by the same author

Skirmish
The Paradise Complex

Sabazius
THE TEACHINGS OF A GREEK MAGUS

DOUGLAS LOCKHART

ELEMENT
Shaftesbury, Dorset • Rockport, Massachusetts • Melbourne, Victoria

© Element Books Limited 1997
Text © Douglas Lockhart 1997

First published by The Compton Press Limited 1978
as *Song of the Man Who Came Through*

Published in Great Britain in 1997 by
Element Books Limited
Shaftesbury, Dorset SP7 8BP

Published in the USA in 1997 by
Element Books Inc.
PO Box 830, Rockport, MA 01966

Published in Australia in 1997 by
Element Books
and distributed by Penguin Australia Ltd
487 Maroondah Highway, Ringwood, Victoria 3134

Cover illustration by Tony Stone Images
Cover design by Mark Slader
Page design by Roger Lightfoot
Typeset by ABM Typographics Ltd, Hull
Printed and bound in Great Britain by
Creative Print & Design, Ebbw Vale, Wales

British Library Cataloguing in Publication
data available

Library of Congress Cataloguing in Publication
data available

ISBN 1–85230–970–9

Part of this book was originally published
by Peter Owen under the title *Skirmish*

Contents

For my daughter Jennifer

Foreword

It is impossible for any of us to rationally establish at what point, within us or without us or both, psychology ends and philosophy – or, more precisely, epistemology – begins. The threshold is extremely nebulous between what is and what is not the psyche, between the mind and what it apprehends, between cognizer, cognized and cognition. And language, which derives from such distinctions and helps perpetuate them, cannot – at least not in conventional forms – reconcile them. A grammar must be created that manifests the paradoxical nature of language itself, a grammar that both embodies and reflects – not the paradox of facile mystification and fashionable non sequitur, but the paradox which is, paradoxically, logically consistent. This is the kind of grammar Douglas Lockhart has evolved.

Richard Leigh

Part One:
SKIRMISH

1 ❋ A ritual of patience

It is not the time or place that matters now, but the man. He was ordinary, but in an extraordinary sense, for he had the face of an oriental priest and the hands of a workman. I can remember only that we were thrust into each other's company, and that he, in a manner which I was eventually to understand and appreciate, took me aside.

'You seem unhappy with the situation,' he said. His words carried the trace of an accent. 'Could it be that like myself you do not like crowds?'

'Quite,' I replied.

'Shall we walk?'

I nodded and looked around half expecting the others to notice our leaving and fall silent, but they continued to talk. We moved through them to the hall, and down the broad, stone staircase to where it was cool.

'I spotted you earlier on,' he said, offering me what looked like a Turkish cigarette. As he lit it, I glanced at him through the flame. 'And I thought to myself ... now there's a man who likes space.'

'You couldn't have been more right.'

'Where are you from?'

'London.'

He looked at me as if what I had said contained vital information.

'And you?' I asked.

'Greece.'

I immediately conjured up a vague picture of the Acropolis.

'But I have not been home for some time,' he added; then he said: 'What brings you to Africa?'

'Business.'

'You do not look like a business-man.'

The way he separated 'business' from 'man' amused me. 'I

don't feel much like one at this moment,' I replied.

We walked out through the large doorway and stood on the building's steps. My eyes moved across acres of closely cut, newly wetted grass. He was standing some four feet from me, his back straight, his arms partially folded, his cigarette hanging from his finger-tips.

'I was here two years ago,' he said; and then he paused. 'Are you married?'

'I was.'

'It did not work out?'

'You could say that.'

There was a moment of silence.

'I too am a business-man,' he said suddenly.

'What are you in?'

'In?'

'What's your firm's product?'

'Ah!' He nodded to himself. 'They produce very expensive items,' he said, having taken a deep breath. 'Most people can't afford them!' He laughed at this as if it were funny.

'What kind of items?'

'Machinery.'

I waited, but he made no attempt to change the word into a topic, so I said: 'Generators and such like?'

'Yes. Generators.'

The word had reverberated up out of his thick-set body like an object of love. Then that body moved down the steps, and I followed, and we started out across the lawn.

'I like Africa,' he said next. 'I always feel as though I've come home.'

'What about Greece?'

'Oh ... that is also my home.' He spread out his arms in an expansive gesture. 'But this is my adult home, where I feel good, in here.' He prodded at his stomach with two fingers.

I liked him for that, there was a certain freedom about his movement which made me feel comfortable. 'I'm just wondering to which of those people you intend to sell a generator,' I said. 'Or have you already sold one?'

He laughed lightly, but did not look at me. 'No, not yet. I'm looking out for a buyer, but I always choose my clients with great care.'

4

'I suppose you're supplied with a hot lead before you come to a country?'

'But of course,' he replied, and to my astonishment he nipped out the remains of his cigarette between thumb and forefinger and put it in his pocket.

'I never journey without a reason.'

'I wish I could say the same.'

'I would have thought you successful to be invited here.' He glanced at me curiously. 'Your firm must have faith in you.'

'I suppose I am quite successful,' I said, thoughtfully, but there was a touch of hopelessness in my voice which I found impossible to eradicate.

'Then why do you talk sadly?'

We stopped walking and stood in the middle of that green wilderness. I did not quite know how to answer his question. I fumbled for words, 'Oh, I don't know … it's just that I don't really get much satisfaction from what I do.'

'Then why do it?'

'I've been doing it too long to change now,' I said. 'It's the only thing I know.'

'You must be capable of other things.'

'Don't mistake me,' I said, worried in case he thought me inadequate, 'I could certainly change my job, but I can't see that changing it would change how I feel.' I laughed. 'It must be middle age draining the life out of me.'

'Yes, I know what you mean,' he said.

'Is that how you feel?'

'No.'

'Then you are lucky,' I said, wondering whether to believe him or not. 'It seems to have attacked me very early on.'

'What has attacked you?'

Looking up into that perfect sky, I said: 'Boredom, I suppose.'

'But you are a young man; at least in comparison with me you are young!'

'Think yourself lucky,' I said again.

'No, not lucky,' he replied. 'I do not believe in the world's luck.'

'Then it's just how you happen to be made.'

He smiled and nodded at me vigorously. 'Yes, yes indeed. I would agree with that.'

We walked on in that dazzling light, our eyes narrowed to counteract the reflected glare. I was finding it difficult to keep up with him; his steps had the spring of youth, an inherent vitality which I could not match. He noticed my difficulty and slowed a little.

'You're very fit,' I said.

'Breathing.' He pronounced the word with great care. 'I breathe properly.'

'I didn't know there was a wrong way.'

He stopped again, faced me. 'Let me see you breathe,' he asked, and he obviously meant it, for he looked at my mouth.

I breathed.

'No, no,' he said, brandishing his hands. 'You're doing it all wrong!'

'What am I doing wrong?'

'You are not taking in air.'

'I must be ...'

'You are not taking in enough.'

'I'm alive.'

'Just!'

We laughed and continued towards a small group of trees and bougainvillea bushes. 'It is something you have to learn,' he said seriously. 'Very few people breathe properly.'

'What does breathing properly do for you?'

'It makes you run like this,' he replied, and before I could say anything he was off across the grass, his heavy body gliding without effort. He ran like a fourteen year old, head back, fingers cutting the sultry air like pink knives. When he reached the trees he sat down. 'Try it!' he shouted.

I ran. I threw myself forward and lurched into bone-cracking strides.

When I reached him I was completely out of breath.

'Now you have a concrete example of how not to breathe,' he said, beaming at me boyishly. 'But if you wish, I will give you your first lesson.'

'Please do,' I said.

He stood up. 'First, you have to learn to attack the air, like this ...' His body contracted, and as it opened out again he filled his lungs to bursting point. I could almost see them filling up, every nook and cranny being jammed tight with that

6

invisible substance. He exhaled. 'That is the first step,' he continued.

I tried to copy his action.

He burst out laughing and staggered back. 'You have to believe that you're breathing!' he exclaimed. And then suddenly he was serious again. 'You must learn to believe in air.'

'I'm afraid I don't understand.'

'Like this,' he said, and his face was momentarily arranged into a grotesque expression. He sucked at the atmosphere, drew it down into his body as if it were to be his last action of importance.

I watched him breathe over and over again. It was fascinating, almost frightening. Each time he drew breath he seemed to grow, until suddenly he was huge and I was the size of a grasshopper.

'Take it easy,' I heard him say, and he tapped me lightly on the forehead with a knuckle. 'You overdid it.'

I was lying flat out on the grass and he was kneeling beside me.

'What happened?'

'You blacked out.'

'It must be the heat,' I said, shaking my head to clear it. 'I must have fainted.'

'No, you did not faint, you fell into a rhythm. You were really breathing.'

'I don't remember doing it.'

'Don't worry about it,' he said, nodding at me as if he understood only too well what had happened, 'it is easy to get caught up in.'

'But I don't actually remember starting the rhythm!'

'We will go back now,' he said, helping me up, 'and you will drink a little iced water.'

We walked in silence. I looked at him from time to time, tried to determine what had taken place beneath the trees, but I was still dazed. 'By the way,' I said, 'my name is Peter Derwent.'

'And I am Alexis Sabazius,' he replied grandly.

The crowd had thinned. The long table on which had rested an exotic buffet was almost bare. Sabazius snorted in faked anger. 'Look,' he said, pointing at some African delicacies.

'They do not know the good things in life, only the trivia!'

I stood watching him eat.

He turned suddenly and looked at me. 'I said you had to drink iced water.'

I poured myself some and sipped at it. It went down through my body like a frosted knife. 'Which ... which hotel are you staying at?' I asked.

'I have my own place. It's not much, but it's comfortable.' He surveyed the table, chose some small biscuits, some squares of brown bread topped with smoked salmon, placed them in a napkin, and with a delicate, unconscious movement inserted them in his pocket with the cigarette butt. He caught my expression. 'I have a cat,' he said, smiling at me. 'She likes such things.'

It occurred to me at that moment that there was something odd about Alexis Sabazius. He was, on the one hand, a high-powered salesman of considerable charm; on the other, a walking contradiction.

'Do you cook for yourself?' I asked.

'Of course.'

'Don't you find it boring?'

He looked at me intently. 'To cook for oneself is to be on guard.'

'Against what?'

'Laziness.'

It was almost as if he were saying to me: 'You are lazy.' I shrugged, turned from him, selected one of the same squares he had pocketed for his cat, and placed it whole in my mouth.

'You do not believe me,' he said. 'You think to cook is to do a woman's work. Isn't that right?'

'Not really,' I replied. 'I just don't see the sense when the firm's paying other people to do it for me.'

'Ah!' he exclaimed. 'You mean you like to have things done for you.'

'That's not what I said.'

'It is what I heard you say!'

'I meant ...' I was momentarily confused. 'I meant only in the sense that I'm a linguist attached to a big company and simply don't have the time.'

'So you do cook?'

'A little.'

'What do you cook?'

'Oh, bacon and egg, toast, the odd chicken if I'm entertaining …'

He waved a hand at me to stop. 'Have you ever worked through the night to prepare a meal?' he asked.

I laughed and stared at him. 'Never!'

'Then you do not cook,' he said emphatically. 'To cook is a mystery, a ritual of patience; it is a way of becoming a man.'

Not wishing to be rude, I said: 'Our cultures are very different.'

'It has nothing to do with culture.'

'I don't agree.'

He slapped me lightly on the arm. 'Now you are angry with me,' he said good-naturedly. 'I like a man who can show anger.'

'I'm not really angry,' I replied, smiling to prove it. 'I just think you've got the wrong end of the stick.'

'Stick?'

'You see things differently.'

'Yes. That is true.'

'Let me put it this way,' I said, determined to iron out the problem with a little logic. 'Is there a garden attached to your house?'

'There is, but it is not mine. I have two rooms high up, high up to see the city, and the sky.'

'Do you ever work in it, dig it?'

'No.'

'Well then,' I said, rather pleased. 'I think digging a garden helps to make one into a man – more so than cooking.'

He laughed so loudly the remaining guests turned to stare at us. 'I also dig,' he said, manufacturing a frown out of existing lines, 'but I dig because I am a man, not to become one.'

'But one could say the same thing about cooking,' I answered quickly. 'If you are already a man, then everything you do is manly.'

He nodded slowly and chewed at the inside of his mouth. 'But you do not cook,' he said at last.

'But I dig!'

'With your hands?'

9

The sudden lowering of his tone, the bulk of his shoulders bending forwards slightly stunned me. 'Of course not,' I said, wondering what he was getting at. 'I use a spade, or a trowel.'

'Then you do not dig, either,' was his reply.

In spite of myself, I could not think of anything to say. There was something in his words which annoyed me profoundly, but I could identify neither the cause nor the meaning. He was Alexis Sabazius, and his thought processes seemed to be different from mine.

Sensing that I would not, or could not continue, Sabazius said: 'When you understand what to "cook", or to "dig" means, then you will quickly learn how to breathe.' I was thrust into the memory of my fainting. 'All things are subtly related,' he went on, 'that is the foundation of *Weltanschauung*.'

'Oh,' I said.

'You understand me?'

At that precise moment I considered him a crank, for *Weltanschauung* referred to some kind of world philosophy, and Alexis Sabazius obviously believed that his was the best.

'Yes, I think I do, now,' I said, looking at him with fast-declining interest. 'You've worked out some kind of pattern for living. A philosophical *Gestalt*.'

He made no reply.

'There are an awful lot of patterns knocking about,' I continued, feeling sure of myself for the first time in his company. 'Every other person you meet has one, but they're all quite subjective.'

'You have changed,' he said suddenly, in a new tone.

'In what way?'

'I can see the iron.'

I frowned and waited for him to continue.

'When I say "iron",' Sabazius went on, 'I refer to emptiness. The emptiness of continual rejection.'

'One has to reject logically a great number of things,' I replied, giving him a half smile. 'Wouldn't you agree?'

'But of course.'

'And as there aren't many things worth accepting, one automatically becomes empty, to use your word.'

He stood looking at me for what seemed an age, then he

said, without malice: 'Empty vessels make the most noise.'

'Almost as much as those that think themselves full,' I said, not wishing to hurt him, but at the same time wanting to get my point home. Then I said, continuing to look directly at him, 'You're a funny mixture of things. I can't quite imagine how you ended up selling machinery.'

'I also make carpets.'

I was now perplexed. 'You're trying to say something to me,' I said, 'but I don't understand it.'

'Of course you don't understand it,' he replied soberly. 'If you understood it, you would have beaten me to the trees!'

'But – '

'No, no ...' He stopped my reply short. 'Your problem is that you do not listen.' His voice was abrupt, commanding. 'You thought I was offering you a personal philosophy, a private view of the world – but I am not! As you said, such things are subjective.' He looked at me carefully. 'I see I will have to appeal to reason,' he said, as if it were a circuit he did not much care for.

'When I said that all things were related, I was not referring to some fixed pattern or mere idea in my mind. I was referring to "fluid" perception: the ability to see what is really there. When you say that you understand something, you mean that you perceive it whole. Is that not so?'

'Yes, I suppose it is.'

'But to perceive something whole, you have to be supplied with all the relevant details. Correct?'

'Yes.'

'And because I have not offered you the details of my perceiving, you reject what I say.'

I nodded.

The smile Alexis Sabazius threw at me contained congratulations and contempt. He turned, leaned on the table, and allowed his gaze to travel out through the large picture-window. 'What do you see out there?' he asked.

'Grass, and a few trees,' I replied.

'What else?'

'Lots of sky, and a man walking across the lawn.'

'Go out to him.'

'Why?'

'I do not mean physically. Go out to him in your mind; become him, look back at this house, this window.'

I was on the point of saying that such an exercise was silly, merely imagination, when I actually felt something in me project. I was inside and outside the house simultaneously, seeing the man one moment, seeing Sabazius and myself the next. Suddenly I felt dizzy.

'Go out again!' said Sabazius.

The feeling returned. I had the momentary impression that I was looking through the man's eyes, seeing what he saw, but being curiously 'myself' in that seeing. I shuddered and turned from the scene.

Sabazius laughed and slapped me again. 'I knew it!' he exclaimed. 'You have the touch, the feel for it!'

'For what?'

'For *Weltanschauung* of course!' He was staring at me hard, as if to rivet my silence and astonishment into place. Then he said: 'Explain that with logic, if you can.'

2 ✻ *Switching on the world*

I spent the rest of that evening with Alexis Sabazius. We drove
back to his place, and with great show he introduced me to his
one-eared cat. 'Cat!' he shouted. 'This is Peter Derwent.' I bent
down thinking she would come to me purring. She did not.

'That is how they are,' said Sabazius.

'She looks a bit wild.'

He nodded, picked her up and rubbed his nose behind her
good ear. 'That is what she likes,' he said. 'She may bite the
approaching hand, but if you love her with your nose, she will
always show pleasure.' He handed her to me. 'Try it!'

I held her as best I could and bent forward. She raised both
paws and clapped me round the ears with a swift boxing
action. I dropped her immediately.

Sabazius choked with laughter.

'I don't think she likes me,' I said.

'No, no …' He smiled at me warmly. 'It was your approach,
you moved with the jerkiness of a robot.'

'I've never had a cat.'

He pointed at her.

She was sitting quietly at my feet looking up, as if to say:
'What are you going to do now?' I bent towards her but
Sabazius said:

'I will teach you.' He got down on his kness and bent his
head low. 'Come down,' he said, 'come into her world.' I knelt
beside him. 'Now watch what I do.' He approached her with
his head side-on, but did not look at her directly, then he
tilted his face a little, offering her a cheek. She responded by
sidling up to him, her head at the same angle. In a circular
motion he brought his chin round until it was against her neck,
then he dipped down and applied his nose to the back of her
neck. 'Do you see?' he said softly. 'You must come to her with
caution, with respect, as she comes to you. No fast movements,

no jerky ones, all must be smooth.' He was talking almost in a whisper.

'Can I try?'

'Yes, yes ...' He got up and sat a few yards away.

Following his example to the letter, I moved in towards her. She looked at me. I turned my head slightly, tilted it, offered her a cheek. She arose and approached me slowly. I could hear Sabazius breathing deeply in the background. I suddenly felt her fur against my face, the warmth of her thickly furred body against my face and neck – pressing. I moved my head up in the same circular motion and brought the tip of my chin down on her neck. She turned her face fully in my direction, looked at me, and with a suddenness which made me fall back, clipped me around the ears a second time.

I got up in disgust.

Sabazius sat perfectly still and looked at me.

'What did I do wrong?'

'You thought about it too much.'

'What else could I do?'

'It is not necessary to think when dealing with animals,' he said; and then to qualify his statement he added: 'You must learn to think like a cat when dealing with a cat.'

'Is that possible?'

'Oh, yes,' he replied matter-of-factly. 'To think like an animal is to move like one. They do not differentiate.'

'How do you know that?'

'Experience. How else?' He beamed at me. 'When next you try it, allow yourself to sink into thoughtlessness, think of nothing, approach her as if you too were a cat. She will understand.'

'We don't pay much attention to cats in England,' I said. 'We fuss over them, but that's about all.'

'That is because you are a rational nation. You reduce everything to the level of an ornament.'

Later, seated in the semi-darkness of his lounge, he said: 'It is very difficult for rational people to change into animals.'

I stared at him, wondering what he meant.

'I do not mean total change,' he added, detecting my attitude. 'I mean the entering into that primitive state for a moment.'

'Can it really be done?'

'You have witnessed men fighting?'

'Yes.'

'Then you have seen the animal consciousness at work.' He was silent for a moment. 'But that is not truly it,' he went on. 'The animal consciousness is neither violent nor passive, it is more like a state of "waiting", like being perpetually on guard.'

I waited for him to continue.

'It is also a state of perfect concentration.' To illustrate his point, he scratched the chair's fabric with his nails. The cat immediately raised her head. 'Now watch,' he said. 'She will stare, depending on how I scratch at this material, for a long time. Then she will drop into the hunting posture, on her belly, with her face well down and her back feet edging into position, and if I change the intensity, she will spring.'

Turning my head slowly, I looked at her. Her eyes were wide and staring, fixed on his fingers. He intensified the sound. She snapped onto her feet without losing visual contact. He drew his nails down the fabric in a slow, tearing motion. She sprang at his hand and buried her teeth into the back of it.

He made no attempt to brush her off.

'Isn't she hurting you?'

'It is a game we play,' he said. 'She knows it is not serious.'

As if in answer to his statement she dropped back to the floor, cleaned herself for a moment, and lay down again.

'Do you take her with you everywhere?'

'I never take her.'

'Then how ...' I was again perplexed. 'How can she remember you after two years?'

'Two years, twenty years,' he said with a shrug, 'what does it matter?'

'But who looks after her?'

'No one that I know of.'

I could feel myself being drawn into another of his mysteries. 'What you're saying,' I said with disbelief, 'is that you come back to this country every so often and she just appears!'

'Something like that.'

'I'm not quite with you.'

'I mean,' said Sabazius, 'that every time I come back to this country a cat appears. That's all.'

I let out a sigh and laughed. 'Oh,' I said.

He surveyed me with amusement. 'Once again you are tripped by logic,' he said. 'All things are not in neat boxes.'

As he did not seem inclined to take the point further, we sat in silence, a mixture of night sounds filtering in through the open window. There was something about his room which stopped me wanting to think. I sat watching him, for he had closed his eyes. His breath came and went gently in an even flow. I listened to it. Each breath was long, inhaled and exhaled through slightly parted lips. And then I looked at the cat, for she was chattering in her sleep, her bottom jaw working in a living dream. I had only just closed my own eyes when Sabazius said:

'Can you feel it?'

'What?'

He got up and walked over to the window. 'I would like to show you something of importance,' he said in a low voice. 'Come and stand by me.'

When I looked out of the window, the city of Johannesburg looked like any other.

'Look,' said Sabazius.

'What am I supposed to be looking at?'

'It's big,' he replied.

I looked from one silhouetted building to another.

'Don't look at things,' he said impatiently. 'Just look.'

I gave up almost immediately and turned to him. 'What do you want me to see?' I asked.

He thought for a moment, then he closed the window and pulled the curtains. The room was in almost total darkness. 'Face the window,' he said.

I faced it.

Suddenly, with dramatic force he pulled back the curtains and threw open the window. 'LOOK!' he roared.

His outburst nailed my attention to what was beyond the opening. I felt a moment of panic, feeling sure that I would not see what he wanted me to; then I heard what seemed like my own voice say 'The World?'

It was some seconds before he spoke. He said quietly: 'Does it take you so much effort to see the world?'

'If you had told me what – '

'I should not have to say anything,' he replied briskly. 'A Man of Feeling always sees the world.'

'But everyone sees or feels it,' I responded irritably. 'It's nothing new.'

'They do not!' He was emphatic. 'They see grass and trees, rivers and mountains; but that is not to "see" the world, to "feel" it.'

I had a momentary glimmer of what he was getting at.

'I think you understand me now,' said Sabazius, and he allowed me a smile. 'Now look again.'

There was the same jagged skyline.

'Feel it,' urged Sabazius.

I kept staring, but nothing happened.

He rapped the top of my head with his knuckle. 'Don't reduce it to an idea ... FEEL it!'

I did as he asked. I tried as best I could to look at nothing in particular, but rather to 'sense' what was out there. Sabazius stood behind me, breathing deeply. Then there was a pin-prick of a sensation somewhere in my head. I refocused my eyes and looked. The feeling disappeared, leaving me with a curious emptiness. A few seconds later it returned, stronger this time, more positive. I tried to stop myself thinking about it, to let it grow uninterrupted; but it again fizzled out, and I almost turned to look at him.

'Look,' he said again.

I trembled. A shiver ran up my spine, reached the back of my neck and was changed into a tiny electrical charge. Suddenly I felt it coming in through the window, a huge, overpowering force, a magnificent being alive and vital.

'It's alive!' I said, in a low voice.

Sabazius took me gently by the arm and led me back into the room. 'You don't have to stare out of the window now,' he said. 'The world won't run away.'

She was no longer a dark horizon of bric-a-brac, she was a living presence, incomprehensible, yet knowable. I sat in silence for some minutes, amazed that Alexis Sabazius should know such things, and not a little puzzled as to his reasons for communicating them to me.

'Why me?' I asked.

He tilted his head, frowned at me, as if he did not

17

understand my question; then he said: 'Because I think you are the right man.'

'For what?'

'A Man of Feeling would not have to ask.'

'I am not yet a man of feeling,' I said.

'Only a Man of Feeling would say "not yet",' he replied.

I laughed and lay back into the chair. 'You imbue everything with a sense of mystery,' I said. 'In fact, you *are* a man of mystery!'

'Only to you,' said Sabazius. 'My mystery is in you, not in me.'

I did not answer immediately. I thought around his words, analysed them carefully, and came to the conclusion that he must be referring to the projection of an attitude. I asked him if this were so.

'You are almost correct,' he said, nodding at me, 'but that attitude is the totality of something else: it is based on your interpretation of me.'

'But my interpretation is based on evidence.'

'What kind of evidence?'

'What you do and say.'

'And what do I do and say to make things so mysterious?' he asked. Before I could reply, he said: 'I have asked you to breathe properly, and to look out of a window twice. Where is the mystery?'

'You just have a peculiar method of asking me to do ordinary things.'

'Maybe they are not as ordinary as you think.'

'That's why you seem mysterious,' I said quickly. 'It is because you see ordinary things as extraordinary that I get the impression of mystery.'

'That is once again your interpretation,' he replied. 'To me breathing is to move, and looking to feel the world. So it is really you who are extraordinary; you devalue things, render them meaningless.'

If he had made that statement an hour before, I would have called him subjective; but as I sat there looking at him, I could 'feel' the world, sense its dynamic quality, its massive presence.

'You look perplexed,' said Sabazius.

'I can't understand why I've never felt this before,' I said quietly. 'It seems so obvious, now.'

He got to his feet. 'I'll make some coffee,' he said. 'It is not good to get too wrapped up in such things. Take them as they come, enjoy them, then dismiss them. That is how a Man of Feeling operates.'

'How can I dismiss the world?'

'By allowing it to exist in its own right,' he answered. 'It is an unfortunate thing, but human beings are either unaware of the world, or over-aware of it. The ones who are not aware think of it as an inanimate object, and those who are over-aware, as all there is. It is the stuff of poets, and it can be the ground of madness.'

'I don't feel inclined to switch it off.'

He laughed and shook his head at me in bewilderment. 'The truth of the matter is, Peter, you do not know how to switch it off, just as you did not know how to switch it on.'

I was about to question him further, but he turned and walked through to the kitchen.

'What do I do then?' I shouted after him.

'Nothing!'

I could hear the clink of cups, the sound of a tap running. Everything seemed natural, and yet was somehow overlaid with meaning. He was right. If I attempted to live constantly with such a presence, it would drive me mad: but it was also deliciously inviting ...

He returned with the coffee.

'Now I will contradict myself,' he said. 'Once a man has switched on the world, he cannot switch it off, so he must learn to live with it, make it part of the larger picture available, and when that is done, then he has control, although only consciously.'

'But what can be larger than the world?'

'The universe.'

'Can that too be felt?'

'Oh, yes; but luckily for you it cannot be felt as one feels the world; that requires a great deal of training.'

'Can you feel the universe?'

'What I feel is no concern of yours,' he replied flatly. 'I am Alexis Sabazius, you are Peter Derwent.'

I did not pursue the point.

'To be a Man of Feeling,' said Sabazius suddenly, 'is to be continuously in danger. It requires an attitude which cannot be moved by externals. What I mean by that is this: To feel the world is a marvellous experience, but to be swamped by it is merely to return to primitive consciousness. You must never allow that to happen.'

'What does one do to avoid it?'

'Nothing.'

'But if you do nothing – '

He waved at me to be quiet. 'What I mean by nothing, and what you mean are two different things. For most people, to do nothing is to float off into a dream world, to enter their private mental flux and follow associations; but to me it is to be myself, to arrive at my Centre.'

'How does one do that?'

'It is not "done",' he replied, 'it just "is".'

I remained silent.

He waited until my mind was exhausted by trying to understand, then he said: 'Firstly, you must *become* what you know.'

My expression made him chuckle again.

'An hour ago you thought you knew the world,' he said pointedly, 'and then you felt it as it really is. That's what I mean by "become".'

I nodded slowly.

He relaxed into his chair again. 'A Man of Feeling does not know things,' he went on, 'he *is* things.' To illustrate this point he raised his arm and held it out. 'I do not *have* an arm,' he said, staring at me fixedly, 'I *am* an arm.' He pointed to his head. 'I do not *have* a thought, I *am* thought, and I do not *have* laughter, I *am* laughter. Do you follow me?'

'I think so.'

'You *sense* what I'm saying?'

'Yes.'

His next statement dumbfounded me.

'When you put all of these things together,' he said quietly, 'that is to *do* nothing.'

Everything evaporated, became mixed up, a mere jumble of words and emphasis.

'It is because you are *composed of disbelief* that you do not understand what I'm saying,' said Sabazius. 'For the truth of

20

what I'm saying is already in you, but it's back-to-front.'

'You mean the reason I could not feel the world earlier was because I believed it to be separate from me?'

'Just so.'

Something in me spiralled up.

I was no longer Peter Derwent, linguist, I was a confused, upside-down idiot who had attempted to live in a world of badly focused truth.

He snapped his fingers, drew me back into the room away from my private world.

'That,' he said, pointing at the cat, 'is how you must live.'

'But she's sleeping!'

'No, no ...' He threw back his head in despair, scratched at the fabric again. The cat opened her eyes. 'She is totally "cat",' he said urgently, 'She *is*.'

I thought about that and said, 'So what I have to do is abandon ...' I never got to finish the sentence.

'*Never* abandon yourself to anything, or anyone.'

'But it's – '

'Dangerous,' he said. He added quickly: 'To be human, fully human, is to be awake. To be awake means to live like a cat, to be constantly on guard.'

'You frighten me sometimes.'

He laughed, lifted the small china cup of dark unsweetened coffee and sipped at it. And then he said, 'You do not know the meaning of fear.'

'When will I know?'

'When you have become a Man of Feeling.'

'When will that be?'

'It may never be, and yet, there again, it may be very soon.'

Suddenly, inexplicably, I was angry with him, furious that he should toy with me in such a fashion. 'What are to trying to do to me?' I asked.

He did not reply; he just sat and stared at me.

I stared back defiantly, felt as if I might attack him, tear at him, cripple him for not being as other men. What right had he to demand so much from a stranger? Okay, so he knew strange things, but that did not mean that he could lord it over men like a tin god. I was ...

'What are you thinking about?'

'Nothing,' I said defensively.

'Nothing?'

'Nothing important.'

'Is that why your jaw was working overtime? Were you scolding someone? Were you scolding me?'

It was almost as if he had read my mind; I did not know what to say in return.

'Am I wrong?' he asked.

'So now you're a bloody mind reader.'

'No, not a mind reader, a reader of faces.' He paused. 'I only read what is put in front of me, Peter, so stop throwing it around.

3 ✻ *A man of feeling*

I left South Africa two days later and returned to London. I had spent every moment of those days with Alexis Sabazius. We had talked about many things, and in his usual fashion he had astonished me with one piece of knowledge after another. Knowledge, I might add, backed by experiences which defied logic – my logic. But the most important thing I learned during this short period was that I argued for arguing's sake. Each time I entered the role of 'arguer', he pointed at my secret motive with unerring accuracy, and by the afternoon of the second day showed me that it was I, not he, who inflicted the pain in such situations. Thus I carried a strange new burden back to my home city, the burden of not only listening to others more carefully, but of listening to myself. Even before I set foot on the plane, I had decided to resign from my job. And that, as it turned out, was the most telling decision of my life.

A few days later, I bought a cook-book, some iron pans, a wooden spoon, a set of metal skewers, and filling a carrier-bag with expensive spices, herbs, and other items which took my fancy, set off for home.

I was going to cook!

My next step was a chicken; but this time I intended to do extraordinary things with it: I would curry it Burmese-style (Sabazius had spent four hours showing me how) and eat it at one sitting. 'To cook properly,' he had said, 'you must love and understand the ingredients.'

I had watched with interest.

'How do you know how much oil to use?'

'You sense it.'

'How does one sense a quantity of oil?'

'By looking at it.'

That was how our conversation had gone that day from item to item, from process to completion. When we ate, he demanded total silence.

I spent two weeks alone, walked a great deal, cooked furiously, and ate everything whether bad or good. For the first time in my life, I was being myself.

Alexis Sabazius telephoned me on a Wednesday afternoon at exactly three-fifteen. He was in London, he said, and would be staying for a few weeks.

'Whereabouts are you?' I asked.

'I've taken a flat in South Kensington,' he replied. 'You won't like it.'

'Why not?'

'Because it's very dull.'

'Then why have it?'

'Because I like it,' was his answer.

I was again thrust into his world.

I attempted to describe what I had been doing since I arrived back, but he said he would prefer to hear it from me face to face. It occurred to me suddenly that he must have known he was coming to London, so I reprimanded him for not telling me. He said he had not known for sure until that very morning.

'A client on the horizon?' I asked.

'Yes.'

We arranged to meet.

He appeared wearing a thick astrakhan coat with a fur collar. 'Ah!' he exclaimed when I opened the door. 'You have been *working* with food!'

I smiled proudly.

We ate without talking and drank a tiny quantity of dry white wine. He passed me a Turkish cigarette and, in his usual fashion, lit it for me.

'What is this you were telling me?' he said.

'I've given up my job.'

He nodded, chewing at his mouth as if trying to dislodge a piece of meat.

'Why have you done this?'

'Because I needed time to think things out.'

'What things?'

'My life, what it's all about.'

'And what have you discovered?'

24

'As yet, nothing.'

He smiled. 'My nothing, or your nothing?'

'Mine,' I admitted.

'Have you looked?'

'I've tried to.'

He stared at me, then he shook his head from side to side. 'It is impossible to try,' he said. 'Either you look, or you do not look!'

'It keeps going out of focus.'

'Then you are on the verge of returning to your old world. You must fight to keep the world, just as you must fight to stop the world overwhelming you.'

'But I remember you saying that the world could not be switched off?'

'It can't.'

'Then why am I returning to my old view of the world?'

'Because you are switching off. You are being dragged back into the dream.'

'But how does one fight to keep the world?'

'By always looking.'

I knew I was taking a wild gamble, a blind leap. 'You are the only person I've ever met who seems capable of telling me what I want to know ...' I hesitated, felt myself blush. 'Will you teach me to be a Man of Feeling?'

He remained expressionless.

'I mean it!'

'But of course,' he replied. 'When a person is full of passion they always mean what they say.'

'What are you saying to me?'

'I am saying that you are asking me now, but that later you may change your mind.'

'I don't think I will.'

'You have no way of telling. Only a Man of Feeling can truly say what he means.'

I sat staring at him not knowing what to think.

'Yet there is a chance it is your Centre talking,' he went on, offering me hope, 'and if that is the case, then you will not change your mind.'

'Can you tell if it's my centre?'

'If you cannot tell, how can I?'

I thought for a moment, then I said: 'If I prove to you that I'm serious, then will you teach me?'

'How would you prove such a thing?'

'By doing whatever you ask, without question.'

He seemed to ponder my statement, weigh it, and I thought he was secretly pleased. Getting up, he opened the window. 'Jump,' he said.

I froze.

'What's the matter, have you changed your mind already?'

I felt tears come into my eyes.

He seated himself quietly at the table and toyed with a fork. 'A man's life is his own, Peter,' he said quietly. 'He must never hand it to another.'

That, as it turned out, was my first proper lesson in becoming a Man of Feeling. Sabazius eventually agreed to teach me, but he laid down one stipulation: a Man of Feeling, he said, could always be trusted, so I had to learn to trust him at all times.

'But isn't that the same as handing over your life?' I asked, a little perplexed.

'No, it is not the same. What you were suggesting was abandonment, and I have already spoken to you concerning that. But to trust is different. To trust is to *sense* that the other is worthy.'

'Trustworthy.'

'Just so. Most people do not understand the meaning of trust, they have devalued it into financial honesty and lost the vision; but trust, real trust, has nothing to do with money, it refers to a mind able to assist without prejudice, on behalf of another.'

I did not see Alexis Sabazius for a few days. He said he had business to attend to. Not quite knowing what to do with myself, I went out one afternoon and walked to Hyde Park. It was a bright, cool day in late September. I stood for almost an hour on the edge of the Serpentine gazing across at the far bank. I seemed to be waiting. Suddenly, I had the illusion that I was high up and looking out on a vast sea. This feeling stayed with me for some minutes, then slowly subsided. When I returned, Alexis was stretched out on the sofa, asleep.

'Alexis?' I said.

He showed no sign of life.

Not wishing to wake him, or rather disturb him (I had seen him like this once before, and he had not been asleep), I went through to the kitchen and prepared a light snack of cheese and tomatoes. When I walked back into the room, his eyes were open.

I said, wanting him to define the situation: 'I'm never quite sure if you are asleep or not.'

'Is that a question?'

I nodded.

'It is something like sleep,' he replied immediately, 'and yet not like sleep.'

'Meditation?'

He looked at me with interest. 'What do you know of meditation?' he asked.

'Not very much really. I've just started reading a book on it.'

'And what does the book say?'

'I've only read the introduction.'

Sabazius lay there looking at me, waiting.

'Making your mind go blank?' I said, taking a shot in the dark.

He laughed, swung his legs onto the floor and sat straight-backed. He took three mighty breaths, held the last one for a few seconds, and relaxed.

'To meditate,' he said, 'is to live.'

That was not exactly how the book had put it.

'It says in the book –'

He cut me short. 'Forget the book.'

'Aren't they any good?'

Making a face as if to say 'Who knows?' he said: 'I am not a book.'

I smiled.

'No, no. I'm serious! Do I look like a book?'

'No.'

'You are quite right,' he replied. 'I do not look like a book, and neither do I feel like a book.' He paused to let my incomprehension deepen. 'I feel like a man.'

At that moment, I felt like an idiot.

He got up suddenly and walked over to my book-shelves, took out a book and brought it back. He then held it up to my face. 'Look at it,' he said.

I looked.

Sabazius tore the book in half. 'That is why I am not a book,' he went on, 'I cannot be torn in half.'

I was somewhat stunned by his illustration.

'A man and a book are different for that very reason,' he said, handing it to me. 'A man does not have words inside of him, he has only himself. A book, on the other hand, is not a book without words, and if the book is lost, then the words are lost.'

'The words can be remembered.'

'Of course they can; but they may not be understood. A Man of Feeling understands.'

'Everything?'

'It is possible to understand that you *do not understand*,' he replied obliquely. 'That is perfect understanding. On that foundation a Man of Feeling learns to ask the correct question, and having conceived of that question, is led to the answer.'

It crossed my mind that Alexis Sabazius was either very clever indeed, or the biggest egoist I had ever met. However, I had 'felt' the world, and it was he who had shown me how.

'Now, as to your question,' he went on, 'what I was doing is extremely simple.' Taking me gently by the arm he led me over to the sofa. 'Lie down a moment and close your eyes.' I did as he asked. 'Allow yourself to drift towards sleep; but remain aware of your condition.'

'It's very difficult.'

'No it isn't,' said Sabazius.

I did not argue.

'I am not telling you to go to sleep. I am telling you to *approach* sleep; and yet at the same time to *know* that you are approaching it.'

'It isn't working.'

'I haven't asked you to make anything work!'

I lay very still for almost ten minutes before I was able to forget that he was standing there. Then suddenly he spoke again:

'Where are you?'

I felt a tiny shock and opened my eyes.

'Well?'

Feeling rather foolish, I said: 'I think I dropped off.'

'Think back,' said Sabazius. 'Was there not a point where you were aware of going to sleep?'

'Yes.'

'That is the point to which I refer. It is there you must stop. You went over the brink.'

'What's the purpose of not going over the brink?'

'It is self-explanatory,' he replied. 'When you have mastered it, you will know.'

'What will I know?'

He sighed, and looked at me despondently. 'If I told you that,' he said, 'it would no longer be self-explanatory.'

When we had eaten our cheese and tomatoes and smoked one of his cigarettes, he said: 'You must find yourself some work.'

'But I don't particularly want to work.'

'Why not?'

I hesitated, wondering what he had in mind.

'Now you are unsure whether you ought to work or not. Correct?'

'I gave up my work to attend to my life.'

'And what would you have done with your life if I had not come to London?'

'I don't know. I didn't get the chance to find out.'

'Then I will tell you,' he said flatly. 'You would have dried up like a stick.'

'Maybe not.'

'Ah!' he exclaimed. 'You have been keeping it from me all this time. You are already a Man of Feeling!'

'I'm not a Man of Feeling.'

'Half a Man of Feeling?'

'I still don't totally understand what you mean by a Man of Feeling.'

He turned off his mockery, became quiet. 'A Man of Feeling,' he said slowly, 'is a man who lives NOW! He does not live in a potential future, nor does he drain his resources and then look for more. When I said that you would have dried up like a stick, I meant just that. You would have lived with yourself, and come to the end of yourself; that is a most dangerous state to be in; it is emptiness of spirit. And when a man is empty, when he no longer has strength of mind to work, to think, to rationalize, to discover, he hangs suspended in a premature death, neither able to go back, nor forward.'

'But isn't it possible to realize your mistake?'

'Oh, yes; but there is then no energy to change direction.'

'None?'

'It is living death,' said Sabazius; 'but it is a curious death. For a man who finds himself in it has generally attempted to push himself through and beyond it. He is generally the kind of man who has a little knowledge of what it is to feel, a man like yourself, but that knowledge is not enough, for it has no foundation but reason, and reason is always limited.'

I still did not fully comprehend what it was he was trying to say; but in a curious sense, I could feel it.

'Such a man,' continued Sabazius, 'has strangled himself with truth.'

I fell into a deep silence, remained motionless inside myself. And then I said: 'Is that always the case?'

'No, but it is generally the case. Sometimes a man will have a vision of himself in time, see what is happening, understand the inner pressures, the twistings and turnings which are spiralling towards emptiness; and when that happens, his very recognition reverses the process and sets him free. But such a man's "recognition" is intrinsic, it is *all* of him recognizing, not just his head. Such a man discovers fear.'

'I've always thought of fear as an emotional reaction.'

He laughed suddenly, breaking the spell of his words. 'Do you think reason is separated from emotion?'

'Isn't that the meaning of being clinical?'

'You are putting things in boxes again,' he retorted. 'If you would look inside yourself for one minute you would find neither reason nor emotion. All you would find is yourself. To use such words is a reduction of what you *are*. You do not have a psyche and a body; neither do you have a spirit and a soul. You simply *are*!'

'I don't understand.'

'That is because you have been educated not to,' he replied. 'It is what I said to you before: You are *composed* of disbelief. Men of Feeling are like animals, they do not differentiate.'

That's when I saw it. 'To move *is* to think!' I said in astonishment.

Sabazius slapped me hard on the arm, roared with laughter, applauded my sudden insight. 'Now you are becoming what you know!' he exclaimed. Then, drawing the argument round full circle: 'To work, is to *think with your body*. That is why we eat in silence, for even to eat is to think.'

I had started. I could now see clearly what a Man of Feeling was, and why he was thus named; and I could also see what he meant by a 'premature death': to die in such a fashion was to be broken apart through segmented and segregated reason.

'What are your responsibilities?' asked Sabazius suddenly.

I shrugged, tried to think of them. 'The rent for this flat's about all,' I said; 'and I have some insurance policies to keep up.'

'A Man of Feeling is his own insurance policy.'

I frowned, waited for him to continue.

'As a Man of Feeling gets older his task is more difficult; it sometimes happens that age or a past mistake relaxes his vigilance, so making him momentarily vulnerable. But if his perception is properly linked to the world, and his being to Elsewhere, he is safe.'

'What do you mean by Elsewhere?'

'Elsewhere is where Men of Feeling go when they die.'

'You mean like heaven?'

Sabazius gave a sharp crackle of laughter, then he said: 'When a Man of Feeling dies, he enters Elsewhere, because there is nowhere else for him to go.'

'It sounds like nothing!'

'It is nothing; but it is *his* nothing.'

I felt annoyed with myself. I now understood what a Man of Feeling was, but I could not understand where a Man of Feeling went.

'What are you thinking about?'

'Elsewhere.'

'How can you possibly be doing that?'

'Is it impossible?'

'It is impossible for you.'

'Why?'

'Because you are thinking words.'

Becoming slightly impatient, I said, 'I know it's an abstraction.'

'If it were merely an abstraction,' he replied, 'then I'm sure

31

you would have it in your pocket by now.'

I felt my face redden.

'To become a Man of Feeling, you must learn how to recognize Elsewhere,' said Sabazius.

'But you said it was where Men of Feeling went when they died?'

'When the body is removed, the man is removed,' he said obliquely, 'there is then only the feeling, and the feeling is Elsewhere from the body.'

'I don't understand.'

'To find Elsewhere, a man must start by waiting on the brink of sleep. When he has mastered the waiting, then the approach to Elsewhere opens like a flower.'

'Is that what you were doing earlier?'

He nodded his head slowly and smiled at me. 'It is there for the finding,' he said; 'in fact, it is everywhere for the finding.'

4 ❊ *Projecting and reflecting*

Despair. Everything I attempted to do over the next few days ended in failure. I was somehow out-of-line with my knowledge. Sabazius, when I told him of my difficulties, made hardly any comment, and I had the feeling he was leaving me to sweat it out. At the end of our first week together, he confirmed this.

'You're chewing yourself up,' he said.

'I can't help it.'

'That is because you are trying to become a Man of Feeling,' he replied. 'Such a man is not made, he happens.'

'Then why is it necessary to work so hard?'

'Why does anyone work hard?' asked Sabazius. 'They work hard to gain something; but in your case the gaining is not tangible.'

'I know that.'

He glanced at me, walked across the room and stared out of the window. 'When I was being taught to be a Man of Feeling,' he said, 'I thought success lay in the accomplishment of a task; in other words, getting to the *end* of something. And then, after a long period of heartbreak, I realized that there was no end, and that there was not even a beginning.' He remained silent for some seconds, before saying: 'To be empty is to work at full pressure.'

'But you told me recently that to be empty was a dangerous state, rather like a premature death.'

'We are not talking about the same thing. There are two ways of being empty, just as there are two ways of being full.'

'What are they?'

He laughed and looked round at me. 'That is one of them! You are already hoping that I will dispel your emptiness through reason.'

'That's true,' I admitted.

'A man finds himself empty because reason is a process of elimination leading only to *more* reason,' he said in one breath. 'There is no end to it; it goes on and on for as long as the man is willing to follow. But at certain points in his reasoning he finds momentary pleasure, for to reason is always to approach an end; albeit a temporary end. So every so often he is not empty, but filled up with the end of his reasoning: only to discover that he has to start all over again.'

'I think that's it,' I said. 'I got depressed a few days ago because I could not reason out where a Man of Feeling went when he died. The whole idea of Elsewhere escapes me.'

'That is indeed why you became empty,' said Sabazius, nodding at me. 'You attempted to reduce Elsewhere to an idea, and in return you were reduced to emptiness because you could find no pleasure in it, no end.'

'But I haven't been able to work due to my emptiness,' I said, 'everything has come to a standstill.'

'Only partly. Because you are already on the way to becoming a Man of Feeling, your emptiness is different, it contains feelings. So what you have to do is "feel" your emptiness, and when you learn to do that, you'll traverse it.'

'How does one feel one's emptiness?'

'If you did not feel it, you would not have been able to tell me about it.'

'Then everyone feels their emptiness,' I said, not seeing the subtle difference of his approach. 'I felt emptiness long before I met you.'

'Maybe so, but you did not *feel* the feeling!'

'I'm afraid you've lost me.'

He took out his Turkish cigarettes and passed me one. 'The feeling of emptiness,' he said, 'is a tangible mental state allied to the body: it is the body that feels the state. And as you have pointed out, everyone feels this; but you have felt it in a different way, because you have "felt" the feeling of emptiness, and when you learn to feel it properly, you will automatically transform it into fullness.'

'Will it just go?'

'It cannot go,' said Sabazius, 'for emptiness is an indication of your internal level of being, it is a warning signal, a command to "look" at yourself.'

'Then I will still feel empty even though I can feel the feeling?'

'Think of it in this way: when you feel empty, remember what I have said about it being what you are demanding, that you look at what you are; if you do this properly, then you will *see* your history, and the seeing of your history will cancel out your emptiness.'

'What will happen then?'

'You will move on through fullness towards further emptiness, for emptiness is the punctuation of your history, its meaning at any given moment.'

We remained silent for perhaps an hour, seated at opposite corners of the room.

'What was your teacher like?' I asked at last.

'You mean: "What is he like?",' was his reply.

'Is he still alive?'

'Yes.'

'When do you see him?'

'All the time.'

'How is that possible?'

'It is possible,' replied Sabazius, and he looked as though he were about to laugh, 'because I am my own teacher.'

'Oh ...'

'Do you think it is impossible to be one's own teacher?'

'I don't know.'

'I am telling you that it is possible.'

'But how can one teach oneself things one does not know?'

'Do you mean by teach, "learn"?'

'Yes, I suppose I do.'

'What a man finds within himself is not learned, it is felt and known.'

'But you must have started somewhere?'

'But of course – the day I was born.'

'And you have had a teacher, apart from yourself?'

'Yes.'

'What did you learn from him?'

'That he was unnecessary.'

'You mean you superseded him.'

'No, I do not mean that I superseded him,' he replied briskly. 'He taught me what was necessary, then I taught myself.'

'But – '

'There is a point,' said Sabazius, 'where a teacher – if he is a good teacher – must stop. He cannot go further, because what is "further" is *in* the man he teaches waiting to be felt and known.'

'But how does one learn from oneself?'

Sabazius stared at me, then he said: 'You must stop using the word "learn" in that way. A man does not learn from self, for he is self.'

'Then where does the "knowing" come from?'

'It does not "come" from anywhere; it is known through looking and feeling.'

'As one looks at and feels the world?'

'Yes.'

'What happens?'

'For quite some time, *nothing* happens.'

'Then what happens?'

'You begin to see.'

'What does one see?'

'Yourself.'

'Is that all?'

'There is nothing else.'

'How can seeing self be the same as seeing the world?'

'When a Man of Feeling looks at the world, it reflects self back to him.'

'Then why is it that humanity does not see itself when it looks at the world?'

'Because humanity is too busy identifying with the world,' answered Sabazius, obviously enjoying the to and fro of our conversation. 'It is only when a man stops identifying with the world, that the world can act as a reflector.'

'What exactly do you mean by identify?'

'To let what you *are* escape.'

'How does that happen?'

'When a man does not know how to *look*, he overlooks. And you know what to overlook means.'

'Not to see something, to miss it.'

'Well, that is what he does, he misses the world, and because the world has the power to reflect self back, he also overlooks self.'

'You make it all sound very simple.'

'It is simple.'

'But man has been wrangling with the problem of self since the beginning of history!' I exclaimed. 'And he doesn't seem to have come to any satisfactory answer.'

'That is because he "wrangles",' replied Sabazius with a grin. 'The very sound of that word tells you why he has missed self.' He laughed again, shook a finger at me. 'And the word "history", as you have used it, is the other reason.'

'In what way?'

'What have you learned about history today?'

I panicked momentarily, then with relief I said: 'That history is what I am in moments of emptiness.'

'Quite. And that is what man's history is,' he said quietly. 'He thinks of it as a mere chain of events, but it is his moments of emptiness strung out and recorded.'

'You mean that history is a reflection of what man is at any given moment?'

'Just so.'

'Then why can't he read his history and understand it?'

'Because he uses his history to blind himself, just as he uses the world for the same purpose. Why else would he perpetuate his history if he were not blind through overlooking!' I must have looked sad, for he said immediately: 'When you look at the world of man, Peter, do not allow yourself to fall into pity; a Man of Feeling knows no pity.'

'But surely to show pity is to feel?'

'To show pity,' he replied, 'is to be dragged down by another's despair because of your own despair. A Man of Feeling, when he is confronted by another's hopelessness, weakness, fear, jealousy, misfortune and even death, remains centred.'

'Why?'

'Because he knows why he feels, knows what he is.'

'I would have thought people who show pity know why they're showing it.'

'They know only one level, and that level is basically meaningless. When people of this world show pity to the other, they are unwittingly seeking forgiveness for their own history; but instead they delude themselves into thinking that they are beings of feeling and understanding: man's pity is his way of side-stepping reality, it is how he fools himself into a false security.'

'But if man did not have pity, then the world would be in an even worse state!'

'Not really. It would just mean that man would destroy himself and his world all the faster; he would get it over with in one fell swoop instead of building towards it through pity. Pity is what man uses on himself before murder, and what he uses on others after murder. It is the seed of his fear, the fear of what he is and what he is becoming. Pity comes to the surface when a man does not wish to look too deeply at, or into himself; it is an escape hatch from the vision of inadequacy which would reveal his lack of love, his inability to love. That is why man resorts to pity, why he lays such emphasis on it.'

The interpretation of pity Sabazius had put forward bothered me considerably, for this last statement had opened my eyes to something in myself, something I did not much care for: my desire to show pity arose because I did not know how to muster love; or rather, how to find love within myself.

'All societies are built on pity,' continued Sabazius; 'that is why the poor are poor and the helpless remain basically helpless. Pity never really changes anything, for it does not have the ingredients within it to bring about the changes necessary; it is always a half measure, that which falls short because of its nature; and the nature of pity is the nature of man, unevolved man attempting intrinsic change, but never quite making it.'

I sat thinking about the implications of what he had said for some time, for it was the only real answer I had ever heard, the only explanation of why man's system of living was inexorably breaking down. The rich pitied the poor because they could not love them, and in turn the poor, when they became rich, fell into the same trap.

In his characteristic fashion, Sabazius stopped me from exploring further the question of pity; he said suddenly: 'To "look" is to be awake, and to be awake at the moment of death is to be its master.'

Attempting to adjust to this new line of conversation, I said: 'How can a man look at his own death?'

'To look at death,' he said, 'is to walk out of one's history with clarity; it is to *see* one's history, recognize it for the last time.'

'Then death is emptiness,' I said, trying to relate it to what he had said before, 'the last emptiness.'

Sabazius smiled at me. 'Now I know that you have understood,' he said. Then he added: 'All men see their history at death, but only Men of Feeling understand their history, for at the moment of death they *are their history*; whereas others, those who have spent their lives in dream and pity see, but do not understand totally, for they are without bodies and have not developed the other body to complete their understanding.'

'What other body?'

'Enough,' said Sabazius. 'Now you are seeking pleasure.'

'But it's fascinating!'

'To be fascinated is not to work, it is to be carried off into dream.' Getting up, he approached me. 'You have asked enough questions for one day, now you must work at becoming the answers.'

He reached into his pocket and took out a small black box bound with silver. Turning it upside down, he extracted a wooden tray with his fingernail. Laying the box aside, he removed from the tray a paper-thin wooden lid and showed me the contents.

'What are they?' I asked.

'They are doorways to history,' he replied obliquely.

'Drugs?'

'Of course not!'

'But they must be drugs,' I said sharply.

'I have already told you,' retorted Sabazius, 'they are doorways to history.'

I eyed the tray's contents with suspicion.

'What is the matter with you?'

'I have the feeling you're going to ask me to take one of these things.'

'So – '

'I don't want to.'

'Why not?'

'Because I'm against drugs.'

'Are you against history?'

'No.'

'Then how can you be against the doorway to your history?'

'It's still a drug to me.'

'It is The Awakener.'

'A stimulant?'

'Ah, good!' he retorted. 'Now you have found a word which does not frighten you.'

'What do you mean?'

'The word "drug" frightens you, but the word "stimulant" does not.'

'That's true.'

'Why is that?'

'I suppose because coffee and tea are stimulants.'

'So if I told you this were merely a stimulant, you would take it.'

I hesitated.

'Look,' he said, and he extracted one of the small black grains and popped it into his mouth. He then made a face at me. 'What will you do with my body if I die?' he asked maliciously.

'You wouldn't have taken it if you were going to die!'

'Then you will not die if you take it.'

'It's the effect that worries me,' I said. 'I've heard of people going out of their minds taking things like that.'

'You mean going "into" their minds.'

'That can be the same thing.'

'Indeed it can,' replied Sabazius. 'But if a man goes into his mind and appears to go out of it, then the man is merely terrified by his history.'

'Merely?'

'Better to be terrified by one's history, than not to know it at all,' he said quietly, pointedly. 'Are you afraid of your history?'

'I don't know whether I should be or not.'

'To be a Man of Feeling,' said Sabazius, 'is to face one's history. If you do not wish to be a Man of Feeling, then you will sidestep it.'

'That's a blatant trap!'

'Of course it is a trap; and it is for you to get out of it.'

I could feel my heart beating. I seemed to be all heart and no body. 'I don't know what to do!'

'Feel the answer.'

Taking a deep breath, I exhaled slowly. I was now visibly shaking.

'Well?'

'You've put me in a terrible position!'

'I have done no such thing,' he replied. 'You are your own position.'

'But it's synthetic!'

'What is?'

'Whatever's in this tray.'

'Am I synthetic?'

'No.'

'I am in that tray.'

I looked at Sabazius, then at the black grain. 'What are you saying to me?'

'I am saying that history is in *you*, not in it.'

I hesitated, then pressed the tip of a finger against one of the grains and extracted it from the box; it looked like a tiny fleck of coarse graphite.

'You don't have to swallow it; just put in on your tongue.'

'Is it that potent?'

He put his head back and laughed.

'I'm sorry, but I'm scared,' I said, staring at him. 'I've never taken anything like this in my life.'

'You still think it is a drug?'

'Isn't it?'

'It is The Awakener.'

'So you keep saying – but what *is* The Awakener?'

'It is whatever you think it is.'

'That's mystification,' I said.

'No, it is the truth. If you think it is a drug, then it is a drug.'

'I'm stuck,' I said.

'What does it look like?'

'Graphite.'

'Then it's graphite,' he said, smiling at me.

'It's so gritty. So hard.'

'It's special.'

'Will it dissolve?'

'No.'

'Then what's the point of putting it in my mouth?'

'Trust me.'

'Oh dear,' I said, seeing the door of his trap closing on me.

'What better time to trust than when so unsure?'

I was still shaking, and there was nothing I could do about it.

'It's up to you,' he said.

I looked at his face, looked right into it for some sign of dishonesty but could detect none. And then quite suddenly my hand came up and I decided to do as he asked – it was as if the computing part of my brain had finally solved some cryptic puzzle and given me the go-ahead.

'Bravo!' he said.

The grain felt like it looked.

'When will I know it's working?'

'You'll know.'

I looked away, looked back at him, took a deep breath and lent forward on my knees.

'Relax.'

Easier said than done. I took another deep breath.

'You are not without courage.'

I accepted his observation and said, 'You're right, it isn't dissolving.'

The hardness of the grain mystified me; how could it be a drug if it didn't dissolve. I took another, and then another deep breath; it was as if my breathing was suddenly under someone else's control.

'Do you see,' said Sabazius, 'you are now breathing with your heart.' My puzzled expression made him add, 'It is the heart that breathes, Peter. Why? Because it is the heart that feels.' He paused. 'The heart is the pulse of man's life.'

'And the blood?'

'The blood carries life to every part of the organism.'

For some reason I blurted out. 'What have I got myself into?'

'You've got yourself into a mess,' he replied. 'You're just a big mess inside.'

'Correct,' I said. 'A mess. My mess. Your mess. Our mess. Their mess. A me-eeeeessssss.'

'Breathe,' he said.

'What?'

'Breathe.'

'I am breathing.'

'I can't hear you.'

I began to breathe so that he could hear me.

'That's better.'

'I ...'

'Yes?'

The words would not come; they congealed in my mouth and I was suddenly so afraid that I spat the little grain right across the room. Something was happening and I wanted to stop it but there was nothing I could do. I couldn't speak, and without warning I couldn't move either.

'Close your eyes,' said Sabazius.

I resisted his request. He got up and came over to me, bent down and closed my eyes with his finger tips. It was as if I were dead and he was delivering the last rites.

'*Kalee-neekhta*, Peter,' he said in Greek. And again, '*Kalee-neekhta.*'

5 ✤ *The eye of the awakener*

After about an hour Sabazius released me from a deep, blank sleep, got me to my feet and walked me around my flat until I was again physically oriented. Then, with a cheery slap on the back, he informed me that we were going out. Wrapped firmly in The Awakener, I found myself on Oxford Street, with the back of my head throbbing like a Jew's harp, and Sabazius's arm around my shoulder much of the time as he steered me this way and that. In every direction I saw faces torn with an inner agony; a fleeting agony rising up like a shadow to demolish human beauty and dignity. I looked and I looked and could not at first understand what it was I was seeing; then it began to dawn on me that what I was seeing was a highly developed form of what we think of as 'normality' – the normality of faces racked from the inside with all kinds of emotion, but apparently normal on the outside but for the odd twitch or two. The odd twitch or two had now become magnified into a highly visible stream of distortions signifying that all was not well with the world.

'It's too much,' I said, glancing at Sabazius. 'I don't think I can take any more …'

'This is only level one,' was his startling reply. 'The Awakener has three levels.'

'Are they all as bad as this?'

He laughed, steered me through a knot of tourists. 'What you are seeing is not "bad",' he said quietly, 'it is the truth of what is.'

'So what do the other levels contain?'

'The others are the natural extensions of what you are now seeing; but they can only be seen and felt when certain things in you come together.'

'When will I enter the second stage?' I asked.

'When you look, of course.'

I allowed my eyes to fasten on objects and people, to enter into them beyond vision. 'They are still the same,' I said; but even as the words tumbled out of my mouth something happened.

There was a beautiful girl walking towards us. She was tall and elegant with a full figure, and carried an expression of worldly contempt.

'Look!' urged Sabazius.

Suddenly she was no more.

In her place there was now a ball of colour, a violent oval shooting out flecks of green and red in thick clusters. I would have stopped, but Sabazius took me firmly by the arm and dragged me forward.

She pulsated past.

'I could barely see her!' I exclaimed.

'She is buried in jealousy and anger,' he said to me. 'That is her penalty.'

Each time I allowed a vision to erupt, people changed into coloured ovals. Oxford Street, it seemed, was a street of anger.

'This is nothing,' said Sabazius suddenly. 'If you reach the third stage then you will *know* what really exists.'

'Does it too come through looking?'

He was silent for some seconds, then he said: 'It comes through accumulation and looking.'

'What kind of accumulation?'

He laughed, wetted his lips. 'What you *are* at any given moment is your accumulation,' he said, 'and if your accumulation is not quite right, if it has a blockage, then the third stage will not appear.'

'Then my "accumulation" is my history?'

'Correct. But that does not automatically mean that you have become every part and section of that history. When I speak of accumulation, it is to that I refer. You *are* your history, but you do not as yet know or recognize it.'

'Only parts of it.'

'Yes. The third stage depends on what you have become; in other words, what you have felt in the true sense of that word. Memory is your history in detail. You carry it with you at all times, and in moments of emptiness you enter into it, or are thrust into it, seeing this, or that, bringing together sections which do not appear to be related.'

'So when you are finally all of it simultaneously,' I said, 'then you are a Man of Feeling?'

He drew me to a halt and looked at me. 'No,' he said, 'A Man of Feeling just attempts more than others. It could be said that a Man of Feeling is continually becoming a Man of Feeling as he becomes his history, just as those who are not yet Men or Women of Feeling are continually approaching that level through momentary glimpses of what they are. There are two "alls": there is the *all of the moment*, and there is the *all of the end*. To become what you have suggested is to reach the historical end, the nothing of being.'

'How can that be?'

'To "be" your history totally,' he said forcefully, 'is to no longer remember it, for at that point accumulation ceases and you enter Elsewhere with a roar.'

'Roar?'

'The roar of a liberated man.'

We traversed Piccadilly Circus, Leicester Square, and wound slowly down towards the Embankment. I had become immersed in considering what he meant by the word 'roar', and as I thought about it, trying to equate it with what he had said, I suddenly saw a large triangle, its point facing down, flowers and blossoms growing up inside of it. I was momentarily stunned.

Sabazius, knowing that something had happened, stood by me silently.

'It's gone …' I said.

I described quickly what I had seen.

He looked puzzled.

'Is it unusual to see a triangle?' I asked.

He said that it was not unusual, but that he had not expected me to see it.

'Why?'

'How can I, Alexis Sabazius, determine the direction of your will?' he replied mysteriously.

I smiled at him.

'Don't glory in it,' he warned, 'or it will melt.'

Understanding what he meant, I said: 'I feel as if I have *something* built around me, Alexis. It's almost tangible.'

'You are being sewn up,' he replied. 'The Awakener is being gentle with you.'

'Isn't it always?'

'Sometimes it kills a man.'

'Why?'

He sighed and tilted his head. His smile was almost sad. 'To take The Awakener without preparation,' he explained, 'can be like walking into a furnace. It requires courage and knowledge.'

When we reached the Thames, he said: 'Sometimes a man has to make a decision without knowledge, that is why he must have courage; but his courage must be fashioned out of prior knowledge, the knowledge of his history, and his feeling for the path.'

'Is there only one path?'

'Every man is his own path, every path is a man.'

'So religions are wrong,' I said, almost hopefully.

'Nothing is wrong if it leads a man to Elsewhere,' replied Sabazius, 'and even things which lead men away from Elsewhere are not wrong, they are just useless.'

'How does one recognize a useless path?'

'By fixing your eye on it, and looking,' was his answer. 'A useless path has no life in it.'

I did not have to ask what he meant by 'life', for something in me said: 'The life of a path is joy ...'

Sabazius laughed and slapped me hard on the back with the flat of his hand. 'Now you are asking yourself questions!' he exclaimed. 'I can see it in your face.'

'But I didn't actually ask anything,' I said. 'The moment you said life, and I heard the word, an answer sprang into my mind, just like that!'

'You have learned something very important,' said Sabazius. 'You have learned to ask questions without asking.'

'How can one do that?'

'You received an answer immediately because you were working outside of logic's limitation,' he replied. 'When that happens, you "experience" the answer, just as you experienced the question. In other words, you *know and feel* simultaneously.'

'Why is it then,' I said, reverting to the logic he had

47

dispensed with, 'that experience in general does not illumine the mind?'

'Experience,' said Sabazius, 'has been relegated to the position of memory bric-a-brac. It is no longer the stuff of life. It has become a story told endlessly to friends, an elaborate jungle of second-hand information.'

I shook my head in amazement, for he had pinpointed the essence in an immediate reply.

'We had better go back now,' he said.

'Am I going to miss the third level?'

'It would seem so.'

'Does that mean there's something wrong with me?'

'Of course not. It only means that something has not yet come together.'

'I saw the triangle.'

'That is something else,' said Sabazius.

We emerged on the Strand and headed for Trafalgar Square. Each time I fixed my eyes on someone they changed into a coloured ball and rolled by like a firework on legs. By some means, The Awakener had opened my visual senses; but even under its powerful influence I still had to perform the visual trick of *seeing* what was there. The door was unlocked, but I had personally to pull it open. The one thing which never ceased to amaze me was my energy level. It seemed that the little generator under my rib-cage was pouring out a flood of impetus. I did not have energy, I was energy! And this energy I felt was not only in myself, it was all around, bubbling and bursting from every stone and tree. Was this how Sabazius felt all the time? My scrutiny of him must have been rather blatant, for he said suddenly:

'What are you looking at?'

I told him what I had been thinking.

'Ah,' he said,'you want to know how I feel in myself.'

'Yes.'

We reached a fountain and he drew me to a halt. 'I will do better than tell you,' he said, grinning at me. 'I will show you.'

Behind him the waters sprayed.

'Look at me!' he demanded.

At first, there was just Sabazius wrapped in a black coat, and then suddenly the flesh of his face and hands melted away, dissolved, and as I watched, reformed into an intricate pattern of hieroglyphics, each wedge of characters built on the next. He was no longer Alexis Sabazius, he was a 'word', a message of other things.

'That is what I am,' said Sabazius when the vision had gone.

'You were made of stone!'

He chuckled and we moved off again. 'I showed you my history,' he said, 'and someday you will show me your history.'

I was suddenly sad. 'Maybe I will never be able to show you my history,' I said, realizing the size of the task which faced me. 'I don't seem to have the strength of mind.'

'But you have seen the world!' He held out his arms as if to embrace it physically. 'If a man can see the world he is not weak.'

I tried to smile, but the feeling of being useless persisted. How could I ever hope to be like Alexis Sabazius? He was a man of strength. He had applied himself to all the tasks, given his life away that he might find it ... and he had found it – or so it seemed.

We walked back to the flat at what seemed breakneck speed. Sabazius remained silent. I played half-heartedly with my new-found vision, switched it on and off, teased it into action; but I was all the while getting lower in spirit, flat and empty and horrified by what I could feel in myself. We had just turned off Oxford Street when it happened. I let out a yelp and stood motionless. Sabazius spun around, gazed at me with interest, then, without a word, lifted me from the pavement and carried me home like a sick child. The next thing I knew I was being submerged in a bath of cold water. I struggled for breath, but he kept pushing me under, my hair firmly knotted in his hand.

'How do you feel?' he kept asking.

'Everything's blurred!'

He submerged me again.

'And now?'

I opened my eyes and saw the green tiles of the bathroom.

Pulling me out of the bath he rubbed me vigorously with a towel. Then he threw it at me, laughing, and walked through to the lounge. When I joined him a few minutes later in my dressing gown, I found that he had made a large jug of coffee.

'You reached the third level,' he said before I could speak.

'I don't rightly know what happened.'

'What were you thinking about just before you broke through?'

'I felt miserable,' I said. 'I came to the conclusion I wasn't worthy of what you were trying to do.'

'And what am I trying to do?' asked Sabazius.

'You're trying to make me into a Man of Feeling.'

'I am not,' he retorted adamantly. 'I am guiding you to the point where you will become a Man of Feeling of your own volition.'

I stood quietly in the middle of the room and stared at him. 'There were no longer any people,' I said slowly, 'just a fuzz of energy darting this way and that.'

Sabazius asked me to be more precise.

'That's all I can remember.'

He poured me a coffee and told me to sit down. 'What kind of energy?'

'Bright energy.'

'What colour?'

'It was all kind of silvery.'

'Did you see any shapes?'

'No ... '

He pursed his lips, sucked at his cheeks. 'But everything totally changed?'

'Yes.'

He seemed satisfied. 'You found what was blocking the path,' he said, glancing at me. 'Didn't you?'

I nodded, then breathed deeply to steady myself. 'Arrogance,' I said.

'Yet so subtle an arrogance,' he replied. 'On the surface you were meek; but under that face of yours ran a mighty pride.'

'You knew?'

'Yes, I knew it; but I could not tell you. If I had tried, you would have played games with me, and yourself. It would have been interesting, but a waste of valuable time.'

As we turned that corner, everything in me had fused into a monumental accusation. I felt a small knife-edged pain ricochet throughout my body. I was laid bare to myself, and the horror choked me like a metal hand. Parts or segments of me were laughing out loud, pointing at me in ridicule. And then the pain tore at me, gutted me like a carcass.

'I thought I was going to die,' I said, looking straight at Sabazius. 'It was dreadful.'

'But you did not die.'

Freedom. The people of Oxford Street vanished as something in me surged up blindingly and lodged in my head. There were no people ... there never had been! Just silver energy cascading in all directions; and in front of me Sabazius, Sabazius in his black coat, staring at me – unchanged!

'What was it I saw?'

'The day we met,' said Sabazius, 'you saw the world, felt its huge being radiating across the horizon; but today you saw the inhabitants of that world, manifestations of that being, energy particles of the world-mind. That is what you saw.'

'But they were no longer people!'

'They are what they are,' he replied. 'If you saw them as oscillating energy, then that is what they are.'

'But what about their ability to love, to feel, to ... ?'

'You may think it a terrible thing for me to say,' said Sabazius, 'but that ability is generally no more than a subtle exploitation. Under it lies a relentless machinery, a blind electrical history. If man were awake, he would see it; but he is not awake, he merely walks in his sleep.'

'How is that possible?'

'It is possible,' was his reply, 'because he does not *see* when he looks. He stumbles about on his world because there is no light, only a glimmer, a mere suggestion of seeing. If man could see, he would tear his civilizations down and rebuild them overnight. He would feed the hungry and clothe the poor, ask forgiveness of his neighbour and sleep in dignity, not dream-ridden fear. It is because he does not see, does not even know that he has lost himself, that he walks dressed in artificial splendour to a roarless death.'

I was numb inside.

The words he had fitted together out of his seeing left me speechless.

'Your coffee's getting cold.'

That was when I laughed.

It came up from deep inside of me like an object, entered my mouth, and fell out into the room. My jaws cracked open. I smiled with my head! I turned to say something, but the words congealed and would not come out. And then suddenly there was a circular rainbow in the room, a bright multi-coloured circle with a black centre: the centre was an eye – it winked!

'Alexis!' I managed to yell.

His head was clasped in his hands.

The eye approached slowly until it was suspended above the little table, then it began to vibrate, its colours merging and separating like a child's top. Was I going mad? Why did Sabazius not move?

There was a sudden 'pop' and the room was empty.

When I looked at him again, he was drinking his coffee as if nothing had happened.

'Did you see it?' I asked.

'See what?'

'The eye!'

'You saw an eye?'

'It was in the middle of a round rainbow!'

'Really?'

'What was it?' I asked fearfully.

His body heaved with laughter. 'You saw the eye of The Awakener,' he replied, as if it were something quite ordinary. 'You're very fortunate.'

I closed my eyes and took a deep breath, then I said: 'How can a drug have an eye?'

He frowned at me, fitting an expression of mock horror onto his face. 'You think what has happened to you today is the result of a drug!'

'But – '

'It is *in you*!' he bellowed, and for a moment I thought I saw a flicker of anger.

'I'm sorry ...'

'For whom?'

'For saying what I said.'

'But you are not sorry for what you said,' he retorted. 'You are sorry for yourself because you cannot pigeonhole what has happened into a logic-box. Through The Awakener you have seen what exists in the world, and through The Awakener you have even seen The Awakener! *What more do you want?*'

I reached shakily for my coffee and drank it down. 'Maybe

you've got the wrong man,' I said.

Sabazius thought carefully, then he said: 'When I first saw you, you were only an ear and a blurred eye sticking out of energy: but now you are half a face.' He paused to let his words sink in. 'You are being born, Peter. You are emerging from the stream of cause and effect ... so don't talk of dying at birth!'

6 ❖ *Making boxes*

It was Sabazius who instigated my taking a part-time job in a cardboard-box factory. I was to work three days a week, for which I would be paid a small wage. Never in my life had I had such an occupation! The owner of the factory, a huge Turk with a scowling face and a mouthful of decaying teeth, looked me up and down, chewed a fat lip, and decided I was okay. My past working history melted away as I looked through the window of the tiny office and saw the conveyor belt and the brown and grey boxes being pushed into shape by a crew of men and women all around my own age. When I returned to the flat, Sabazius was waiting for me.

'Well,' he asked, 'did you get the job?'

I said I had, but the idea of it did not appeal one little bit.

'And why would that be?'

'Isn't it obvious?'

'Ah!' said Sabazius. 'Your pride is hurt.'

'I'm a linguist,' I told him. 'I've travelled the world first-class. What do you expect?'

'I expect you to make boxes,' was his reply. 'It isn't as silly as it looks.'

I shrugged and walked through to the kitchen to make us coffee. 'Have you ever met the owner?'

'Yes,' he shouted back. 'I've known him for many years.'

'Where did you meet?'

'In India.'

'From what I saw of the factory,' I said with sarcasm, 'it might as well be in India!'

When I turned, Sabazius was standing directly behind me. I had not heard him approach.

'There is something I want you to do,' he said, ignoring my surprise. 'I want you to say nothing of your past to anyone who works there. And if they ask you directly, be vague, avoid the issue, change the subject.'

'Why?'

'Because that is how it must be,' was his reply, 'at least for the moment.'

'But they'll think I've got something to hide.'

'Then let them think it. What does it matter what they think?' He paused, and then he said ominously: 'And watch the Turk carefully, do not anger him, I have seen him kill a man with one hand.'

'In India?'

'Yes.'

'What happened?'

'Nothing happened. He was not suspected.'

'You're telling me that my employer is a murderer!'

'Only technically.'

I asked him to explain.

'The less you know the better,' said Sabazius, taking the coffee pot from me. 'If you have no knowledge of a man's history, you cannot judge him.'

'That's true,' I said, 'but what you've just told me is a slice of history I would prefer not to have known.'

'I only told you so that you would not get into trouble with him. If you do your work, and behave yourself, everything will be fine.'

My future was temporarily laid out. I was to make boxes and assemble them in virtual silence – and not annoy my murdering boss!

The factory, on that first morning, with its slapping overhead belts of canvas and droning generator, produced in me an abject sense of horror. I was out of my mind to do such work! Why had I allowed Sabazius to talk me into it? The Turk, his body a mass of white shirt and braces, pointed to a small lean-faced man:

'That is how it is done,' he said thickly. He pointed out my space. 'You will soon pick it up.'

My training session was over.

Draw the flattened box towards you, slide the flat of your hand inside and turn it up, insert a second hand and push apart, draw the flaps in and bend them until the sliced notches lock, turn the box the other way up, bend the opposite flaps out and over the sides, twist your body round and lay the box on the conveyor going in the other direction. Within minutes, I had refined the operation and reduced the number of movements required. Within an hour I was an expert. Or so I thought.

A bell rang at ten-thirty.

The conveyor belt stopped, ushering in a deep silence. The lean-faced man looked at me, nodded, said it was a tea-break, and asked if I had a cup.

'I haven't got one,' I said.

'Didn't he tell you?' He meant the Turk.

'Never mentioned it.'

'That was stupid. Better bring one tomorrow.'

A small boy with bright, dark eyes and a swarthy complexion carried in a tray on which were a selection of cups and mugs. The 'boxers' – that's what we were called – took their personal china and returned to their positions quietly. There was not, as I had expected, an agitated buzz of voices, just a murmur of people talking in subdued tones. Were they all afraid of the Turk?

'It's very quiet,' I said to the man.

'It's been like this since I came.'

'Have you worked here long?'

'A few weeks.'

I nodded absent-mindedly and took stock of my surroundings. The walls, bare brick painted with a scratchy white, had small windows near the ceilingless roof. They were all shut. Fluorescent tubes had been suspended above the work benches – two of them were on the blink. At the far end of the factory – some twenty yards away – the Turk sat with his back to us. At his side was the boy.

Incomprehensibly, the bell which had announced the tea-break did not ring at its termination, there was just the sudden whir of canvas above, turning the diminishing cogs linked to the conveyors. We were off again: draw the flattened box towards you, slide the flat of your hand inside and turn it up, complete the process, and then do it again, and again, and again . . .

Sabazius, I should point out, had talked me into doing this kind of work with a very plausible piece of cosmological reasoning. He had said that to make and assemble boxes, or anything similar, was like taking a holiday from ego consciousness. Unlike more demanding and intricate occupations, where the individual was called upon to exert personality projection, or high technical concentration, to assemble boxes produced in you a state of mind equal to, and sometimes greater than, deliberate meditation. It was, he said, a vegetable state which could be transformed into a glorious exercise of self-discovery. Everything in you was working. The intellectual sense was being held in check by an automatic modicum of concentration; the body in all its aspects was being held in check by a repetition of fluid physical movement; and above all, self, now open to scrutiny by the Central Personality, would slowly manifest, the intensity of its presence growing as the meditation or awareness cycle lengthened through practice.

When I walked out of the Turk's factory that evening, I was depressed but enlightened. My attempts to *Identify* self had mostly been abortive. Continually, on following the instructions Sabazius had given, I found myself returning from some kind of mental reverie. I had visited the Caribbean, talked animatedly with friends (on important subjects of course!), argued with enemies, dictated attitudes to past subordinates, elevated myself (I?) to numerous stations in the cosmological structure, bought and sold imaginary possessions, returned to my old job with its attendant security, flirted with oriental girls whom I had known, and performed a host of other unmentionable mental contortions; all to escape my basic reason for being in that factory – to know self. I was, to say the least, a monumental flop.

But I knew it!

At the end of three days, through concentrated effort and stubborn alliance with my conscious Central Personality, I managed to intensify knowledge of self and, at the same time, *look* at the boxes I handled. For something like eight minutes, a scattered eight minutes diffused through a twenty-four-hour internal battle, I glimpsed self. This showed me clearly that I was, most of the time, floating in a semi-conscious dream world of internal and external bric-a-brac. I was a shadow; but a shadow with the possibility of becoming solid. On the Friday evening, with rain plummeting wave-like against the window, I realized how accurate Sabazius had been, and simultaneously noticed a slight change in my attitude. But this was only a flash of insight (only?), a momentary cognition, or ignition, based on an awareness of mental density. When I attempted to Identify self through this density, the shockwave was intense: a double backlash from self and object which electrified the personality-core. The density, brought about through making the attempt to self-Identify, was each time strengthened, allowing the next attempt – if it were rapidly made – to heighten the self-awareness principle and produce a further state of density, so completing the cycle. But to continue indefinitely with this process was impossible, for at all times other parts of the mind, the sub-personalities and *their* attitudes, brought it grinding to a halt by short-circuiting the subtle psychic action, and dragged me back into awake-dream. As I sat there in my chair thinking of the process, a deep dread overtook me, for if this was the path, the doorway through which one had to push oneself to find self, then I doubted if I would ever manage it. But then I remembered that Alexis Sabazius was a man like myself, albeit a Man of Feeling, yet basically flesh and blood, bone and tissue, cell and atom: a man, but cosmologically restructured through persistence.

I would persist.

My doorbell rang at ten the next morning. I let Sabazius in and finished preparing my breakfast. He seemed in good spirits, but said little. Over lemon tea and thickly buttered toast, I told him my thoughts of the night before.

'You've got it wrong,' he told me. 'To be persistent does not mean straining yourself. You must "allow" with gentleness what is in you to come out. If a baby is pulled violently into the world it suffers damage, and if you are pulled out of it you too will suffer damage. To work, in the sense a Man of Feeling uses it, is to continually *make room* for the "other" to manifest. That is why I said that meditation was living, for to live at all times in the sense of making room is to be deeply involved with self.'

'But it's such a battle of will!'

He nodded understandingly, then he said: 'If you can grasp what I mean by "making room", then you are well on the road to appreciating the nature of will. Will *is* to make room, not to strain or rupture the mind.' 'Will,' he continued, 'is a battle won, not a battle in progress. It is a battle won because the man who uses it has already won the battle long before. He is triumphant. He no longer has to exercise will; he *is* will. Do you see?' asked Sabazius.

'Clearly.'

'What do you see clearly?'

'That will is dynamic passivity.'

'Excellent!'

I felt pleased with myself.

'Do you know why will must be so?' he asked.

'No.'

'Because it is the purest expression of Elsewhere known to man. When a man masters the medium of will, he is a true creator, not just an interpreter of what is, but a participator in what is self-evident. To *become* will is the final leap in becoming a Man of Feeling, for it is all that he is, gathered up and given to self. He is simultaneously the master of self, yet mastered by self. He is stable and immovable.'

'But how does one approach such a state?'

'There is no approach,' replied Sabazius. 'But if you wish to think in "directions", then the approach to will is identical with the approach to self. I will give you an example. When you draw a perfect circle, the pen or pencil must necessarily start somewhere. But when the circle is complete, the starting point is lost, for it was only a temporary start, an illusion. The circle is man's guide to all truth. So the approach, as you call it, does not exist in cosmological reality. Will has always existed perfect in the man, and only requires to be identified through self.'

'So I have a perfect will now!'

'No, self has a perfect will. That is why you must *I*dentify self.'

'It's very mathematical.'

He chuckled, sipped at his tea. 'It may appear so, but it has nothing to do with progressions as you understand them. Cosmic law is perfect because it is the Will of Elsewhere manifest in Time. But the Will of Elsewhere cannot be directly equated with man's logic of numerical progression, for the Will of Elsewhere spans that progression in an *ever-comprehending act of will*.'

'Alpha and Omega.'

'Just so.'

I felt suddenly awed by what I had heard. The idea of an 'ever-comprehending act of will' trembled through me, reduced me to silence.

'And that,' added Sabazius, 'is what man interprets as the "presence" of God.'

What I had thought of as removed from me, the distant, incomprehensible Elsewhere of Sabazius, was now in the room – self-evident. From what appeared to be a clinical dialogue had sprung the essence of all things related in perfect harmony. Objects, people, animals; indeed the whole universe moved and had its being within that will. It was all-encompassing, a blistering cosmological bubble ever becoming itself as we, the expression in-universe, returned fully self-willed! From deep inside me arose the words: 'To feel the earth is to witness will ...' I trembled visibly, for although the inner articulation had been mine, the source of that statement was undeniably self. I had, for the second time, heard or experienced self talking in me.

Sabazius stared at me hard, tilted his head in concentration. 'The boxes you have been handling will eventually contain things,' he said, 'but you are not a box, just as I am not a book, and because we are neither box nor book, we must continually make room for the other.'

'What other?'

'Other is the evolving principle of truth.'

'But isn't truth absolute in relation to Elsewhere?'

'Of course not,' replied Sabazius. 'Truth, which I call "other", is an expression of Elsewhere in Time. It evolves within the principle of the *ever-comprehending act of will* continually unfolding itself in Universe. Truth cannot be absolute, just as Elsewhere cannot be absolute; for "absolutism" is man's limited vision theologized.'

'So there is no end to truth.'

He chuckled at my statement, grinned all over as if I had coined a cosmic joke. 'Can you see one?' he asked.

'I can hardly see the beginning of it,' I replied, feeling all that had happened to me since I had met this extraordinary man gather into one incomprehensible question after another. 'It's breathtaking!'

Sabazius stood up suddenly. 'Did you know that the sun was shining?'

I glanced at the window. 'Do you want to go out?'

'Yes.'

'Where shall we go?'

'Where would you like to go?'

'Hyde Park?'

'I have a better idea,' he replied. 'Why don't we visit the Rhodope Mountains?'

'The where?'

From out of that lined face sprang a dazzling smile. 'The Rhodope Mountains lie above the Thracian plains,' he said. 'They are the home of the Sarakatsáns. I am a Sarakatsán.'

I laughed uneasily. 'That would be very nice,' I said, 'but we'd never get back in time for lunch.'

He was still staring at me.

I said, haltingly: 'I don't understand.'

Taking off his jacket and shirt, Sabazius stood in the centre of the room and raised his hands high above his head; then, drawing in an enormous breath of air he expanded his chest – barrel-like anyway in response – some three or four inches. He then held the breath within him for something like thirty or forty seconds (although it may have been longer), and exhaled it slowly through his open mouth and partially closed throat. He instructed me to do the same.

'What will it do?' I asked.

He did not answer, just waited for me to strip off my shirt and tie. When I had completed the exercises, he showed me a number of other ways to breathe, some simple, some incredibly complicated; then he outlined in what order they should be used, and with what intensity. At the end of an hour I was exhausted and dizzy. I felt curiously displaced, not quite in myself, rather like after having fainted.

'Now,' said Sabazius. 'Lie out full-stretch on the floor, make yourself comfortable, relax your limbs as I have shown you, and allow yourself to drift towards the edge of sleep. But no further!'

I did as he asked.

For some inexplicable reason (inexplicable at the time) he lay down beside me and linked his little finger through mine. 'Imagine yourself drawn up into your head,' he said quietly. 'And don't be alarmed when you lose physical sensation, that is what is supposed to happen. It is perfectly natural.'

We lay there on the floor together, two human beings experimenting with knowledge preprepared, a system of exactitude handed down from out of a misty past. The last thing Sabazius said to me was:

'I am joined to you, so do not be frightened.'

The grey twilight zone of mind entered, I lay perfectly still, and waited. At first there was nothing, just the sound of our shallow breathing; our bodies were so filled with oxygen we hardly needed to breathe. I toppled over the brink twice, but a slight pressure from Sabazius's finger linked me again with that subtle region of balance.

And then my body slowly disappeared!

It was like a kind of numbness, a creeping paralysis which ate me up from the outer extremities until I was only a head; then it rose to my chin, and my nose, and then to my eyes ... and then there was a distinct 'click'!

A tremendous pressure attacked the back of my head, as if part of it were trying to work loose. I felt the top part of my body slowly rise, ever so slowly rise, in a gentle swaying upwards motion until I was standing – or appeared to be standing – on my feet. That's when I remembered I was somehow linked to Sabazius, and on glancing in his direction, saw him standing beside me: a glistening Sabazius!

Freedom!

When I tried to move everything went haywire. I wobbled, fell without falling, felt myself being dragged back, back to, well – I didn't know.

We were still in the room, everything visible; but by some means had transformed ourselves into ... and it was at that point I shook with fear and panic, for at my feet were feet, and those feet belonged to a body, and the body was mine!

I stared at myself. Stared down from somewhere above; finally I looked at the other body, for Sabazius too had sprung out of his physical shell, left himself lying peacefully on my brown carpet ...

'Come,' said Sabazius.

Still linked by our little fingers we moved across the room and through the window, out into the bright morning sunshine, afloat and splendid, free as birds. When I spoke I could not hear my words; but I knew that I had said them, and Sabazius had heard, for he smiled at me, grasped me by both hands, and closed his eyes.

Blackness.

Bold shining blackness and a sense of incredible speed. A mere second, or the fraction of a fraction of a second, and then light, a dazzling yet soft light coming up from below and stretching out into a horizon of powder blue.

The Thracian plains ... and beyond them, in mighty splendour – the Rhodope Mountains!

7 ❀ *The essence of being*

Macedonia in the twinkling of an eye!

Linked (by more than a little finger?) to Sabazius, I was carried hither and thither to see this, and to see that, and at one point, found myself standing among a flock of mountain sheep listening to the tinkle of bells.

Then I was shown men.

The Sarakatsáns looked more like monks than shepherds. They were tall, angular men with eagle faces and sharp eyes. Like Sabazius, their faces betrayed an interaction with nature, a deep involvement with wind, snow, rain and sun. Black-cloaked and hooded they stood, their bodies bound in the very animals they tended, in their hands tall crooks carved with snakes, dragons, dolphins and the heads of rams. We blurred from village to village, from mountain fortress to grassy plain, and at all times there were sheep, and bells, and clusters of little cone-shaped huts.

From high above the Rhodope Mountains, Sabazius pointed out the outline of Bulgaria, and intimated that to my left lay Yugoslavia, and to my right, Turkey. How was it possible to see such things? By what medium had we travelled? Who, or what, were the two bodies lying peacefully on my lounge floor?

Glistening, we hung suspended. Never had I felt such freedom, such joy. What we saw was real, but when I tried to touch it, savour it physically, it melted through me like a wisp of smoke, a projected slide.

We returned to my flat in the same incomprehensible manner, and like two aircraft coming in to land, slowly levelled out, dropped lower and lower, and merged with the physical.

Numbness.

A trickle of sensation in my fingertips. The slow pounding of my heart as the machinery of my body woke up.

When I opened my eyes, Sabazius was already on his feet.

He was standing as he had stood before, arms held high above his head, chest expanded mightily in the act of breathing.

'Fill your lungs,' he commanded.

I obeyed immediately.

There was a curious realization of weight. I struggled upwards, held on to the sofa for support, and slowly, almost painfully, stood erect.

Sabazius, having completed his exercises, pulled my arms from my sides and lifted them as high as they would go. Holding both wrists with one hand, he then placed a palm on my stomach and pressed hard.

'Expand the chest,' he ordered, 'and hold it there. When you breathe, breathe from below the chest rapidly, building up the expansion until it is perfect.' He then placed the palms of my hands together and told me to push upwards with each inhalation. 'This will boil your blood,' he remarked casually, and he smiled, as if the term 'boiled' had just occurred to him.

Later, over coffee, he said: 'You have just travelled on the lowest level a Man of Feeling knows. Almost anyone can do it with practice. It is nothing special.'

'It was the most marvellous experience I have ever had,' I said, the freshness of those mountains still vivid in my mind. 'But it defies all reason!'

He nodded, licking his lips.

'How can a man have two bodies?' I asked him.

'A man has two eyes.'

'Yes, but they belong to one body.'

'A man can see with those eyes in two different ways.'

'Are the eyes he sees with when he looks properly part of the other body?'

'There isn't really any *other* body,' he replied. 'That is the trap everyone falls into. What you think of as the other body is still you. As I have said to you, a man does not have a body, he *is* a body. It therefore follows that he does not have another body, but that he is that other, and if he is that other as he is the physical replica of that other, then he is the same.'

I was somewhat confused. He had started out to say that a man did indeed have two bodies, and ended up proving that this was not the case.

I questioned Sabazius on this.

65

'When I said that a man has two eyes,' he replied, 'I was not saying what you concluded. I was saying that two eyes function as one, see as one, are part of the same circuit of sight. It could be said that a man has five, or even seven bodies; but that would not be true either, for they are merely seven manifestations of *himself*, of his intrinsic Being.'

'But logically it could be said so?'

'Anything can be said logically,' was his reply. 'All you need is a beginning, and you can reach what appears to be an end. But a man does not have a beginning, he is immortal in two directions, a perfect circle of being expressed in universe, and as such, beyond logic.'

'I've always thought of immortality as pertaining to the future.'

'But what is the future?' asked Sabazius.

'What lies ahead, I suppose.'

'So what lies behind is the past?'

'Yes.'

His bellow of laughter made me freeze. 'And I suppose this is the present?' he said.

'What else?'

'What a neat little box that is! Behind you is the past, in front the future, and around you the present, eh!'

I nodded.

'I'm afraid they do not exist,' he said softly. 'The past, the future and the present are one and the same thing. They are contained, if one can even use that word, in the *ever-comprehending will* of Elsewhere made manifest. You will soon know what I mean, for you will experience what some people call The Moment of Eternity, and others, like myself, the Essence of Being. It is because man has a fragmented vision that he has broken them apart, and it is through the healing of that vision that he becomes aware of the world, and thereafter enters Elsewhere with a roar.'

The word 'healing' soothed me. It suggested a process of bringing together all man's shredded consciousness of world and universe. I saw that I was not mixed up in some kind of magic or forbidden nonsense, but being introduced to a gigantic cosmic plan which totally and utterly defied the penetration of reason and logic; that is, the reason and logic of fragmented man, but was totally open to man reborn in the spirit of oneness.

'You understand me?' he asked.

'Yes.'

'What do you understand?'

I laid out my thoughts carefully, explained the momentary feeling that all things were truly related in harmony.

'Quite so,' said Sabazius matter-of-factly. 'But at this moment you have only an intellectual appreciation of what I mean by the Essence of Being. It is something you must enter like a door, penetrate, and return from, before proper understanding can take place. It is too often the case that men of intellect grow fat and lazy inside because they can appreciate intellectually what others cannot. That is not enough, it is mere pleasure.'

'What happens to those who do not have the brains for it?'

'They are confronted by love.'

'In what way?'

'They develop a perfect will through prayer.'

'Prayer?'

'At first,' said Sabazius, 'a man who prays to his god asks for this and that, for this to happen, or that not to happen; but one day when he kneels or prostrates himself he is faced with a hard nothing, and the hardness of that nothing is the silence of love.'

'It sounds dreadful.'

'It seems dreadful to the man, at first,' he replied. 'In their ignorance they call it The Gates of Brass, or The Nothing Answer; for it generally happens when they have been asking too much, and for all the wrong reasons, and sometimes because they have come to an end of themselves, seeing their fragmented worthlessness. But whatever the path, they face the hard nothing, and the hard nothing grinds them into perfect beings like a millstone, and they emerge beautiful to behold, unstained and guileless.'

'I haven't seen many of them about,' I said.

'That is because they are too busy working,' was his reply. 'They are doing the will of their god, following the inner dictates of self revealed. And because they depend on joy as the mainspring of their peace, they are at all times deeply

67

involved in purified semi-conscious prayer.'

'So it is possible to know self without intellect being the guide-line?'

'What is intellect?' he asked rhetorically. 'It is what men use to destroy themselves with. It is the foundation of all the errors in this world, all the mistakes, all the wrong turnings, all the blundering, helpless sadness. Intellect, with its degrees and ramifications, has wilfully murdered millions upon millions of human beings in an endless stream of agony; and for those who use it for pleasure, it delivers them to a heartless vision, a profound emptiness and distaste for life. That is intellect,' said Sabazius with vigour. 'Who then can say that those who do not have enough of it are less human, less loved!'

His words produced in me a marked emotional reaction. I felt my eyes burn with tears, my pride wither, my reliance on that very instrument melt into a self-revealed vision of personal arrogance. I had all my life thought myself a sophisticated being, a man endowed with a favourable intellectual capacity; but it was now as dross, a dangerous machine which could make me into a machine, an internal object which could make me view the world and man as objects. But, as Sabazius had shown me from the very beginning, it could be transformed into an instrument of self-realization and revelation, a channel through which the *ever-comprehending act of will* could manifest itself in Time.

Trying to cover up my emotional reaction, I asked him something which had bothered me considerably. 'If man,' I said hesitantly, 'is an expression of Elsewhere manifest in Time, why did Elsewhere express man in the first instance, when, as the *ever-comprehending act of will*, Elsewhere knew that man would return?'

'You have answered your own question,' he said immediately. 'As you have said, man is an expression of Elsewhere as will, and as such, is an integral factor in Elsewhere's comprehension.'

'But –'

He held up a hand. 'No more,' he said. 'That is a question you will have to leave until a later date. To talk of it would be to jest.' He passed me a cigarette, lit it. 'The vision of a man,' he said softly, 'is a remarkable thing. It can span from a grain of dust to the ultimate reaches of universe in the time it takes to blink. It can see and feel that which is not evident in time, comprehend cosmic operations as it would the binding of two sticks, and on occasions, when it is perfectly tuned, even penetrate its origin like a knife through butter.' He looked at me steadily for a second or two. 'But to have such vision requires energy, and that energy is to be had from the world around us. It is continually streaming towards us in the form of sense perceptions, entering us in the form of air and food; but because we prefer the awake-dream to true consciousness, we take it in, and in a moment have squandered it: uttered it out as opinion; used it up in inner wrangling; burnt out its strength in fear, desire and ambition. Instead of gathering those energies,' he said with emphasis, 'transmuting them into the finer, subtler material needed for growth, man throws them to the wind, cultivates his appetite for fantasy, encourages other men to waste the enormous talents they have on peripherally meaningless activities; and the end result is a laughing, amused world devoid of direction. But you would not dare tell them it was so, for they would rend you to pieces, carve you up with humour.'

'And yet they have religions,' I said. 'They know there is something.'

'And they will die knowing it,' replied Sabazius. 'Every so often, when they get fed up with the emptiness around them, they consider death; but they might as well consider a sponge, or a can of soup, for they have no intention of pushing their minds *into* that death. They look at it, they explode with fear, and recoil back into the mess they have built for the very purpose of escape. As I said to you, a circle is perfect, and their perfection is awake-dream.'

'And yet many of my friends can be kind and helpful. Sometimes they go out of their way to offer assistance.'

'Of course they do. If they were incapable of showing human reactions they would not be able to become Men and Women of Feeling. But I will tell you something,' he added, his face reflecting a deep seriousness, 'if you want to lose most of these friends, see them scatter, then all you have to do is talk *Weltanschauung* for a few minutes. At first, they will seem to agree, but as your vision unfolds their attitudes will change, and their faces will become hard.'

'Why is that?'

'Because you will be threatening their awake-dream, making them look at a task, a pattern which frightens them.'

'But it may just be that they do not agree with what I am saying?'

'No,' said Sabazius, 'it is more than that. They will attack because they cannot afford to consider what you are saying. Inside,' he laid a hand on his chest, 'they *know*; but up here,' he moved the palm of his hand to his forehead, 'they reject. For if they do not reject, they have to change, and as they know they have no power to change, they attack.'

'I know some very intelligent people,' I retorted, wondering what they would think of his words.

He sighed patiently. 'Do you mean by that that an intellectual's opinion of the world must be recognized as valid?'

'It surely can't be discarded!'

'Then I'm wasting my time with you.'

'But why?'

'Because not only are you not yet your history, you do not even believe that you can become your history!'

'I don't agree.'

'How then can you take stock of an intellectual's opinion?'

'I suppose because I believe in tolerance.'

'By the sound of it,' replied Sabazius, 'you would believe in anything!'

His voice became quiet, but admonishing: 'The only tolerance you can afford to allow anyone is the tolerance necessary not to do them irreparable damage. When you have tested a man, and found that he not only lacks understanding of *Weltanschauung*, but that he rises against you because he cannot even "feel" it intuitively, then you must remove yourself from that man with grace. If you continue to disturb such a man's systems, then you may very well kill him, for he is not yet enough of his history to respond, and such profundity could paralyse him and turn him against even the "feeling" of truth he feels. That is the responsibility you must have, the sensibility you must develop. It is often far more important *not* to talk to a man, than it is to talk, just as it is sometimes important not to listen to a man who is talking for talking's sake.' He paused and seemed to be formulating his next sentence. 'But you must always take a stand for what you know to be true, for either you know it, or you do not know; either you are convinced, or you are a fake sampling yet another attractive, but basically meaningless idea. Your friends may be nice, Peter, but if they do not have any feeling for *Weltanschauung*, if they do not show any level of aptitude for it, then not only will they disagree with you, they will try to destroy you. For if they do not destroy you, you will remain always a constant threat to what they stand for, and they stand for awake-dream, the fantasy world where sleeping men talk, walk, and even appear to listen.'

'But why is it so?' I asked despondently. 'Why can't man find within him the power to change?'

'That is very simple,' said Sabazius. 'It is because they no longer understand what change means.' He chuckled, shook his head in wonder. 'But it is a curious fact that change is what all men everywhere are seeking. Every second of the day they are hunting for change, clamouring after it, manufacturing it in this way and that. The moment a man opens his eyes in the morning he thinks of change. When he dresses, he will choose a blue shirt instead of a white, a red tie instead of a green; and with that tie or shirt he will then choose this suit or that suit, and with that suit this pair of shoes or that pair of shoes. At all times man is attempting to change, trying to satisfy his craving, his desire for something different. A man will grow his hair, then suddenly cut it short; adhere to a particular style of dress, then suddenly "change his image"; believe in an ideology, then cast it aside. His desire for change penetrates from every item he owns even into his inner thoughts. So everything a man owns, believes in, saves up for, looks forward to, arranges, buys, sells, reads, studies, hopes for, is an indication of his ever unsatisfied desire for change. And this desire for change, reflected from every corner of the earth, has been termed professionally as "economics". All societies are built on an economic-change base, all human beings are governed by it, all change is due to it, all problems grow out of it. That is his stumbling block.'

'Then everything is against true change.'

'It has been replaced with distraction.'

'And the moment you try to bring about real change in

71

yourself, you are forcefully distracted from it.'

'Exactly. And the reason for that is this: Change as the world knows it can be bought and sold. It has been reduced to a commodity. So when a man speaks of true change to another, he is saying to that other that they must "work" at change, gather their natural forces of being together, make a decision not to be distracted.'

'No wonder they reject it.'

'But what courage,' said Sabazius, 'when they accept the challenge!'

I pondered what he had said, digested it. Then I said: 'But why can't they see what's happening?'

'Because they are blind, deaf and dumb,' he replied. 'They have invented for themselves the concept of a "comfortable world" to escape the responsibility of self-knowledge. It is a huge game, many many times more complicated than three-dimensional chess, and the whole aim of it is to sidestep four intrinsic questions: Who am I? What am I? Where am I? Am I?'

'That's a terrifying vision.'

'And what is more terrifying,' added Sabazius, 'is that the vision is true ...'

8 ❈ *Concerning men of power*

On Wednesday the Turk went mad.

I had been in a distracted mood all morning, and had finally succumbed to a random selection of thoughts concerning my future. I neither saw nor heard him approach, but when he reached me, his presence drew me back to reality and I looked up.

'What are you doing, Mr Derwent?' he asked.

'What do you mean?'

'Is my question so difficult?'

I looked at the cardboard box I had just assembled. 'Is there something wrong with it?' I asked.

'No.'

'Then I don't know what you mean,' I replied, confident that I had not overlooked anything.

Turning, he signalled to someone to stop the conveyor. When everything was silent, he said: 'I will show you, Mr Derwent.' Picking up some eight or ten boxes from the stack, he bunched them together like playing cards, and passed them over for inspection. 'What is wrong with them?'

I examined three of the boxes carefully, but found them perfect. 'They seem okay,' I said.

He sniffed loudly, stared at me. A ball of panic formed in my stomach. Everyone was listening.

'They are not okay,' he said pointedly. 'If there was nothing the matter with them I wouldn't be talking to you, would I?'

'They're as good as any of the others,' I replied, my panic momentarily overcome; 'at least they are to me ...'

He continued to stare at me fixedly. 'Compare them with the box you have just assembled,' he then said.

I did as he asked but could find nothing wrong. 'There's no difference.'

'Yes there is.'

'Then hadn't you better tell me,' I said irritably, trying to keep face before my fellow boxers. 'We seem to be holding up production.'

'Are you blind?'

'Do I look blind?'

. I regretted having said that, for it prompted him to say: 'You appear to be more stupid than blind, Mr Derwent!'

Afraid of him, yet incensed by his attitude, I retorted: 'Well if you're so bloody clever why don't you show me?'

The veins on his neck and forehead stood out as if summoned by my words. 'You are not only a fool,' he said gruffly, 'you're a lazy fool!'

'But how –'

'The difference between the box you have just made, and those I handed to you, is that one is assembled and the others aren't! Now do you see?'

'Why are you spelling out what's obvious?'

'Because they bloody well ought to be assembled!' he roared at me. 'It isn't me that's holding up production, it's you!'

I laid both hands on my bench to stop myself from shaking. 'How do you work that out?' I said, determined to keep my voice steady if nothing else.

'Because I know.'

'But how do you know?'

'You require proof?'

'Yes, I do,' I said stubbornly.

'Then I will supply you with proof,' he replied. He then pointed to the other conveyor belt where the finished boxes trundled towards the stacking bay ready for collection. 'At the end of that belt,' he said forcefully, 'is a small metal lever. Each time a box passes that point the lever is pushed back, and each time it is pushed back it triggers off a number on the quantity dial.'

'So?'

'So I know when production is down.'

'But your little dial doesn't tell you who the culprit is!' I exclaimed.

'No, but my eyes do,' was his reply. 'I've watched you get slower and slower for the last hour. You stopped altogether at one point!'

'I did not.'

He prodded at his chest viciously. 'I am telling you that you did!'

'But –'

'I want no more argument from you!'

'Now just a minute ...'

My point was never made. The Turk reached over, grabbed me by the scruff of the neck and hoisted me over the conveyor. The next thing I knew I was being forcefully flung out of the factory like a drunk at closing time.

Devoid of coat and jacket (my wallet was in the jacket), and dressed in a brown canvas apron tied with string, I made my way back to the flat discreetly. I was miserable and almost wet through due to a sudden shower, and had determined to charge the Turk with assault. The man had to be out of his mind. Later, however, when I was again in a smart suit and had regained my composure, I realized that I was secretly pleased. I had hated working in the factory, disliked the Turk enormously, and had only done it to keep Sabazius happy. Now I was free to do what I liked. To my surprise, Sabazius turned up that evening. I welcomed him in, and waited for an opportunity to unload my news. But I didn't have to, for he said suddenly:

'I told you not to annoy the Turk.'

'I don't know what story he's told you,' I said quickly, 'but I'll bet it's crazy!'

He stared at me, chewed at his mouth. 'You think the Turk is crazy?'

'I don't think it – I know it!'

'Why do you think that?'

'Only a madman would do what he did!'

'What did *you* do to make him angry?'

I described briefly everything that had happened.

'Then he had every right,' said Sabazius.

'To pick me up by the collar and throw me on the street like garbage!'

'I want you to go back.'

Words failed me.

'I want you to return to the factory tomorrow as if nothing has happened.'

'Why?' I managed to say.

'Because this is what you must do.'

'I couldn't. And anyway, he wouldn't let me in the door.'

'Try.'

'But for God's sake why?' I shouted. 'There must be a dozen other jobs I can do in London!'

'I want you to do that one.'

'I'm sorry,' I said flatly, knowing there was going to be trouble, 'I won't go back for you or anyone else.'

'I'm not asking you to go back for me,' he replied softly. 'I'm asking you to go back for you.'

'I can't for the life of me see what good it would do.'

'If you do not go back,' said Sabazius, and there was the hint of a smile on his face, 'I'll leave you to become a stick.'

'Please be reasonable,' I said, feeling my anger and astonishment turn into panic, 'surely there must be some other way?'

'There is no other way,' he said, and the tone of his voice told me plainly that I had a decision to make. 'Not for you.'

I stood motionless before him, my mind twisted into a knot of anxiety. If I refused, he might leave and never come back. But to balance this fear was a second fear, my fear of the Turk. There was a good chance that I might get myself beaten up, or worse. But if I lost Sabazius, I lost everything, for I had only started to comprehend what his teachings were all about, and without him I would be at a standstill. Ten, twenty seconds passed. One minute. I looked hard at Sabazius, knowing that I was standing on a knife's edge.

'Well?' he said.

I sighed. 'Okay,' I said.

Instead of congratulating me, he accepted my decision with a nod and changed the subject immediately. 'How good are your ears?' he asked.

'Fine, as far as I know.'

He told me to sit down in the centre of the room and close my eyes. After a short interval, he said: 'What can you hear?'

I concentrated. 'I can hear a clock.'

'And?'

'The traffic outside.'

'Anything else?'

'The sound of your breathing.'

He told me to open my eyes, then he said: 'I want you to choose three sounds and listen to them. Exclude all others; just pay attention to the three you pick.'

'In what order?'

He laughed. 'All at once.'

I opened my eyes in surprise. 'How can one listen to three sounds at the same time?'

'Have you ever tried it?'

'No.'

'Then now's your chance to find out.'

The Turk, my jacket, and all thought of going to the police station dissolved as I closed my eyes again and attempted what I thought to be impossible. I reasoned that it was possible to have a sound interrupt another; but to actually listen to three sounds simultaneously, well ...

'I can't do it,' I said almost immediately. 'I either hear one or the other.'

'Did you feel anything when you tried?'

'Yes, a kind of tingling. But it was only for a moment.'

'To listen to three sounds,' said Sabazius, 'is like entering between the voices of two singers and catching the density created by interaction. Some people would call it strain; but they would be quite wrong to call it that. When a human being listens to two or more voices, or instruments, they call their collective-sound-awareness "appreciation", and leave it at that. However, it is much more. The subtlety of such sound, no matter how it is manufactured, creates in the listener's system a tension between functions; but it is an unconscious tension which they express by saying: "Isn't that beautiful." All sounds produce automatically that relative tension; so when you are able to hear three sounds, or more, the tension produced, or what I prefer to call "density", draws the mind together and holds it steady. But to have full effect, it must be a conscious action.'

It took me twenty-five minutes to hear what I thought to be three sounds at the one time; and even then I was not sure if I really had. They seemed to come together one by one, the first holding the second, the second holding the third, until they were superimposed like identical spots of colour; three layers of colour merged, yet curiously separate. When he again asked me how I felt, I described the band-like feeling in my head, and voiced my doubts as to whether I had managed it properly.

'The first thing you must understand,' said Sabazius, 'is that to listen to three sounds consciously is totally different from allowing them to wash over you like water. The attempt you have made has produced a certain friction in your mind, and if followed through, that friction would assist you to hear four sounds, and the friction created by four would open up a fifth, and a sixth. I have known men who could hear, and hold, seven separate sounds consciously. They became very powerful men indeed.'

'How can sound make a man powerful?'

'All things contain energy,' he replied; 'I've already told you that. When people locked in awake-dream take in the world's impressions, whether it be a tree, or a building, or the sound of a bus, the energy of the world flows into them; but then immediately flows straight back out again because they do not have the conscious ability to hold on to it. So during a lifetime of awake-dream, they only take from the earth the portion of energy required to keep their biological and psychic functions ticking over. The rest they throw back. This is part of the meaning of awake-dream, an important part. But every so often something strange happens to those dreamers, they wake up for an instant, see the world, feel it around them, hear it breathe, know that they are alive; and before what has happened can have time to register, they are dragged back into the mindless to and fro of meaningless activity, and are again asleep. They remember those moments, talk about them, write about them, discuss them in serious chit-chat, but seldom do they realize their true meaning. My "funny feeling" or my "mystical moment" they will call it, when in actual fact all that happened to them was a moment of *proper consciousness*.' He looked at me gently for some time, then he said: 'That's why you must return to the factory: the friction will keep you awake.'

Suddenly, the idea behind the factory came alive for me.

'Do you see?' asked Sabazius.

'Yes.'

'Good,' he replied. 'Now you can start applying a little *heart* to the work.'

78

'The Turk's just going to let me walk in there tomorrow morning, isn't he?' I said.

'Yes.'

'Because you told him to?'

'No,' said Sabazius, 'because he is a Man of Feeling.'

'The Turk!'

'Does that surprise you?'

'It absolutely astonishes me!'

'Why?'

'How can such a violent man, a murderer, be a Man of Feeling?'

'Because Men of Feeling aren't always saints,' was his reply. 'Sometimes what you would term a "bad" man becomes a Man of Feeling; after all, it only requires a huge determination to acquire power over one's I's, and subsequently over the I's of others.'

'But what about self?'

'Self can warn; but it cannot stop a man making his decision to *exploit* the cosmos, rather than join it.'

'Did the Turk ... ?'

'The Turk fell foul of a passing god and was stricken with horror. I did what I could for him, almost brought him back to life in a manner of speaking, and he has been my servant ever since.'

I stared at Sabazius in amazement. 'What do you mean by "servant"?'

'Just that. He obeys my every wish ... and my wish is to serve self and enter Elsewhere with a roar.'

'Can you control him?'

'Most of the time; but every so often he runs amuck, like an animal cornered in a world of hunters.'

'But –'

'The Turk's fall was no accident,' said Sabazius. 'He sought to capture the power of a god for his own use, but made a mistake.'

'Capture?'

'That is a decision you will eventually have to make,' added Sabazius, eyeing me with interest. 'To take power and use it as you will, or to forfeit power for love.'

I would not have believed such a decision was available to a man, but as I sat there looking at Sabazius, it dawned on me that it was, for I could feel the tug of power.

'I'll do what you've done,' I said immediately.

'It's impossible for you to say that yet,' he replied. 'You are with me, so you choose love; but when you walk out into universe in *strength*, you may change your mind. Power is very attractive. A man will sometimes take power instead of love thinking that he can assist the world in some practical way, and indeed he may do so for some time. But eventually power eats the man, gobbles him up, dries out his vision and reduces him to ashes. Power outside of love is too bright a flame.'

'But you saved the Turk!'

'Only because he made a mistake early on. If he had not made that mistake, stumbled through and had his system trodden on by a god, he would today be a Man of Power.'

'So there are two types of men,' I said excitedly, 'Men of Feeling, and Men of Power!'

'You could say that,' replied Sabazius, 'but it would only be a verbal distinction, for they both contain the same basic elements. Until a man's history is complete, and by that I mean when he is finally gathered up and drawn into Elsewhere, he runs the risk at all times of changing into a Man of Power. The Path contains unimaginable subtleties, and these subtleties are in all men in varying degrees of predominance. I once knew a Man of Feeling who at the end of his life turned towards power. He became a great magician, a man of colossal ability. But there was of course a flaw in his power, and the flaw became a black hole, and he fell into it.' Sabazius seemed momentarily sad, as if memory had thrown a face into his mind. Then he laughed. 'But that is not your problem, Peter,' he said good-humouredly. 'You have still to become a Man of Feeling, for until you do so, the other decision is meaningless, mere words.'

'I hope I never make that mistake.'

'You can but hope. It is all any man can do ... ultimately.'

It seemed almost a contradiction to use *will* in such a manner; but it had to be true or Sabazius would not have mentioned it. So what made such men change? How could they know so much, feel and see so much, yet still be drawn to power? What were the fatal flaws in a man's nature which so directed him? Did I have such a flaw, and if I had, would I too create a pit to fall into?

'Three sounds as one,' said Sabazius suddenly. 'That is the basic principle of creation, and if you can master the principle of three, then you will find the stability of four.'

'What is four?'

'That is something else, it comes later.' He motioned to me to get up from the floor. 'I will now show you a trick,' he said, and he held out his hand for me to look at. 'Can you see anything?'

'No.'

'Now my hand is different.'

'It doesn't look any different.'

'I assure you it is,' he replied. 'I've tensed some muscles in it. That is the trick.'

'I don't get it?'

'Stand still and close your eyes.' He let me stand like that for some seconds. 'Now, tense your arm, or part of it.'

I did so.

'You are now an arm,' said Sabazius.

'So any part of me I tense, I become.'

'That's the general idea.'

'And if I tense all the muscles of my body?'

'Don't be carried away,' he said, smiling at me, 'it is only a trick. But that trick has purpose. Now that you have learned how difficult it is to remain awake at the factory, this is what you must do to stay awake. By simply tensing a small muscle anywhere in your body you can stay awake. The moment you fall asleep, the muscle will relax. The moment you realize the muscle has relaxed, you will be awake again. And so it will go on until you can dispense with the trick.'

'Does it stop dreaming?'

'It helps to stop it.'

'How?'

'All human movement is automatic. It has been learned, and like anything that is learned well, it seems to vanish and operate on its own. In other words, you do not have to think about driving a car, or how to lift a cup of hot tea. You simply drive, or lift, automatically. When the automatic system of a man's movement breaks down, that is when he becomes what is known as "neurotic". He will make a vast number of mistakes when driving, just like a learner does, or someone after an accident, and he will spill the tea or drop the cup. Thus, because man is so automatic in his responses, both physically and mentally – he also has automatic patterns of mind – he has time to dream, time to fade into that inner world of fantasy where he can be famous, rich, handsome or beautiful; and the end result is sleep, and then death. Now the reason I call it a trick is because if you tense the same muscle over a number of days, or weeks, eventually that too will become automatic, and you will still be asleep – dreaming of being awake! This is the most difficult part, for a man can even dream that he is conscious, dream that he is alive. So what you have to do is keep on changing the tension from muscle to muscle. I do not mean by that constant change of tension, but a change every so often to stop the automatic process of learning from coming into action. When you are alone, you can be more adventurous, curling a hand at a peculiar angle, or walking with a limp. Anything out of the ordinary, in this sense, will keep you hovering on the edge of proper consciousness. But you must not think of it as an end in itself, for it is only an exercise to keep you at a certain level where more important work can be done.'

'Why didn't you tell me about this earlier?'

'Because I wanted you to really appreciate how difficult it is to stay awake. I wanted you to *know* what sleep is.'

'I'll use it in the factory tomorrow.'

'Ah!' exclaimed Sabazius. 'You only want to be awake when in the factory!'

'Sorry.'

'There are no "tomorrows" allowed to a Man of Feeling,' he said, looking at me sternly. 'What good is being alive tomorrow, when you may die today?'

9 ❋ *The preparation*

From then on I worked at the factory without mishap, but not without falling asleep. What Sabazius had said about the trick was true. On a number of occasions I found myself dreaming of being awake, dreaming that I was Peter Derwent. Without being told, I perfected a further trick to cement the first firmly into place. It was quite simple, I just pressed two fingers together and thought and moved through them. At first, like taking your eyes away from the page of a book, I kept losing my place; but eventually the desired results came, and the band in my head tightened, allowing me an hour or more of startling concentration without the trick.

Sabazius, when I told him of my efforts and the results, showed little interest. He would nod his head, chew at his mouth, and change the subject. His attitude at first dismayed me, for I required encouragement to focus my will; and then I saw the reason for his apparent disinterest: to have lauded my attempts would have been to lay a foundation of pride in achievement. What I was doing was not 'clever', it was not the equivalent of solving a mathematical problem, it was more like double-digging a garden – the preparation.

It was during those days that I realized how a Man of Feeling could turn into a Man of Power. Any man, by hard work on himself could produce results; but those results, although the same on the surface as the results of some other man, were founded on differing attitudes and experience. A man could attain perfect concentration, yet at the same time lay unwittingly the base for a monumental arrogance which would carry him inexorably towards the desire for power. This was the 'subtlety' to which Sabazius had referred, and was to return to time and time again. Every time a man changed something within himself – a gigantic exercise requiring *exact* knowledge – he automatically produced 'modifications' in his system: for indeed everything was related, nothing worked totally by itself, moved by itself or thought by itself. This being so, a man's growing ability to change brought the other invisible modifications to the surface. These peripheral changes were sometimes extraordinary, varying from a heightened sex-drive to a squint of the eye, a stammer, or even a limp. Unfathomable problems presented themselves daily, problems which Sabazius, with infinite patience – and sometimes a few harsh words – turned this way and that until their meaning and relationship became clear. I was still only on the first rung of a ladder which reached from earth to heaven, and there was no safety net but death or awake-dream at the foot of it. But at the other end of that ladder lay . . . well, as Sabazius was prone to say: That was something else.

A few weeks after my incident with the Turk, I learned something which disturbed me profoundly. Being more awake, I began to observe the other boxers. When leaving one evening I overheard a snippet of conversation which aroused my interest at once. The lean-faced man – the one who worked next to me – was talking in low tones to a young girl of about nineteen near to where we hung up our aprons and collected our jackets and coats.

'Don't give in whatever you do, it won't be long now,' said the man.

'But it's so difficult, you don't know what I'm going through!' replied the girl.

Pretending to be busy with the strings of my apron, I moved closer, keeping my back to them.

'If you don't work at it properly, I'll hand you over to the Turk, and you know . . .'

He spun round and looked at me. I still had my back to him, but I could feel his eyes moving over my body like a searchlight. With almost perfect concentration I took off my apron and draped it on a peg, then, slowly, as if I had heard nothing untoward, I lifted down my own clothes, put them on and headed for the door. As I walked away his eyes followed me like a physical presence until suddenly I was outside in the grey evening and the feeling switched off.

What had I stumbled on?

Sabazius showed little reaction when I told him. He just sat looking at me fixedly, then he said, to my surprise: 'Just forget about it, it does not concern you.'

'But I can't,' I objected. 'There's something funny about that little man. I have a feeling he knows what we know!'

'That,' said Sabazius, 'would be quite a coincidence.'

'He knows how to "look"; I felt him looking.'

Sabazius exhibited unease. 'So what are you going to do?'

'I'm going to try and find out what's going on.'

'I thought you might say that.' He sighed, licked his lips. 'I didn't want to have to say this,' he said quietly, 'but under no circumstances must you let the little man know you suspect anything.'

'Why?'

'Don't you know any other word?'

'I can't help it,' I said, all the more interested now that he had warned me off, 'it's my nature.'

'This is a bad situation,' he then said, looking away from me. 'I think I had better explain what's happened or you'll get yourself into serious trouble.'

'What kind of trouble?'

Sabazius allowed a silence to fall upon us before speaking. 'The lean-faced man is a Man of Power,' he said suddenly. 'He has taken the girl under his wing, as I have taken you under mine. But being a Man of Power, his reasons are of course very different from mine. The Turk told me what was going on. The Turk does not like the little man, for the little man rules the Turk. You see, as I've already told you, the Turk tried to be a Man of Power, and failed, almost died; so he automatically hates the idea that such a little blob of human flesh should manage what he could not. But as he no longer has any strength or will to fight with, he has to obey the little man's every wish, just as he obeys my every wish. The girl, according to the Turk, was born with some natural gift that the little man wants to use, but because she's dim-witted and slow, he needs to train her, just as I'm training you.'

'Am I dim-witted?'

Sabazius laughed. 'No, you're too damned quick-witted,' he exclaimed, 'that's half your trouble! You think you can *think* your way into the skin of a Man of Feeling!' He held up a hand to stop me from replying. 'The only reason I've told you all this,' he said, 'is because if you try to communicate with that girl, or take it upon yourself to talk with the little man, a catastrophe will take place. If the little man finds out what kind of strength you have, he may very well throw the girl aside and force you into his service instead. And don't think there's anything you could do about it, you would be as helpless as a baby.'

'Wouldn't you be able to do anything?'

'Of course I could do something,' said Sabazius, 'but I don't want to have to make that decision. To involve myself with the little man would be a waste of precious time, would probably bring about a huge loss of energy in me, and most likely permanent madness in you.'

'Can't you help the girl to escape from him?'

'She would not want to escape,' was his reply. 'The girl has the same spirit as the lean-faced man; if she were brighter she would claim power for herself and make him her servant. That is how some people are.'

'Are such things fixed?'

'That is too difficult a question to answer at this moment.'

'Do you think the lean-faced man knew I was listening?'

'Undoubtedly. But what he does not yet know is if you understood what you heard. Your very cleverness at hiding that fact will make him suspect you.'

'What should I do?'

'We will just have to wait for him to make a move,' answered Sabazius. 'He'll try every trick he knows to make you betray yourself. He'll touch you with his eyes when you're least expecting it, project little pains at you – pains I might add which only a Man of Feeling, or someone approaching such a state, would feel. So if you show a reaction, he'll know.'

'How will I ward off the pains?'

'Now that you know how to be conscious, you can stop them hurting you by remaining at a high level of consciousness all day long. It will be very difficult for you, but I'm sure you can do it. In fact, you *must* do it, unless you want him to take you.'

'Couldn't I just leave the factory and find another job?'

'If you did not turn up at the factory he would know immediately what the situation was and come after you. Don't be mistaken, he would find you.'

'How would he do that?'

'He would call your name, and see you wherever you were.'

'Just by calling my name?'

'Yes.'

I was astonished.

'But there is something else,' said Sabazius. 'If he projects a pain at you, and you happen to be asleep at that moment, and react by raising a defence of consciousness, he'll attack you in the same minute and take you over. Now there is a way out of this, but it would require a tremendous effort on your part, a super-human attempt to call on the strength of self. When I say call, I do not mean shout for self; that would do you no good whatsoever. When a man in danger calls on self, he opens up every segment of his body and mind in an overwhelming cry at the centre of his head. That cry can be heard at the outer limits of universe. But it is a cry which can only take place when a man is terrified beyond belief, when he knows that *all he is* is being threatened. That is the cry you must make to survive if he decides to take you from me.'

'Is there no other way?'

'Yes,' replied Sabazius, 'but it would mean me attacking him, and to do that I would have to drain myself like a jug. For I would not only be protecting you, I would be protecting myself. And if I failed, we would both be in his power.'

'Even you!'

'Men of Feeling and Men of Power generally leave each other alone for that very reason. It's too big a risk for them to take, for the stakes are high, and no one can say for certain which way such a battle will go.' His face was utterly serious. 'So it is better that he take you than both of us. You have only started the work, I am in the midst of it.'

I was now numb.

'But you are strong,' he said, 'and I believe you can come through this, even if it means having to make that cry, that ultimate gesture to self.'

'And if I fail?'

'Do not speak of failure,' warned Sabazius, 'for if you allow for it, you will have it!'

'Can I ask you one more thing?'

'Yes.'

'If he attacks, and I manage to "cry" properly, what will be my position afterwards?'

'He will not be able to touch you, for the arms of self will be around you, protecting you from all harm until you are ready to stand firm.'

'Will I then be a Man of Feeling?'

'No, you will just be protected. When a man learns the secret of the hidden cry, then he can really start to work.'

'So this situation by the very nature of the work would have arisen anyway, at some other time?'

'Exactly. But I will be truthful with you. It has arisen sooner than I expected, so you will have to be on guard constantly.'

'From this second,' I said, remembering my last reprimand.

Sabazius nodded and laid a hand on my shoulder. 'You will soon be your name, Peter Derwent,' he said. 'And when you have become your name, our work will be glorious!'

When I entered the factory the following morning, every cell in my body was alive and vibrant. I had risen early, prepared myself as Sabazius had instructed with special breathing exercises and a wordless prayer for immediate assistance if anything happened. I was like a clock fully wound, a bomb with the detonator already primed.

The lean-faced man paid no attention to me at all, did not even look up as I walked past him to my position at the conveyor. Then I turned my back on him, and waited for the Turk to start up the day's operation.

Tea-break and lunch passed without incident, and it was almost four-thirty before I felt the slight tingle of his eyes on my shoulder-blades. Holding my mind steady, and keeping up the flow of boxes as before, I prepared myself and waited for the first pain. I felt remarkably still inside, as if all that I was was sitting silently to attention. But the pain I expected almost immediately did not occur, and the tingle of his looking ceased after a few minutes. What was his plan of action? Would he wait until I thought an attack improbable, then strike me down?

Five-thirty.

I collected my jacket and coat and left the factory. When I was no more than two streets away, Sabazius appeared. I greeted him, but to my surprise he walked straight by as if I were a total stranger. I stood looking after him, wondering what he was up to, then I felt a tingle at the base of my neck and knew I had been followed. Had the little man seen me greet Sabazius? Was that why Sabazius had walked by me? I was a fool. The little man was clever, he was probably watching me right this minute, waiting for an opportunity to project the first pain.

Dismissing all thoughts of Sabazius I walked on, forming an expression on my face which conveyed that I had hailed someone by mistake.

The tingling moved down and came to rest on the backs of my legs. I breathed slowly through my nose and pressed two fingers on each hand together to hold me steadily awake.

Then I felt it.

The pain did not come abruptly as I expected. It grew like a small fire below the level of my knees and made me want to scratch. It was a clever move, for I had to keep walking as if nothing was happening, or he would know immediately that my sensitivity was not normal. I pressed my fingers tightly together, adding a third to hold them firmly in place. I was determined not to be beaten. But now I was walking down Covent Garden and entering the busy centre of London. There would be so many distractions, so many things to draw away my pointed attention. But if I kept walking round in circles, kept to the quiet back streets, the little man would have further reason to suspect that I was not what I seemed. There was no choice. I headed at a regular pace towards Charing Cross Road, checked and double-checked visually, yet all the while holding my mind in a steady stream of concentration, for if I were suddenly shocked by a car or stray dog, he might intensify the pain and cause me to fall. And if I fell ...

Sabazius was somewhere around, but he had stated categorically that he would not attack the little man on my behalf. So I was on my own, rather like a rabbit waiting for an eagle to pluck it from the ground.

When I reached Cambridge Circus, I waited an age for the traffic to thin before attempting to cross. On my face was an expression of boredom, an expression I hoped the little man would somehow detect and translate as innocence.

But where was he?

The pain in my legs was quite intense, growing, spreading up past my knees and into my thighs. How long could I withstand it? Should I find a café and sit down? Go into a pub and pretend to drink a pint of beer? I decided against both those modes of action and headed for Oxford Street, winding my way through the maze of Soho.

The basic problem of holding simultaneously the one-pointedness I required to ignore the pain, yet remain conscious of my surroundings, manipulating myself physically across roads, avoid others hurrying home in the opposite direction and project an expression which relayed a totally different state of mind was almost crippling. There were now beads of sweat on my forehead. My fingers were numb through the pressure I was exerting. My breathing was not as steady as it ought to be. How could I possibly survive if the little man sent that gnawing pain all the way up through my body and into my head? I would then have to call on self, throw everything in me out into universe, and *believe* utterly and incomprehensibly that I would be rescued! I did not allow the *other* thought, the alternative, to surface. Sabazius had warned me sternly about that. 'Under no circumstances consider the possibility of failure,' he had said again and again, 'for if you do, he will take you from me in an instant.' And so, with that wordless fear lying on me like a heavy hand, I eventually reached my flat, opened the door, and walked in.

Everything was quiet.

I lifted the telephone off its stand and laid it on the table; then stripping off my shirt and trousers, I placed myself on my usual spot on the floor, regulating my breathing until it was almost imperceptible, and drew every iota of energy I could muster to my assistance.

The pain intensified.

It had now reached my waist and filtered down to envelop my ankles and feet. I could not have risen if the building had been burning around me. I was locked so rigidly into a stream of mind that nothing and no one could have disturbed or entered.

That was when the pain burst like a firework and rushed up through my chest, captured my arms, hands and fingers, exploded in my neck, and like gushing lava crept up into my face and eyes. I held it for a second, controlled it for an instant of time, then, with my bones, my lungs, my heart, my very flesh, I cried out.

10 ❊ *Like a drunk man*

The face of Alexis Sabazius.

I was lying on my back staring up into it. He placed a finger on the tip of my nose and pressed gently, affectionately. 'Well, you survived,' he said, as if I had just recovered from a severe illness.

As his words registered, the feeling of certainty I had had earlier returned. 'I can hardly remember what happened,' I said. 'In fact, I remember nothing after the pain reached my head.'

'You conquered.'

I smiled weakly.

'And you conquered consciously.'

'I feel as if I've been dead.'

'That is because you *were* dead,' replied Sabazius. 'Before a man can be born, he must first die in self. The path demands everything that a man is before allowing him to continue.'

'But I don't remember anything,' I said again.

'That doesn't matter.'

'Why can't I remember?'

He laughed and helped me to get up, suggesting that I put my clothes on again. 'There are certain things you must understand about memory,' he said, ' ... before a proper appreciation of self is possible. You cannot understand why memory fails you, because you expect there to be a picture, an experience-picture in your mind with which you can relate, but there is not. Is that not so?'

'Yes.'

'It is like this,' said Sabazius. 'When an ordinary man remembers something, he remembers out of awake-dream, and as the thing he tries to remember was itself experienced or conceived in awake-dream, the remembered incident or thought becomes a dream in itself. So the man, the incident, and the man's memory of the incident is a treble dream. When he remembers, he sees but a flat image on the surface of his mind, or he attempts to recreate in words what he *thinks* he remembers. Now it is often the case that that man will forget most of what he saw, read or experienced in awake-dream, just as he generally forgets what happens in his sleeping dreams, and the end result is a lie. Man is at all times lying to himself and others concerning what he remembers, and that lying becomes "hyperbole", "embellishment" and "exaggeration". All of which are totally acceptable, because the I's of ego, the multiple personality structure, demand that he stands out as special among his fellow dreamers, who are also inveterate liars. But when a man who is properly awake remembers, he remembers at a dynamic level what he exprienced at a dynamic level, so the man, the incident, and the man's memory of the incident is dynamic; or, if you like, three-dimensional. Such a man cannot forget what he has experienced, for when he remembers, the dynamic quality of his memory produces not "recall", but the *act* itself.' Pausing, Sabazius offered me a Turkish cigarette. 'So there are two reasons why you cannot recall entering self. Firstly, to remember self is to look at that which looks directly on Elsewhere, and as I've told you, that is the final act of a Man of Feeling. So to remember self in a total sense would be to enter Elsewhere; but as you are not yet sufficiently your history, even as a Man of Feeling until the day he exits life is not sufficiently his history, then you cannot remember self in an intrinsic fashion. And secondly, as self cannot be thought of as something exterior to you, but what you *are* intrinsically, then it is impossible for you to have memory recall in any ordinary sense, for self is not an incident or an idea in your mind, it is *all* Peter Derwent, and necessitates as such not recall, but "re-entry".' He sat staring at me, waiting for me to catch up, then he said: 'Today, you consciously walked out of awake-dream, and although you do not realize it, you have opened the Double Gate of joy and fire. The fire of self will burn the dross out of your history, and then bathe you in joy.'

'When I again attempt to remember self,' I asked hesitantly, 'what will happen?'

'You will burn.'

'Burn?'

'Up until twenty minutes ago,' said Sabazius, 'you had never remembered self, or anything for that matter. You had only felt the shock of passing backwards and forwards across the point where entry into self is possible. What you were doing was "observing" what stopped you from remembering; but today you were thrust into a situation where *not to remember* self meant subservience to a Man of Power, so you sidestepped awake-dream and pierced what you are.'

'I almost feel as if I should thank the little man for doing me a service!'

'Why not?'

I smiled at Sabazius, wondered what his 'Why not?' meant.

'If a man has done you a service, then he ought to be thanked.'

'But he's dangerous!'

'I'm afraid that was all a fearful dream,' replied Sabazius innocently. 'The little man is not a Man of Power, he is a Man of Feeling.'

My mouth fell open.

'Does that matter to you?'

'I ... I don't know what to say!' I said, shocked that he should trick me in such a manner.

'Look,' continued Sabazius, 'such situations can arise, and they're highly dangerous when they do. Far better to be tricked into such a terror, and reap the reward, than face the real thing with no avenue of escape. If you had not succeeded, I would have told you I attacked the little man; that would have satisfied you, for you would have known no better. But you did not fail, you conquered, you cried the cry and you came through. So what does it matter?'

'But the pains ... '

'They were real enough.'

'Did the little man project them?'

'Of course.'

'Can you project pain?'

'Yes.'

'When do you use it?'

'There is something you must understand,' said Sabazius. 'A Man of Feeling does not really "use" anything in the normal sense. When he becomes a Man of Feeling, many things are

93

possible to him, but he did not become a Man of Feeling to acquire these things, they are extras, of no meaning to him except when they can assist someone else to become a Man or Woman of Feeling. It is just something that happens on the path, and we ignore it, for it contains the seed of a trap, a hole into which a Man of Feeling can fall through weakness.'

'Becoming then a Man of Power?'

'Exactly.'

As I sat there thinking about what he had said, the pattern which lay behind human existence slowly opened up to my inner eye. Man had a choice, and his ability consciously to choose filtered into every level of his earthly life, even up to the gate of death. For if a choice was not available to a man at *all* stages, then the *ever-comprehending act of will* would be limited in its act of comprehension, and such a limitation would mean the appearance of blatant power in universe. All things were governed by love, and man, as an expression of Elsewhere in Time, was himself love partially veiled by awake-dream. That was the mystery.

The room in which I sat was suddenly filled with joy.

Sabazius watched me calmly.

'I'm alive!' I burst out.

'And you must stay alive,' he replied.

'How can I ever possibly forget to stay alive now!'

'By falling back into awake-dream.'

'Even now?'

I was trembling.

I sat absolutely still and looked at him. 'I don't have to go back to the factory now, do I?'

Sabazius thought for a second, weighed my situation up. 'No, I suppose not,' he said.

'What is the factory?'

'The factory is a School.'

'What kind of school?'

'One of the few places left where a man or woman can be taught to feel.'

'And the girl who was with the little man?'

'She is a pupil like yourself, but more advanced.'

'And the Turk?'

'The Turk is what I told you,' said Sabazius. 'He is a broken

Man of Power, a man whose history had a flaw.'

'What happens to me now?'

'I don't know,' replied Sabazius. 'In a matter of a few weeks you have become a face and part of a body; but it may take you the rest of your life to join all the parts of your history together.'

'Will you continue to teach me?'

'I will teach you until you no longer need me.'

'How will I know when I no longer need you?'

'You will know because you will tell yourself so.'

'What will I do when I know such a thing?'

'You will walk the world.'

'Alone?'

'A Man of Feeling is never alone. For company he has light and love. He moves continually among men that they might see and feel for a moment, glimpse for a moment what really exists around them, and in them. He has no home, no bed and no pillow; everything he does, everything he thinks, adds to humanity yet another moment of reality.'

I smiled, for a number of things had suddenly come together. 'The firm you work for,' I said, remembering his description of it, 'I think I understand it now.'

'What do you understand?'

'There is no firm, just Men of Feeling who know of each other's existence, who have the same purpose.'

'We are as one man,' he replied.

'When can I join you?'

'When you're ready.'

'I suddenly feel very far away from you.'

'One can only say that of someone when you are close to them. It is your knowledge of your own ignorance showing you the path. If you did not know that you would still be a fool living in awake-dream.'

'I feel afraid.'

'To learn true fear is to learn wisdom. Without true fear, a man is nothing.'

Universe unimaginably out-of-time. I could vaguely sense it all around me. As I sat there with Sabazius, the room slowly grew dark, melted away into itself from the nothing of visual sight and became real. It was then I saw my triangle again, only this time there were more flowers and less undergrowth, and at the flat top edge I spied an infinitesimal patch of blue sky, just a suggestion, a glimmer of something else.

And then the first *real* pain came.

Something sparked from out of that blue and entered into me. I choked on it mentally, tried to swallow it with my mind but could not. The pain grew. I cried out, became suspended in that silky darkness and felt what was my history grinding piece by piece one against the other. I would surely die. Surely I would die and it would be over, not with a roar, but with a cry of terror, the ultimate terror of an unmade history faced too soon, opened up too soon ...

Tears.

Huge tears burning down, through and into my being.

Laughter.

I turned this way and that, then I realized it was my own laughter – an empty laughter; the laughter before fear is born and a man reached the end of all he is ... caught on the hooks of pride ... hanging on the gallows of self-pity ... a man facing universe.

White light.

When I opened my eyes I was cradled on Sabazius's chest. I was crying like a child, sobbing out the hate, arrogance, pity, pleasure and horror I had experienced in my life. A scream rose to my lips, spewed out into the room. The box of my mind split open, shattered glass-like; there erupted within me a knowledge that I had been fettered, bound and locked away from true joy by a world of sleep-walkers.

'Peace to you,' said Sabazius.

I drew breath and felt the vision pass on, move on to capture another.

'I'm empty,' I said.

The knot of my mind slowly relaxed, untangled itself and became still.

Sabazius stretched me out on the sofa, got a blanket from the bedroom and covered me with it. 'What did you expect?' he replied, smiling down at me. 'Did you expect to be born without pain?'

I found it impossible to answer.

'Birth is glorious,' he said. 'When a man is born, the whole universe sings a song. You may even hear that song very soon, hear it whispered in sleep, as if a beautiful woman were humming in your ear.' He laughed suddenly, but quietly. 'And do you know what it is! It is the planets shouting to each other as they pass; distant stars smiling; galaxies breathing; energy everywhere flowing; and above everything, Elsewhere comprehending.'

I marvelled at his words, wondered if I were supposed to take them literally or metaphorically. Could stars really smile? Did galaxies really breathe? It was all too much, too much for my intellect to handle. All I knew at that moment was that I was utterly empty. Never in my life had I felt so empty; yet it was a clean emptiness, a totally satisfying knowledge that I was at least momentarily free from dream. I closed my eyes slowly, only to open them again instantly, for the picture I had glimpsed inside my head was identical to that outside. I closed my eyes a second time, and there standing behind the sofa was Sabazius. I laughed in wonderment and told him what I could see.

'You are experiencing "dynamic vision",' he said casually; 'but it will fade.'

'It's fantastic!'

'It's nothing,' was his reply.

My mind was like a piece of crystal. I could think of anything, and it immediately appeared. By chance, I happened to close my eyes again as I remembered something I had read in a book some years before, and to my astonishment the book appeared in my head open at the page with the words clearly visible. I had total recall. It did not take me long to realize that I could do the same with places and people, and within minutes I had again revisited Africa, watched Sabazius run towards the trees, walked down Oxford Street looking at the human firework display and produced childhood companions complete with school caps and short trousers. No wonder Sabazius had little trouble answering my questions; the answers he spun out so efficiently were at all times ready and waiting, detailed and perfect in his mind. If this was dynamic vision, I wanted to have it more than anything else. I considered all the things I could do with it, the exams I could sit, the degrees I could take, the people I could astound by quoting not only passages, but whole books if required. I could be a genius overnight! I could ...

'What are you thinking?' asked Sabazius.

'I was just thinking how handy such vision would be if I ...'

'Yes?'

. I flushed, could not look at him.

'You were thinking how *powerful* you would be,' he said. 'You were thinking of all the people you could impress, all the wonders you could perform.'

My head throbbed, ached inside.

'That is "power",' he said, 'That is how a man loses sight of the path.'

I took a deep breath and turned to look at him. 'I'm glad it's going to fade,' I said, wondering if I really meant it. 'I'm not ready for it yet.'

'Some men are never ready,' he replied, 'and sometimes even those who find the path and walk on it for a little while, stray off in search of power, and then *more* power.' Looking at me fixedly, he said: 'I don't know which man you are, yet.'

11 ❋ Elsewhere

'Some people,' said Sabazius one afternoon when we were out walking, 'think there must be a strict pattern when teaching a man to feel and see; but I have not found that to be the case. Every human being has developed certain strengths and weaknesses long before they tackle a path, so one must always deal with their strengths first, then use these strengths to modify or change their weaknesses into further strengths. It is quite silly to follow a strict pattern of weakness eradication – as is the case with most religions – for what may appear to be a weakness, can easily turn out to be a strength in disguise.'

'Can you give me an example of that?'

'Well, let us say that a man has a violent temper, but that inner violence – which is generally grounded in frustration – can be turned into a rock-like determination to stay on the path. If, however, that violence is eradicated as an evil, the quality of "determination" will then have to be manufactured out of some *supposed* strength – which may be a weakness in disguise – and the end of that man may very well be that he does nothing at all. Such a man will eventually leave the path because others took it upon themselves to "judge" that man externally, so rendering him incapable of true work.'

'When you say "some people",' I asked, 'are you referring to certain Men of Feeling?'

'It is seldom that a Man of Feeling will make that mistake,' he replied, 'but it is certainly not impossible. It depends greatly on the teacher the Man of Feeling had. It is possible for a great truth to lie fallow in the minds of men who *appear* to know and understand. Many such men build vast systems of belief to convince their followers that they "know" the truth; and in reality that is just the case, for they only know the truth, but they are not themselves that truth.'

'You mean by that they have not become their history?'

'Yes. Most of the great truths have been changed into philosophical systems, programmes almost, because man desires always to present everything neatly, in a box.'

'But you yourself utilize logic.'

'Of course, but I am not deceived by logic! Many men think that an intellectual appreciation of a truth is enough; but that is the basic lie which makes them impotent. It is true that some men will approach truth in such a manner and gain tremendous insights into the most difficult of problems; but if that appreciation does not become an integral part of them, if it does not make them into *new men*, then it is worthless.'

'So the work is really the translation of "ideas" into practice, making the man *into* what he believes or conceives.'

'Just so,' said Sabazius. 'What good is it if a man says there should not be another war, but is secretly manufacturing a war out of that very wish to stop all war? That is stupidity. We are surrounded by such men. But the basic issue is often not what the man believes, but what has already been created demanding a fixed line of belief or action. Economics, or man's desire for change, is the basic evil driving him in and out of confrontation. Economic development of a country is called "progress", but it has nothing to do with progress, it has only to do with "use". The spiral of trade demands new products to feed man's desire for change, and man's desire for change makes him "use" whatever is available, even if all that is available is a weapon of destruction. Even the great peace treaties of nations are but temporary respites between wars so that man can swap his product and use the "changes" provided by others. The very term "work" has been changed into "for the use of" others. Men no longer work to become new men, they work to change their personal product, and in working, supply others with new personal products which keep the wheel of desire and blindness turning. So the men of learning follow suit, providing other men of learning, or men who want to be men of learning, with the product of knowledge, the new toy they will evenutally tire of and change for another, or complicate so much so that they are among the few who *seem* to understand it.'

'Then what hope is there for humanity if everything is so fixed?'

'There is no hope in the sense you mean.'

'What do I mean?'

Sabazius laughed, glanced at me in amusement. 'You are lamenting the fact that the whole world cannot be made to see what is self-evident.'

I nodded my confirmation.

'Does that worry you?' he asked.

'It makes me sad.'

'Why?'

'Because surely they ought to have the chance?'

Taking a large, coloured handkerchief out of his pocket, Sabazius blew his nose like a trumpet. 'Did you see what happened?' he asked.

'Not really.'

'They did not notice.'

'Pardon?'

'I gave them the chance of hearing me blow my nose,' he replied, 'but they rejected it.'

'They must have heard it!'

'Oh yes, but they didn't stop to look, did they?'

'You mean that a man *is* given the chance, but ignores it, passes it by.'

Sabazius pocketed the handkerchief, then he said: 'A man is every day of his life faced with himself, and all the other little selves which bob backwards and forwards. There is not one second of his life when he is not confronted with the internal and external truth of what he is, and what he could be. There is also not one human being on this planet who does not consider his death at one moment or another; he is surrounded by death, reads about it every morning, or sees it first hand. But he makes no attempt to change, even when he knows that change is not only possible, but vital. That, however, does not mean that he does not *want* to change. If you listen to him carefully, you will hear him at all times talking about and discussing real change; the only problem is, he is generally not talking about change in himself, but in another. It is always in another that real change must take place. He dishes out change to others in the form of advice, and in exclamations to enemies. It is always *you* who must change. Some men are even conscious that real change must start at home, so they adhere to religions or systems of belief; but generally all they get is a veneer of personality change: they become nice, good, cheerful or honest; and then they generally become smugly self-satisfied and fall into the trap of telling others to change once again. But in spite of all this dreaming, and veneer, there appear men who have *faced* their history, and these men change and slowly, often painfully, evolve through terrible suffering and hardship until they emerge victorious. They swim against the stream, seek out battles others cannot see, and develop out of "will" comprehension, and out of "comprehension" more will. Others, however, remain in awake-dream, wallow in self-pity; and although exposed to the same stupidities, hatreds and blind folly, will not even attempt the first step.'

'But it may not really be their fault!' I objected, sensing a loophole in his argument. 'They are the product of their environment, their education.'

'You are not thinking straight,' replied Sabazius. 'A man may very well be the product of all the influences that can possibly be imagined, but underneath he is still a man, and like all other men he is spoken to and wooed continually by self. All men are subject to the inner voice which tells them what to do on every occasion; there is never any occasion when the inner voice does not instruct a man. Now a man may argue that this is not true, give example after example of how he has made mistakes and taken the wrong turning; but that was never the fault of self, it was the fault of the man for not listening. If a man but stops for a second and listens, he will hear self in his heart. This is what I meant when I said to you that every man is his *own* path. He does not have to belong to anything or anyone to know and become the truth, for he is himself the truth at all times.'

'Then why doesn't he know this?'

'He does know.'

'It wouldn't appear so.'

Sabazius stopped and looked at me. 'Are you trying to tell me that *you* did not know before we met that your life was a mess? Are you trying to tell me that you did not make many attempts to rectify what was wrong with you by facing yourself squarely?'

'Yes, but –'

'There are no buts,' he replied. 'All men, no matter where they live, or how they live, are being touched by self – and they know it!'

We walked on in silence and I found myself looking at others as if for the first time. Was it true? Did self talk to all men at all times? Were they continually sidestepping the truth of what they were? I thought back, tried to prove to myself that this was not the case; but each time I recalled an incident, an experience, a relationship with some other human being, I was confronted with the startling knowledge that I had known exactly what to do, but on most occasions had not done it. I was my own fool! But on the occasions when I had obeyed that inner certainty – even when my actions or statements were derided by others – I had been filled up inside with a kind of joy, a joy which spoke to me of 'knowing' and 'understanding' what life was about. Those were the occasions when I walked with a spring in my step, did my best work, knew I was somehow 'together'. But as Sabazius had pointed out earlier, it was often the case that others would not *allow* you to obey what was within, for to do so made them face the blatant fact of their own sidestepping; so you were pulled down, or 'allowed' yourself to be pulled down because it was easy, less bother, if not generally more pleasurable. When I told Sabazius of my discovery, he said:

'If a man requires proof of this, all he has to do is ask himself where everything he knows, everything he believes in has come from. From where else but out of the mind of man could it come?'

'Many would say it came from God?'

'And they would point at the sky,' added Sabazius. 'They would point at something external because they have mastered the external. They would point at a projection because they have mastered the art of projection. Everything they are is hanging out in the world like a tongue, and like their own tongues they are controlled by it, manipulated by it, hypnotized by it. But when a man becomes himself, everything returns to its rightful place, for that man then knows his history, and his history informs him through self that he does not *have* a god, but that he *is* a god.'

'But what of Elsewhere?'

'That is where gods return to in their perfection; into which they roar with joy!'

I was again quite overwhelmed by his words, but this time attempted to take the argument one step further for clarity's sake. I said: 'Many would say that Elsewhere was God, and that it was Elsewhere who would intervene in human history.'

'If Elsewhere were some kind of being, or mind,' answered Sabazius, 'then they would be correct. But Elsewhere is not a man, or a woman, or anything imaginable in the mind of man. Elsewhere is Elsewhere. If a man hunts for Elsewhere, he will not find Elsewhere; if he cries out for Elsewhere to assist him, nothing will happen; if he attempts to make Elsewhere into some mighty spiritual force or projection, all he will have is his own mistake. Elsewhere will not have changed.'

'Then it is not possible to conceive of Elsewhere?'

'Of course it is.'

'But how?'

'By a trick of eyesight.'

We had now stopped on a traffic island in the centre of the Strand. I could see nothing, hear nothing but Sabazius. I said: 'I don't understand.'

He chuckled merrily to himself, then he said: 'Elsewhere is nowhere to be found, for as I said to you some weeks ago: When a Man of Feeling dies, he enters Elsewhere, for there is no-where-else for him to go!'

'Then Elsewhere does not exist.'

'I meant by that that Elsewhere does not exist *by* existing.'

'Then how is Elsewhere conceivable?'

'By simple *looking*.'

'But how can one conceive of the existence of something that does not exist, by looking?'

'Try it.' He held his arms out in both directions.

I looked but could see nothing.

'What do you see?' asked Sabazius.

'Nothing.'

'How can one *see* nothing?'

'Because there's ...' I stopped short, stared down the Strand, allowed my eyes to come to rest slowly on everything in sight; every stone, every colour, every turn and twist within my line of vision.

'Now look at the sky,' said Sabazius.

I looked up at patches of blue, grey clouds, and saw birds flying there.

'And now look at your hand,' he said.

Pink, with lines and topped with fingernails. A bit of dirt under one fingernail. A scratch on my left thumb.

'Now close your eyes.'

Blackness with splotches of colour, zig-zagging lines and the odd picture or two.

'Now look at me.'

I opened my eyes and looked at Sabazius, at his hair, his eyes, the brown suit he always wore under that heavy coat.

'That,' said Sabazius, 'is Elsewhere. Elsewhere is to be found "nowhere", because Elsewhere is everything. Elsewhere is not "contained" in anything. Elsewhere *is* everything!'

Taking me by the arm he almost carried me across the street. I was dumbfounded.

'That is why man thinks God is up there,' he said casually, pointing above his head. 'Man can *sense* Elsewhere "up there"; and sometimes when he's looking at a flower, he senses Elsewhere in the flower. But as you now know, that is a limited conception, for Elsewhere is not "in" any of these things, just as Elsewhere is not "in" any direction, for Elsewhere is that direction, is that flower, is that sky.'

Having gathered my wits together again, I said: 'Some people would call that pantheism ...'

'What is pantheism?'

'The theory that God is everything, that everything is God.'

'We are not talking of the same thing.'

'It sounds like it.'

'I am not talking about a theory!' exploded Sabazius, 'I am talking about Elsewhere! If you want to replace Elsewhere in your "seeing" by a theory that God is everything, and everything is God, then you will be back where you started! Elsewhere is *not* God; God is the lost self of man which man has projected from himself and, having made his God external, become impotent. Elsewhere is the *ever-comprehending act of will* made manifest.

I cannot say that I grasped the words, because even now, they refuse to deliver up their internal meaning in any ordinary, logical sense. The shock of realization seemed to paralyse me until my body stuttered to a halt. I leaned against a wall and breathed deeply to stop the intolerable shaking which was rippling through my limbs and trunk.

'When a man becomes his history,' added Sabazius quietly, 'he enters Elsewhere – the not-existing Elsewhere – and on entering, continues.'

'And if a man does not become his history?' I managed to ask.

Then it is too late to I-dentify with self; that can only happen as an *act of will* while in the physical body. You see a man carries into his death what he "is"; in other words, he becomes a summation of whatever particular history he lived, and as his knowledge of that history has not come to him in a dynamically conscious fashion, he is momentarily stranded between "continue" and "return". Only a man who has refined his history consciously and developed will can pass through the needle of death and continue.'

I again looked around me.

I was not looking at Elsewhere. All that existed was the "act" of that will, the ever-comprehending and evolving act!

'I can only just take it all in ...' I said, and as I moved, a further realization hit me. 'Man's will,' I said in astonishment, '*is* the will of Elsewhere!'

'Now you can "see",' he replied, 'but such a thing can only be truly seen by those who are dynamically conscious. That is the work which lies ahead.'

We walked slowly on.

I could never be the same again; my view of everything had changed.

Sabazius smiled at me. 'It is impossible for a man to work with energy until will is established in that man. What you have at this moment is only a suggestion of will, you have barely touched it, and it has barely touched you.'

'What do I have to do?'

'You now have to live *as* will, not just *with* will.'

I was too full of wonder to even attempt to understand; but I knew Sabazius would eventually lead me into that understanding, if not trick me into it! Deep inside me was the vague memory of what I had once thought of as 'evident reality': it had indeed been a puny conception. In some curious fashion, the hidden logic of his teachings was now coming together, not into a pattern, but into an 'evaluation' through will.

I laughed, and my laughter made me stop. Sabazius stood waiting for me. 'I've just had the most extraordinary thought,' I said, staring at him; 'but I'm not absolutely sure if it's meaningful!'

'And what is that?'

'I am now an atheist!'

His smile gathered the lines of his face together, thrusting his expression of congratulation at me physically. 'That is an interesting observation,' he said back.

12 ❈ Digging

The garden.

It was two-thiry in the morning, very dark and heavily over-cast. I was standing with Sabazius on a patch of waste ground where I generally threw the odd stone or two when raking the flower-beds.

'Just there.' He pointed a little to my left. 'That's where you'll find it … all going well.'

'How can you possibly know that something's buried there?' I asked, knowing that Sabazius had never been in the garden; at least not to my knowledge.

'I don't really know,' he replied, 'but I suspect that's where you'll find it.'

'What exactly do you think I'll find?'

'Who can tell?'

'Then I'm looking for a mystery object.'

'You could say that.'

Clearing the small stones from the surface with my feet, I glanced at Sabazius. 'Shall I just start digging?'

'Not right away. You must sit on the spot for an hour first.'

'An hour!'

'What is an hour to you,' said Sabazius, 'you who intend to conquer death …?'

'Why is it necessary to sit on the spot?' As I spoke, the first drops of rain touched my face. I added immediately: 'Hadn't we better get coats?'

'What for?'

'I don't particularly want to get soaked.'

'If you wear a coat,' he replied, 'you will not find what you're looking for.' He motioned for me to sit down, then he said: 'I will be here with you, but we must not speak, so you must listen carefully now to what I say. Firstly, you must not look at your watch until you are absolutely sure the hour is up.

If you look at your watch, and there is even a minute of that hour left, then you must sit for a further hour; so beware of impatience or it will have you here all night. If, however, the hour is up, then you must immediately start digging.'

'How far down will I have to go?'

'Roughly two feet, and wide enough for your body to curl into. Now when the hole is dug to the correct depth, and the object of mystery is found, you must stand in the hole for a further hour, and the same thing applies to the second hour as it did to the first. Do you understand?'

'I think so.'

'Where are you going?'

'To get my spade.'

'You will not need a spade, use this.' He handed me a small, flat stone.

'You will find it quite sufficient.'

'But it'll take me ages!' I exclaimed. 'Why can't I use proper tools?'

'Because you would damage what is in the hole, and that must not happen.'

The rain was now falling steadily, running down my forehead and into my eyes. It was going to be a miserable night.

'Sit down,' said Sabazius.

It crossed my mind to ask him if I could sit on a piece of wood, but the look on his face stopped me. I sat down on the spot indicated and resigned myself to his incomprehensible logic.

'We must now be silent,' he said, and he too sat down, some five or six feet away. But instead of facing me, he turned his back and allowed his head to fall forward. It was almost as if he had entered instant sleep.

There I sat, my clothes slowly turning black as the rain drenched me, my hands and face slightly numb, my mind empty but for a certain curiosity concerning the 'object' in the hole. What could it possibly be? What would I do with it when I found it? It crossed my mind that Sabazius had possibly placed it there earlier. I smiled. If he had dug up this ground in secret, then it would be easy for me to uncover again. Maybe he had not thought about that. But, there again, Sabazius generally thought about everything.

When roughly an hour had passed, I was so cold and wet I could not stop my body from shivering. What would happen, I wondered, if I just started digging now? Would Sabazius be any the wiser? Would the object I was supposed to find melt away into further mystery? Deciding against it, I tried unsuccessfully to concentrate on holding my mind steady.

Sabazius had not moved a muscle since he sat down. He looked like a black rock, or the stump of a hefty tree. I sat there staring at his back, wondering if he were thinking about anything, or if he had entered some other level or region of mind known only to Men of Feeling.

To stop myself from getting utterly bored, I started breathing in a long, steady rhythm, and attempted to listen and hold three sounds simultaneously. As a result of this, I almost fell asleep sitting up, and only managed to catch myself in time before ploughing my face into what was now a pool of mud. That was when my circumstances really hit me, for the lower part of my body had become completely numb, and the numbness was creeping up slowly into my chest. Even if I found the object, I thought, I would probably die the next day.

But Sabazius too must be numb.

I stared at him, tried to work out why he was subjecting me to such rigours.

It really was quite silly, I thought. No man in his right mind would allow another to dictate such a stupid and senseless course of action. What good was it going to do me to sit here all night? Did he want me to catch my death? That's when I remembered what he had said earlier: What's an hour to you, you who intend to conquer death ...?

I reconsidered.

Maybe there was a purpose in it; albeit a veiled purpose. If I proved to Sabazius that I could withstand rain, cold and numbness, then maybe he would open new doors of revelation, initiate me into new truths. I laughed to myself. I was now able to justify anything he did on the grounds that he was a Man of Feeling. He was right, I had made him into some kind of formula. But he *was* a Man of Feeling, and as a Man of Feeling his methods of teaching were quite often untoward.

So I kept on sitting there, and slowly, as the minutes merged into the time dictated by my own stubbornness, a sense of peace rose up – along with the numbness – and when I looked at my watch the hands said: Work.

The top soil, wet to a depth of some six inches, was easily removed; but the next layer, a hard and gritty compound of earth, resisted my feeble scraping, making me use the small stone Sabazius had given to me like a handleless adze. As I worked, the rain slowly changed each loose deposit of earth into congealed mud, making is extremely difficult to move from hole to mound. After what seemed an eternity of digging, I surveyed my efforts. The hole was certainly large enough in circumference, but still dismally shallow due to my hitting a course of broken brick, not to mention a stray tree-root. Even as I sat there looking at it, the rain was gathering in pools under my legs, rendering my task slowly invisible.

I glanced at Sabazius.

Despair again arose to choke me.

What could be so important that it made a man act like an idiot! And not only that, Sabazius had said that he was not really sure if this was where the object was to be found. Was I digging ... scraping and scooping with my hands for nothing? With little enthusiasm I again attempted to make the hole deeper. Maybe he had only said that to produce this very feeling. I worked on, laid bare the root, manipulated the sucking bricks from their beds of water, and found myself breathing mindlessly through clenched teeth.

Eventually, oblivious to the elements and my shaking limbs, I reached what appeared to be a depth of two feet. Scrabbling about I searched for the object, pushing my fingers into the dark mush in the hope that they would locate what my eyes could not possibly detect. But there was nothing, just more bricks and more earth, more coldness and numbness. Slowly, and painfully, I got to my feet. Should I tell Sabazius I had found nothing?

It was five-thiry-eight in the morning.

My second problem hit me. Had Sabazius meant me to stand in the hole even if I did not find the object; or did that only apply if it was found? Should I ask him? A great sorrow overtook me, a heart-felt sorrow for myself and all I had been through. What did it matter if I stood in the hole for an hour, a day or a year? If I walked away from the hole things would be just the same – wouldn't they? I clambered out, looked momentarily at Sabazius, and decided to leave him to his senseless vigil. What I needed was a bath and a mug of hot coffee ... oh, what I would have given for a mug of hot coffee!

I was only six feet away from the hole when the sickness came upon me, doubled me up. Dropping to my knees, I clamped my arms round my middle and swayed from side to side. It was obviously a stomach cramp. When it relaxed a little I would get upstairs as quickly as possible and drink some whisky. I was not at all sure if whisky would help, but it seemed the sensible thing under the circumstances. If it did not help my stomach, at least it would warm me up.

Each time I made for the steps however, the pain increased, intensifying until I thought the death I was trying to avoid would surely take me to itself that instant. Death! I again remembered why I had dug that hole, sat for hours in drenched silence. I was not only staggering away from Sabazius, I was turning my back on the task. But there again, it was all very well having high-flown thoughts, but would they save me from illness, from more pain and suffering extended into the future! I looked through the darkness at the steps, then back at the hole, and thought: Okay, so I have not found the mysterious object; but did that really matter, was it so imperative for me to gain an end product? Sabazius himself had once believed that each task had a conclusion, only to discover, as I was discovering, that a task completed *was* a conclusion. The task Sabazius had set me lay uncompleted.

That's when a very unusual thought struck me, a thought related to the moment, yet not intrinsically related to the man I thought myself to be: if I'm going to die, I said to myself grimly, then I might as well die in the grave I have dug with my own hands ...

The pain evaporated.

From where I stood, I could still see Sabazius. He had not moved. Was he waiting for me to return, waiting for the other man in me to respond?

I wiped the water and mud from my eyes and face and walked slowly back to the hole. There was a foot of water in it. I looked at it for some seconds, evaluated its meaning, its lack of meaning, and then I stepped in ...

Blackness.

When I came to I was no longer in that hole. Sabazius had carried me upstairs, washed me from head to toe and placed me in a warm bed. As my eyes flickered open, he started to laugh.

'How do you feel?' he asked, his face lost in smiling.

'Exhausted ...' I replied.

'Tell me what happened.'

'Don't you know?'

'I want to hear it from your own lips.'

Slowly, I recounted every segment of the struggle, every thought and curse that had entered my head.

'And still you *worked*!' he said in astonishment.

'Didn't you expect me to?'

'I expect nothing,' said Sabazius, 'so I am never disappointed.'

'But I didn't find anything,' I said, wondering if this modified my attempt in any way. 'There was nothing there.'

'Of course you did.'

'I found nothing tangible.'

'You found something both tangible and intangible,' he answered. 'Don't you know what you found?'

'I haven't got the faintest idea!'

He pulled back the covers suddenly. 'To take *that* out of your grasp, I would have to cut your hand open with a knife!'

In my hand was the little stone adze; it had broken in half.

'That is the mystery,' added Sabazius. 'So you did find something.'

'But I had that when I started,' I said, 'I didn't find it.'

'Then it found you.'

'I didn't have it in my hand when I walked away from the hole. I know that for a certainty.'

'It was in your hand when I brought you up here.'

'Does the stone have special significance?' I asked.

'The stone is *of* you, and you are *of* the stone. All Men of Feeling have had a stone.'

'What do you use it for?'

'We don't use it for anything, just as we don't use ourselves for anything. The stone "is", and we "are".'

'Then what do I do with it?'

Sabazius chuckled and sat down on the bed. 'The stone is

very special,' he said reverently. 'It must be kept with you at all times.'

'Why is that?'

'Because the stone contains your will.'

'But surely "will" belongs to the man?'

'Of course it does; but without the stone the man could not at first regulate his will.'

'Then I must carry it about with me?'

'No, no,' said Sabazius. 'The stone must be fashioned into a pendant, and what is left of it, every grain, has to be made into a powder.'

'What's the powder for?'

'That's something else. When you're ready, I will tell you.'

Sabazius then told me to sleep, for I would require a great deal of energy for some experiments that evening. So, with the stone firmly clasped in my one semi-washed hand, I fell asleep, fell into a deep, deep sleep which lasted for twelve hours, and from which I awoke refreshed.

When I had had something to eat, Sabazius made me sit once again on the carpet, or to be exact, kneel on the carpet, with a hand placed on each thigh. I was to look, he said, between my hands at the floor, yet attempt to *sense* both hands together.

After almost three quarters of an hour, I noticed an indistinct ripple.

'There's something there,' I said quietly, 'but it's very vague.'

'It will become stronger when you focus properly,' he replied from behind me. 'Just look gently at it.'

I attempted to look gently.

The ripple slowly took on the appearance of a double-ended cone, a cone measuring some three or four inches from tip to tip. It was, I remember thinking, not really on the carpet, but just above it. It was composed of tiny dots of energy, rather like silver fireflies in flight, yet contained, or at least apparently contained, within that curious shape. I described what I could see to Sabazius.

'That,' he replied, 'is your will made manifest. It is the subtle bisecting point of vision, the line of projected sight.'

'What's it for?'

'It is what a Man of Feeling uses to "see" with. When he looks at something, or someone, in the special sense, he looks at them through the point where projected sight crosses. So if he looks far away, at the horizon for instance, the perspective of his vision determines automatically where the point of will rests; and although he can no longer see visibly that bisecting point, he is consciously aware of its existence, and therefore dynamically affixed to it.'

Still slightly puzzled, I said: 'But if everyone has a point of will, why don't they ever detect it?'

'Because they are continually lost outside of themselves,' answered Sabazius. 'When they are in awake-dream, the energies required are dissipated in all directions. They never really focus on anything, hear anything, or touch anything. At all times, except on very rare occasions, they are being carried this way and that by the flow of the world's energies. But when a man approaches the region of self he forms a barrier which holds him in place, and being in place, his natural energies have time to generate and accumulate. But the moment he again enters awake-dream, those energies flow out and are lost in the world.'

'And if he stays consciously awake over long periods?'

'The energies produced give him the ability to stay awake more and more, and because he is more awake, he becomes properly conscious of his moments of sleep.'

'Until finally he is totally awake.'

'When a man is totally awake,' replied Sabazius, 'he is then composed of self-knowledge through having become the momentary culmination of his history on this planet. And because of this, he walks carefully, and with superb attention, towards the exit from physical life.'

My double-ended cone of will vanished. 'It's gone!' I said. 'It just faded out.'

'There are three reasons for that,' said Sabazius immediately, 'and you must at all times know, or attempt to know which one is operative. It can be because you have switched it off and applied yourself dynamically to something else; because you are looking far away through it, rather than at it; or because you have momentarily dropped back into awake-dream. Now it doesn't really matter what you're doing or thinking at any moment, for awake-dream can be entered without warning, and the only guide you have to that fact is when you suddenly reawaken. So you must train yourself to take words "in", not flow out to meet them; just as you must learn to take the world's impressions "in", yet not flow out into them.'

'It sounds like an impossible task,' I said, seeing everything being complicated yet another degree. 'Can a man really think simultaneously on so many levels consistently?'

'If he does not,' said Sabazius, 'then that man remains until his death merely a biological machine. If you remember that, you will desire to remain dynamically awake.'

13 ❋ *The cutting of the stone*

Sabazius made me keep the stone on my person for three days. On the morning of the third day he informed me that it was time to make the pendant. Following his instructions carefully, I washed the stone in a solution of tepid water mixed with salt, then, with the help of a small magnifying glass, and a sliver of freshly cut wood from the garden, I removed all traces of earth from the veins on the stone's surface. When my will-stone was to his satisfaction (he would not touch it), he handed me a small piece of metal some six inches long – not unlike a file, except that the serrations on one edge had been hand-cut – and told me to mark the stone into two portions, the top portion to be exactly one third, and the bottom portion two thirds. To make absolutely sure, he insisted that I measure the stone with a wooden ruler. When this was done, he then told me to cut through the mark with infinite care, each stroke of the file being made towards my body. To assist my concentration, he intimated casually that if I botched the job, I might well become very ill.

To make sure that nothing of the stone was lost, he placed a sheet of finely grained paper on top of my wooden breadboard, laid the board on my coffee table, and then placed the table near to the window where an early morning sun was struggling to show its face. At no time, he said, was my shadow to fall on the stone, so this required a straightbacked posture, with my arms held out in front of me. At first, I found the single strokes of the file easy, but after an hour each stroke took on the proportions of a mighty act of physical strength, and to my horror, the stone's dense consistency had blunted the file.

'I don't seem to be making any impression,' I said hopelessly. 'I've hardly marked it.'

'You must remember,' said Sabazius, 'that this is no ordinary stone. It contains your will, so cut it with will, imbue the file with your will until each stoke is meaningful.'

'How do I do that?'

'That's for you to find out. If you do not find out, the stone will resist your efforts indefinitely.'

At the end of three hours I was exhausted, and only one eighth into the stone's three eighths of thickness. If the next quarter of an inch took me as long, I would have to spend nine hours at the task. This thought made me stop.

'What's the manner?' asked Sabazius.

'I can hardly hold my arms up.'

He looked at me intently, then he said: 'No man will ever attain self-knowledge without the *application of heart*. If you do not have the "heart" to cut that stone, you're finished.'

'But it's resisting me like mad!'

'That's the clue to cutting the stone.'

'How do you mean?'

'Think about it.'

I considered what he had said, turned it this way and that, and then a thought occurred. If the stone contained my will, then in some peculiar fashion, I *was* the stone! So what was actually happening, was not that the stone was resisting me, but that I was resisting myself! If I could resist myself, it followed that I could *assist* myself, so what I had to do was enter into the stone consciously through the file, and allow *myself* to be cut ...

The very next stroke robbed me of breath and almost knocked me over, for as the file grated across the stone's surface, it was as if someone had cleft me with an axe.

'Don't drop it!' roared Sabazius.

I bit into my bottom lip and drew blood.

'Now you know how to cut the stone,' he said in a controlled manner, 'but if you drop it, shatter it, or score any other part of the surface, you will wish you had never been born.'

Taking a deep breath, I applied the file accurately to the groove and pulled it towards me, only to again undergo that terrifying experience. It was almost as if every atom of my physical and mental structure was on the point of rupturing, and being scattered.

'I don't think I can do it,' I said, laying clenched fists on the table to steady myself. 'It's tearing me to pieces.'

'On the contrary,' replied Sabazius, 'it is solidifying your being, giving you the "heart" you still lack.'

'But - '

He frowned at me, raised a hand. 'There is no time for talk,' he said gravely. 'Either you cut the stone, or you do not cut the stone.'

'Isn't there some other way to acquire will?'

'There are many ways, millions of ways; but each way must contain heart, and when a "Way" or "Path" has heart, it demands everything that a man is.'

'But surely when you put your heart into something you're enthusiastic about it?'

'Man's enthusiasm is awake-dream,' said Sabazius. 'It is how he fools himself into self-importance and remains asleep. A man's heart is his living pulse, so when heart is applied to a task, the *whole* man responds.'

I looked at the stone.

'Cut it,' said Sabazius.

Uniting everything within me in a conscious act of will I drew the piece of metal towards my body in a slow, deliberate stroke ... there was a flash of white light inside my head followed immediately by a searing pain, and the stone, inexplicably, and to my utter joy, was cut clean through like a piece of cheese.

I stared at it, then I said, looking at Sabazius in wonder: 'What happened?'

'You cut the stone.'

'I know I've cut it ... but how?'

'You applied heart. You entered into the spirit of the hole where you found the stone, and the spirit of the hole gave you strength.'

I stared at him. 'What do you mean by "the spirit of the hole"?'

In answer to my question, he said: 'When you dug the hole you laid the foundation of heart in your being, you captured the secret essence of will, and the essence of will entered the stone. So to cut the stone, you had to release the essence of will from the stone by again applying heart, so multiplying the structure of heart in your being, and the essence of will in the stone simultaneously. What you experienced was both of those things rapidly coming together in the act of cutting, for to cut the stone successfully means that you have acquired the ability to control will, and through it apply heart to any task.'

'Then I can do anything!'

'I would hope not,' said Sabazius, and he smiled at me. 'As I said, you have acquired the ability to control will through the application of heart, but the will you have acquired is only so you can again apply heart to the manufacturing of more will, so perfecting the circle. If a man acquired perfect will before he acquired a perfect heart, the end result would be disastrous. He would have no control over it, for fantasy would drive him to use will in the most extraordinary manner. He would kill his friends, bestow riches on those who did not deserve them and, against all his better judgements, eventually kill himself through aberrated imagination. Balanced will can only appear within a balanced man, and a balanced man is he who through the application of heart has refined all that he is, all that he thinks and so on. Such a man is "master" of his will, because he *is* will.'

The same simple foundation was presented to me again. Why could I never remember that a *man is a man*, not a bundle of bits and pieces fragmented and scattered like a broken car? There was nothing in what he said that did not eventually find its completion in 'unity'. Man was a unity, and when he became *consciously* conscious of that unity, realized, thought, acted, believed, felt, willed, evaluated through his unity of being, then all things became possible, for all things were in themselves a unity. Having allowed me to think my thoughts, Sabazius said:

'Even a Man of Power must follow this principle. He must perfect firstly the application of heart, manufacture will out of that heart, spiral upwards until he has conquered and integrated all levels of consciousness, and at all times be on guard against making a slip which will send his will out of control.'

'But you said that all Men of Power had a flaw?'

'Indeed. Men of Power never really intend to become Men of Power. It is a mistake they fall into because a certain aspect, or aspects, of their modified systems backfires at a later date. They go through the same process of change; but the end result is breakdown, a form of madness from which there is no escape.'

'So a small conceit can become madness.'

'For men who attempt "all", yes; but for those in awake-dream it matters little, for their conceit suffices but to make them look in mirrors, not to attempt the destruction of humanity.'

'I'm beginning to understand,' I said. 'Every task you give me is designed not only to manufacture will through the application of heart, but also to refine my basic nature.'

'Yes,' said Sabazius.

'Are you succeeding?'

'I will tell you something,' he replied. 'The moment a man believes he *has* succeeded, that man is in trouble. To succeed in the true sense, you must doubt every action, every word, every proof of your success. Death will not claim any Man of Feeling who lives by that law.'

'How can "doubt" be a law?'

'It is a law firstly because it stops a man abandoning himself, and it is a law secondly because it arouses a series of modifications in his system which eradicate potential flaws, or flaws which have just appeared. It could almost be said that a Man of Feeling stands in the midst of three pillars: Heart, Will, and Doubt.'

At that particular moment my 'will' was in the shape of two small stones lying on a breadboard, my 'heart' was a hole in the garden, and my 'doubt' a man called Alexis Sabazius. It was indeed a curious thing to receive 'doubt' as a gift.

'But there is another aspect of this,' continued Sabazius, 'for even a man who has built the first of those three pillars can be caught by death. It sometimes happens that his doubt becomes the very flaw it is supposed to eradicate, and instead of feeding him with balanced energies, produces a desire for awake-dream which makes him turn his back on all he knows. And then there is the man who shuffles backwards and forwards between serious intent and awake-dream as if the whole cosmos was designed for his benefit. This man switches cosmological vision on and off when it suits him, wallows in awake-dream when he's tired or hungry, and only attempts anything positive when things are bright and to his advantage. Such men are a danger to everyone they come in contact with, for they demote the vision to their own level, and become a stumbling block to those who seek it.'

'But what – '

'You have work to do,' interjected Sabazius, and he pointed at the stone. 'You have three things before you: you have the upper stone, the lower stone, and the powder. The upper and the lower must be refined by rubbing them together, and the powder obtained crushed until it is like flour. When they have been refined through rubbing, they must then be joined with a thong of leather, and coated with a special varnish.'

'How long will that take?'

'You have answered your own question.'

Five words, and at their centre, will. So the operation of 'refinement' depended on will. Through will I had to refine will, for both stones represented will – although, as I discovered much later, differing aspects of it.

Sabazius then pulled the curtains until the room was almost dark. 'This part of the task,' he explained, 'cannot be done in the light, for although light is required to cut the stone, the rubbing always take place in darkness.' He stood looking at me for some seconds, then he added: 'To rub the stones, first stroke the lower portion with the upper until its edges are smooth; then, with the lower which has been refined, stroke the upper until its edges are smooth. Only by rubbing the stones in this manner can you master will.'

'How will I know that the task has been done properly without light?'

'Again you answer your own question.'

'Will?'

'What else? You will *feel* the smoothness of your will.'

I carefully lifted the stones and peered at them, then, transferring the small stone to my right hand, I attempted to start.

'There is something else you must know before you start,' said Sabazius. 'If you simply rub the stones together they will become hot through friction, and what they contain will be lost. But if you spit on the stones first, your spittle will stop this from happening, and the smoothness will be like glass. And there is something else, each stroke must this time be away from you, not towards you.'

'Why is that?'

'When you were cutting the stone, you drew the file towards

you so that the stone's will – which you had manufactured out of the application of heart – would come under control; but to refine them, you must direct the line of that refinement towards Elsewhere, for only in Elsewhere made manifest can your will have dynamic meaning.'

He nodded at me to start.

With infinite care (I had applied spittle first), I stroked the larger of the two stones with the smaller and, to my utter relief, was not subjected to my previous experience. At first, the action of rubbing the stones was rather like sharpening a penknife; but as the minutes gathered, multiplied, my attention became fixed on each stroke, and the meaning of my actions became clear. It was like standing in front of a large window at night, seeing at first nothing, then stars, then a faint greyness, then dawn. I forgot all about Sabazius, so wrapped up was I in this memorable task. There was nothing but the two stones, and the sound of rubbing. Nothing else mattered, came to mind or demanded my attention.

When the larger of the two stones seemed as smooth as I could make it, I discovered that the smaller stone, through the action of rubbing the larger, was already faced on both sides with smoothness, so making my task much easier. Changing them around, I then rubbed the smaller with the larger, and as I rubbed it occurred to me that a similar action was taking place in reverse, refining, as it were, that which was already refined. The subtlety of this captured me until the process was complete, whereupon I informed Sabazius that the stones were ready.

He drew the curtains.

'Now you must gather the powder,' he instructed. 'But be very careful with it, for each grain must be split into a further grain, and the grains obtained split until they can be reduced no further.'

'What shall I keep the powder in?'

'I have a small box made of hardwood for you.'

With the blunt end of the file, I crushed the larger grains of stone into a powder as directed. He then gave me the box – which looked as if it had been carved out of ebony – and, folding the paper, I poured the powder into it.

'That must be kept with you at all times,' said Sabazius. 'The powder has a special purpose, but I will only tell you that purpose when you have proved to me that you are capable of handling it wisely.' He pointed at the stones again. 'Now you have to bind them, and varnish them.'

The binding, as it turned out, was easy. Sabazius gave me a black leather thong and two small pieces of copper wire. With the help of some household glue I glued the thong in a figure of eight round the outer edge of the stones (the smaller being at the top), and bound the connection above and below with the wire. While the glue was setting, Sabazius showed me how to make the varnish.

With a needle, and my unwilling consent, he pricked the thumb of both my left and right hand, squeezed out some blood, and with some spittle (mine) and a little powder from my box, prepared the mixture. When this was a reddish paste, he produced a twig, which he said had been taken from the garden near to the hole, sliced it open with a knife and scooped out a pocket of golden resin which just 'happened' to be there.

'How did you know which twig to take?' I asked.

'All the twigs nearest to the hole contain such resin,' he replied matter-of-factly. 'The trees produced it for you.'

'How can a tree know what I need?'

'When a man finds unity in himself,' said Sabazius, 'everything around him responds, especially nature. If this world contained only beings of unity, nature would burst into a paradise.'

'What causes ... '

He silenced me immediately. 'You will find these things out later,' he said briskly. 'First you have to mix this with the paste, then apply it to the stones until they are sealed. When that is done, hang the pendant in a dark place so that the surfaces can dry; but it must not touch anything, especially metal.'

With the help of the little stick I had used to clean the stones, I mixed the resin, then, revolving the stones slowly, I sealed them firmly. I felt very excited at that moment, for this was the first task I had completed which afforded me a tangible result, something I could look at and remember. The pendant was not merely a decoration, it was an instrument of my will.

14 ✳ *The sheath of vision*

On a cold, blustery morning late in December, Sabazius told me I had some important work to do. He said that this work was not unlike what I had done on the day the lean-faced man came after me, but that there would be no terror in it.

'What exactly do you want me to do?'

'I want you to fix yourself in place for five or six hours.'

'How will I do that?'

'Up until now,' he replied, 'you have been laying a foundation of knowledge, and an understanding of that knowledge. You have had certain experiences, and those experiences have convinced you that the work is real, not just in my imagination. But everything you have experienced has been momentary, and most of your experiences have been due to tricks of one sort or another; today, however, there will be no tricks, there will just be *you* walking through London, Peter Derwent attempting to fix himself in place.'

'Aren't you coming with me?'

'Oh yes,' said Sabazius, 'and every time you fall into awake-dream I'll slap you across the shoulders so hard it will hurt!'

'I thought I was out of awake-dream?'

'You mean you *still* think you are conscious!' he exclaimed. 'Do you really believe that?'

I hesitated, smiled. 'I'm certainly more conscious than I was.'

'The only time you've really been conscious is when I've made you conscious. You're still confusing thinking about being awake with actually being awake.'

'I quite often practise being awake while on my own,' I replied. 'I'm not that lazy.'

He laughed, threw his head back, opened his mouth and let out a long sigh of frustration and amusement. Then he said: 'We will soon find out how conscious you are.'

'How will you know whether I'm conscious or not?'

'That doesn't concern you for the moment,' he replied, 'just take my word for it that I will know; so don't go plastering your face with frowns of concentration, that will mean nothing to me.'

Wrapped in heavy winter coats we left the flat and headed for Oxford Street. (We seemed to do nothing else but walk up and down Oxford Street.) Drawing my mind in as tightly as possible, I set out to prove that I could remain conscious longer than Sabazius thought, but before we had covered twenty yards he slapped me across the shoulders as promised. The power of the stroke stunned me, it was like being hit with a log of wood.

'I wasn't in awake-dream,' I said, staring at him.

As I completed the last word of that sentence, he slapped me again, this time across the right arm. On his face was a smile, as if he were greeting me with playful roughness. Still smiling, he said: 'Keep walking.'

My next slap came after ten yards.

Seconds after setting off again, he clipped me on the left shoulder with his fist.

That was when I turned on him.

'For Christ's sake!' I shouted, trying to control my temper. 'You're striking me for nothing!'

'I'm striking you because you are asleep,' he replied harshly. 'You're asleep now, don't you even know that?'

'But I'm not asleep ... '

'If you're awake,' he said quickly, 'then I've already entered Elsewhere with a roar!'

Trembling, I said: 'Then I don't know what I'm doing wrong. What am I doing wrong?'

'You were dreaming.'

'But I was consciously thinking in an exact fashion about staying awake!'

'Of course you were, but your "exact" thinking *was* awake-dream.'

'How can you possibly know that?'

'Never worry about what I know, only about what I do not know.'

I turned away from him and looked down Oxford Street. Pulling myself in mentally, I *looked* at it.

126

'That's better,' he said immediately.

'Wasn't I doing that all the time?'

'No.'

'Then what was I doing?'

Sabazius stared at me, then he said: 'To be awake means that your being is awake, not just your mind. If you cannot sense *all* that you are simultaneously with what you are looking at, or thinking about, then you are in awake-dream. So it follows that to merely think in logical or exact patterns is not to be truly awake, for if that were so, then many people on this very street could claim that they too were dynamically conscious.'

'But surely one thinks logically when awake?'

'But of course,' he sighed. 'However the logic of dynamic thought is rigid, it cannot move from its subject without complete approval from "being" – arbitrary associations cease. When you said you were thinking in an exact fashion, what you were referring to was deep concentration; but deep concentration is that out of which a man realizes that he is asleep. It is only the approach, the entrance to wakefulness. When a man thinks in such a manner, he forgets that the world exists, everything becomes hazy, out of focus. He can walk three miles and not remember a single step on arriving at his destination. Now he may have solved a problem, and the problem may even be, as I said, that he knows that he is asleep; but what good is knowing such a thing if you are powerless to wake up? Such thinking may produce an invention, or marvellous mathematics, but in the end it produces only death.'

'So when I looked, and tried to sense the world, I woke up.'

'Your features flickered to life,' replied Sabazius. 'Your eyes were immediately calm, for you were holding the world and self simultaneously.'

'But I can only do that for a second.'

He laughed, tilting his head in that familiar way. 'And that is the second you must enlarge until it is a minute, and then an hour, and then a day … until it is all you are.'

'But I can't *think* when I'm trying to sense both. The sensing disrupts my ability to think.'

'Exactly. At first, all a man can do is practise *looking*; then, slowly, he can stand over and above his looking and think too. But to think in such a manner is to be controlled rigidly by self through the world. At no time can a stray thought enter in. You are then master of your senses.'

I had noticed earlier that people were looking at me. When Sabazius slapped me twice in quick succession, an elderly woman had stopped to stare. Her expression had said clearly: 'Why don't you slap him back?' That was when my concentration had broken in two, and I had spun round to defend myself verbally.

'Did you see the woman?' I asked.

'Yes, I saw her,' said Sabazius, 'and I also saw one of your personalities slot itself into place without your knowing.'

'You actually saw it?'

'Everything about you changed. You began to walk differently, with your shoulders back and your chin tucked in. It was just as if you were saying: "I'm not really weak ... look at my dignity."'

As usual, he was right. I could now distinctly remember my feelings at that moment. Everything had changed. I had tried momentarily to look 'important' for the woman's benefit. Obviously I was not immune to awake-dream and personality shift, the one being a symptom of the other, allowing the other to manifest. If I was ever to become a Man of Feeling, then, as Sabazius had said, I had to 'enlarge' my moments of looking, stretch them out, join them together until there were no gaps.

We moved on through the crowds of people and every so often the flat of Sabazius's hand landed on my back or shoulders. It amazed me, for I was slowly becoming conscious that I was popping in and out of wake-dream with almost every blink. Would I ever manage to remain static?

Sabazius said suddenly: 'There are three levels of staying awake, but I prefer to call them "distances". What you can see just in front of your feet is the Lower-Distance, then there is the Middle-Distance where moving objects begin to appear, and beyond that the Upper-Distance where everything is in flux and mixed together. To enter "wakefulness", one should always view the Lower-Distance first, that will give you a chance to sort your mind out; then, when that is done, and you feel reasonably confident, switch to the Middle-Distance at intervals to strengthen your ability to look, and when you cannot be shaken in the Middle-Distance, direct your gaze at the

Upper-Distance. But if something happens, either externally or internally to break that looking, then do not drop your eyes completely, always come down through the levels one by one, as if your mind were a gear box. If you do it this way, you'll find that your ability to "look" will be recaptured much more quickly.'

'Why is looking at the ground easier?'

'Each of the levels, or distances,' replied Sabazius, 'carries its own time sequence; in other words, depending on the angle of vision, a man can see less, or more. And the more he sees, the more he is confused by the differing rates (times) of energy rushing towards him. When you look at the ground, however, the distance and the similarities of compound produce almost a level influx of energy, so giving you a chance to get your looking "balanced". The Middle-Distance throws a more complex variety of energy-rates or energy-times at you, so demanding a tighter grip on your looking; and the Upper-Distance is a barrage of energy time-rates, both moving and static, large and small, far and near, powerful and weak, which demand "total" looking. But curiously enough, when you have mastered the technique, you will find the Upper-Distance not only easy, but thrilling. For mastery produces an "envelope" round your looking which automatically holds it in place. When that happens, you can then start to pin your *looking* on objects, or people, and the results of that are quite astounding.'

'In what way?'

'Well, firstly, the external is cut off from the internal. By that I mean that you are inside a "sheath of vision" which stops you flowing out into awake-dream, and similarly stops you flowing in, into awake-dream. So you are suspended between the two, being able to look out at the external world and in at the internal world without losing sense of being for a second. So when you think, each thought leads immediately to a conclusion, either yes, you do understand, or no, you do not; and anything you pin your looking on becomes what it really is, not just a flat uninteresting picture thrust upon you. The beauty of this state is that you are taking in the world's energies, plus the energies of your thoughts, but throwing nothing out, thus building up a store of energy with which to tackle your work.'

'What causes the "sheath"?'

'I think my answer to that question will interest you considerably,' replied Sabazius. 'When a man has perfected his looking, or at least reached a reasonable level of consistency, his looking causes chemical changes in his brain, and the chemicals produced by the interaction of other chemicals with electrical energy cause him to "see" for longer and longer periods. Now the curious thing about this is that the chemicals produced by his "looking" do not immediately react upon him, but are sent down into the saliva ducts, whereupon they are taken into the body like food, enter the bloodstream, and are pumped back up into the brain. Now you may think that a pointless exercise, but there is a very good reason for it. Certain chemicals which have the power to change a man's vision are already in his brain, but they lack a third ingredient to become active, and that ingredient is not another chemical, it is the man's own will. Before a man can produce the chemicals necessary for him to "see", he must *want* to see, so the chemical which has the power to give him vision travels, as it were, on the strength of the man's will and, on its return to the brain, produces sight.'

'How on earth do you know that?'

'By taste.'

'You mean you taste the chemicals when your saliva ducts produce them?'

'Just so.'

My attempts to 'look' suddenly took on a further importance. It was not just a matter of autosuggestion, or imagination, as many of my friends would think, but a chemical, electrical and psychical reaction which meant that everything in me, everything I *was*, was working to create a Man of Feeling. I now understood what Sabazius had meant when he said my 'history' was in me, not in The Awakener.

'What – '

'Don't you want to see?'

'Of course I do.'

'Then get on with it,' said Sabazius.

The smile on his face intimated to me that the abruptness of his tone was consciously directed to start up my looking. Walking slowly, we made our way down to the Thames and followed the river to Westminster Bridge. With infinite care, I graduated from the Lower-Distance to the Middle-Distance, and being presented with a people-free view of the river, soon attempted Upper-Distance looking. At first, the sheer enormity of the landscape robbed me of my sense of 'being'; but with practice I learned to hold 'being' in place, thus making what I saw remain intrinsically *in* itself.

After two hours of such looking, I realized that my ability to 'see' was now switched on, and that the breaks, when they came, were not so intense, and generally a result of sudden external influences rather than internal wanderings. I then experimented by moving up and down through the levels, and by the end of the third hour could even move my eyes rapidly without that curious non-concentration being broken.

The one thing which stood out from all of this was the fact that I had no desire to think in normal terms. Thoughts did not arise, I had to make them; or as Sabazius was prone to say, manufacture them. It was utterly impossible to just think about this or that, for one was totally caught up in the 'act' of seeing, and the seeing in itself was so calm, so beautiful, that the only involuntary action, or reaction, was the occasional smile which forced itself upon me.

Amidst noise, hustle and bustle, the world was still!

Then, as if to deny the fact that thoughts could not arise associatively in this state, it 'occurred' to me that my knowledge of 'being' – that through which I was able to see – was somehow connected with my spinal column. It came into my head that the brain did not extend halfway down the body for nothing, and that the basic reason for this, apart from the nerve-bunches leading off to sensation centres and eventually erupting into an unimaginable number of tiny skin sensors, was to allow 'being' to be realized. Through a total sense of one's body, consciousness changed from something you 'had', into what you 'were'.

This was the meaning of 'awareness'.

Sabazius, when I told him of this, nodded but did not reply. He had not struck me for two hours, and seemed to be taking little interest in the operation now.

At the centre of my body, a pulse was beating; and at the nape of my neck I could feel a faint vibration which seemed to be feeding a pulsation at the base of my brain. I tried to fathom these things, but could not. How mysterious, how marvellous, I thought, that the body should be so constructed, so knowledgeable in its own chemistry and general function, that when a man took his first faltering steps into consciousness, it should follow like a loving friend, regulating, manipulating, changing, adding and subtracting.

Everything was related.

From points of light, seen and unseen, in the depths of universe, to the smallest particle of matter which constituted one's being, there was a connection.

I shook my head in wonder.

Sabazius said: 'Now you must learn to talk.'

'Learn?' I said.

'Now be careful,' he warned. 'To talk and hold being in place is even more difficult than to think and hold being in place. It requires more energy, much more. Thinking breeds thinking. Chaos breeds chaos. But in this world we have lost sight of the difference between talking because *we have something to say*, and talking because we *have to say something*. This breeds talking for the sake of talking, just as it breeds thinking for the sake of thinking; and from this arises the world's multiple logics which are based eventually on meaninglessness. Such logics, when they are firmly established, then further the meaningless continuation of words and thoughts, and the result is organized stupidity.'

Leaning for a moment against the concete rim of the bridge, he added: 'Of course talking has its reverse side, and the reverse of talking is listening. Even though a person says nothing in return to another's statement, he can still fall into the trap of thinking about that statement when that statement contains no intrinsic meaning. To think about a basically meaningless statement is to make yourself meaningless, and to reply to it, idiocy. But like all things, there is a third side to this question, and the third side is your personal responsibility to others. If a man makes a statement to you which is meaning-full, and because you are in awake-dream and captured by the I's of ego, your reply is meaning-less, then you endanger that man. Such actions also render you consciously impotent, and push you further into awake-dream, making it more difficult to break out and create the sheath. That is why I say that you

132

must *learn* to talk, just as you have learned to think.'

Standing there as I was gazing fixedly up the Thames, what he said heightened and intensified my knowledge of being; but I also knew that I would soon be subjected to that ordinary level of consciousness which I considered 'normal', and that at that level, the advice and insight Sabazius had given to me might very well fade and go out of focus. So there was only one thing to do, and that was to attempt to remain in 'the sheath of vision'.

15 ❈ *Intellect and intelligence*

When I awoke the next morning, I had completely forgotten about the 'sheath', but within a few minutes the memory of it returned, and I found myself gazing out of my bedroom window, longing for it, hoping I would be again able to enter into that level of mind where everything seemed stable. Sabazius had stayed the night, and as I lay thinking about what I had apparently lost, he brought in coffee and buttered rolls.

'How do you feel this morning?' he asked.

'Empty.'

Placing the tray near to me on the bed, he sat down. 'Do you like being empty?'

'No.'

'Then do something about it.'

I nodded, smiled at him and reached for a roll. Sabazius stopped me by placing a hand on mine.

'What's the matter?' I asked.

'Indeed,' he replied, 'what is the matter?'

I looked at him for some seconds before it dawned on me what he was getting at. 'Now?' I said.

'What else is there to do?'

Lying back I attempted to enter 'being' and *see* the room. Nothing happened.

'Do you like hot buttered rolls?' asked Sabazius.

'Of course.'

'Then start there. If you can switch on your looking fast enough, they might still be warm enough to eat!'

I laughed to myself, feeling like a child promised a sweet if it washed its neck properly.

'You have such a complicated mind,' he said, 'that by necessity you make everything you approach more difficult than it really is. You don't have to "think" your way into the sheath, just *allow* it to happen; open yourself through looking, be conscious of your looking, conscious of the source of your looking and the sheath will form. It's the easiest thing in the world.'

Feeling a sudden need for air, I filled my lungs in one long breath. There was an immediate reaction.

'That's better,' said Sabazius.

A synaptic flash made me connect breathing with the sheath. I again breathed deeply, and immediately noticed a growing density in my head, like a coming together of particles.

Excitement.

'Don't tense yourself,' warned Sabazius. He laid a finger on the back of my hand. 'Tension strangles one's ability to look.'

Within ten minutes my feeling of emptiness evaporated. I knew I was not yet in the sheath, but the curious process Sabazius had described – that of the chemical journey through will – was, I felt sure, already taking place.

Step by step I entered the 'inner room', the room which was somehow suspended between mind and the beginning of sight. All the while Sabazius kept that slight pressure on the back of my hand. When I was obviously well into myself, he said:

'Now you can have your roll.'

In a wordless sense (they seemed unnecessary while in the sheath) I considered the difference between how I now felt and the emptiness I had experienced upon waking. The first factor was that my body had been dead; that is, *not known to me* in an intrinsic manner. However, the moment I looked through 'being' at what lay around me, the small generator of consciousness started up, feeding energy to every nerve and cell. As a reaction to this, my lungs immediately demanded more oxygen, and with a fuller intake of that neglected substance my 'looking' reached another level.

'Don't you want your roll now?' asked Sabazius.

'When you came into the room carrying that tray,' I replied, 'there was nothing I wanted more. A cup of coffee and a roll seemed very important. But that is not the case now, I could quite easily do without them.'

'You're learning,' he said, smiling at me. 'You are now approaching an understanding of what "desire" is built on, and how it can be avoided. When a man captures and retains the vital energies of being, he automatically separates himself from object-desire. And when that happens, what he longs for and seeks after withers into nothing. It's a very simple process, and it has nothing to do with denial. But that of course is too easy for the world to recognize, it has to complicate the issue with self-sacrifice.'

After breakfast, Sabazius put me through a series of exercises combined with breathing. I was, apparently, to do them every morning and evening whatever my circumstances. When I asked him what they would do for me, he said:

'The first thing they will do is make you strong physically. A Man of Feeling must be strong to withstand the huge pressures and influences of the world. And secondly, the effect of them will accumulate and strengthen your ability to stay in the sheath. If a man does not have the sheath to insulate him from the world and awake-dream, then all the knowledge ever conceived and digested will not shield him from disintegration and death.'

'Does that mean that a Man of Feeling does not grow old internally?'

'Of course he grows old,' replied Sabazius, 'no man can avoid that. But growing old is not what matters, what matters is *how* one grows old. As you know very well, advanced age does not only imply a wasting of the body, it also means a slow breaking down of the mind, and that is because man is a unity, not a mind and a body somehow separated. Concentration is based on the interaction of all that a man is. When a man thinks, the cells of his body play just as vital a part in the "concentration" of that thought, and in the "construction" of it, as the cells of his brain. True concentration is total man thinking through the will of being. Any other type of thinking is concentration through body-mind with only a modicum of will to hold the thought in place. For the *will of being* to cement thought properly, a man must not only know that being is necessary to his thinking, but build for himself a body which produces a strong will, so that his thoughts are strong.'

'Some great thinkers have been weak physically,' I said. 'How does that fit in with what you believe?'

'I never attempt to make things "fit" what I believe,' said Sabazius. 'The mere fitting of thoughts together is the work of mechanics, logical tradesmen. What I believe never changes, for it is a knowledge of that which never changes, yet is all the time changing.'

'How can something not change, yet change?'

He smiled at me. 'The change I'm talking about is not logical replacement by something else, it is the ontological evolution of something else. It could be said that Elsewhere never changes, for Elsewhere is always Elsewhere; but Elsewhere is also known as the *ever-comprehending act of will*, and as such, is continually evolving in an act of will which to us *seems* like change, yet to Elsewhere is "constant" reality. As I said, truth, or the "other", is not absolute, for absolutism is the limit man puts on his God through not being able to see.'

'And yet one cannot deny the greatness of thought that has come out of awake-dream.'

'If I were in awake-dream, I would agree,' replied Sabazius, 'but I am not in awake-dream, so I consider the greatest thought of awake-dream mere foolishness.'

'But you must surely agree that man, even in the state of awake-dream, has performed miracles on this planet,' I said with considerable force. 'He started out as a primitive, and through the evolution of conscious intelligence has transcended nature.'

Sabazius chuckled and shook his head. 'It is true that man has made nature almost subservient to his will,' he said slowly, 'and it is also true that he has and will perform miracles of one sort of another; but the "nature" through which he *uses* the products of his advancing intellect is still infantile. You must understand that man has built everything he has out of a grain of will which his early ancestors created. This infinitesimal grain of will has been passed down through the generations. It is a gift from the past. Early man, or if you prefer, prehistoric man, created will in himself through self-knowledge.'

'But early man was primitive!'

'What do you mean?'

'Ignorant, I suppose.'

'Is man today not ignorant?'

I hesitated, then I said: 'He's less ignorant than prehistoric man.'

'What is "less"?'

'He knows more about his world, understands it better.'

'Only the first part of your statement is correct,' said Sabazius. 'It is true that present-day man knows more about his world, but it cannot be said that he understands it. He may have laid nature bare, exposed the atoms of her structure for analysis; but he has not the "will" to recognize what it is he has laid bare. Early man was light years ahead of modern man in understanding. When he looked at nature, he knew nature.'

'Then why don't we know nature?'

'To understand that, one must recognize the relationship between intelligence and being. It is man's ignorance of being which blinds his intelligence. In the Early Time, man was *all* being, he was an animal, but he was a man-animal. Through interaction with his external environment he slowly learned to relate himself to the outer world. Then, after a long moment, he learned to relate parts of his outer world to each other.'

'I suppose that was the birth of intelligence.'

Sabazius stared at me and laughed. 'You are trundling out modern thought without thinking about it,' he said. 'Man's ability to relate one thing to another is not a symbol of his intelligence, but of his intellect. His ignorance of being is intellectual ignorance, and it is this ignorance that cuts him off from intelligent seeing. Intellect is the product of memory, whereas intelligence is not a product, but what the man is. Man sees his world, but he does not know it, for to see the world truly requires all of the man to look, not just the content of his memory. But memory itself, as an expression of intelligent will, not only allows man to relate one thing to another, but to remember that he has related them, not as objects related, but as a synthesis. It is the "all" of memory "felt" at any given moment which allows man realization of his history. And this is the important bit: to become one's history is not merely to remember it, it is to *realize* it. Then, and only then, is memory dynamic, or three-dimensional, for it is not recall but re-entry.

'What happens to a man who balances being with conscious intellect?'

'You know the answer to that,' replied Sabazius.

'He conquers death?'

'What else!'

'Just by forming the balance?'

'No, it's much more complex. Forming the balance is only the beginning. For a man to escape death, he must build out of that balance a *new man* capable of liberty. All the time I have known you I have referred to a third principle. There is always a third principle. When a man balances being and conscious intellect, he sets in motion new forces, forces which are seldom seen in universe. These forces produce further changes in man; but not change as you would understand change. In the Early Time, man was pure being with potential intellect, and in this latter time, he is pure intellect with "being" as his potential. When those two things are put together a third principle, or force, arises, the force of a perfect memory, a memory which spans the "moment" in two directions. Man becomes Past, Present and Future, so cancelling his tie with time. Time is the rope which binds man to the external world, to this dimension. To escape from time therefore means to escape from this dimension to another. But as I have said to you, when a man passes through death with a roar, he "continues", and to continue means that he passes through subsequent dimensions, each demanding further purity and refinement. The further a man goes into Elsewhere made manifest, the nearer he comes to that point where "existing" changes into "not-existing", and when he merges with the not-existing, he is free.'

'Then to escape death,' I said in astonishment, 'is only the entrance to a huge continuing!'

'And it is a continuing *in* self.'

I had never at any point asked him this question, but the desire to know was now overwhelming. 'What is self?' I said.

The smile Sabazius cast at me was dazzling. His face seemed to light up from within, as if everything in him was delighted with the question. He replied quietly:

'You are self.'

'I still tend to think of self as something separate.'

'Of course you do, what else can you do! You are still living *in* the external.'

'But I'm in the sheath!'

'You are only partly in the sheath, but you will know later. Self is composed of three things: Being, Intelligent-Consciousness, and History. Being is the perfect animal-man, the forgotten "unconscious man"; intelligent-consciousness is the animal-man made aware of himself; and history is the summation, the "word" of *all* the man is consciously and unconsciously brought together into perfect unity, cohesively united through the will of a perfect memory.'

'Then I am self.'

'No. "Am" is self.'

'Am?'

'To say "I am", is to add "I" to self. The perfect formula of self is "Am".'

'The "word".'

'Am is the "word".'

It was like reaching the peak of a high mountain.

'You now have the key,' added Sabazius. 'Am will unlock all doors, clear all paths, open up all vistas. Without Am, a man is as grass, he withers and dies.'

'Can a man – '

Leaning forward, Sabazius opened the front of my pyjama jacket. 'Place the palm of your right hand on top of the back of your left hand,' he said, 'and then lay the palm of your left hand on your will-stone.'

I followed his instructions carefully.

'Now say the "word".'

'Aaaa Mmmm,' I said slowly.

'Slower still,' urged Sabazius. 'Enter into the word Am as you pronounce it.'

'AaaaaaaaaaaaMmmmmmmmmmmmmm … '

At first nothing seemed to happen, then, slowly, the sheath formed tightly around me, wrapped me up and away from the external. It was like being inside a bubble, a transparent bubble. Everything was just the same. I could see the room, and Sabazius, hear sounds outside, smell the remains of our coffee; yet I was somehow separated from everything, removed, aloft; yes, that was it, I was 'aloft', curiously 'out' and 'above' the external. My experience of the sheath the previous day, and that very morning, had been only a suggestion, a degree of what was possible.

'If you had told me the "word" when we met,' I said, 'I could have experienced this immediately.'

'The "word" only has meaning to those who *are* the "word",' he replied. 'To others it is but grammatical licence.'

Sabazius stood up. 'Take your hands away now,' he said.

When I removed my hands, the sheath remained.

'Now place your palms together as if in the act of prayer.'

The moment my palms touched, my whole body began to vibrate.

'Breathe!'

The air I took into my lungs was like electricity. I could feel it flickering down into my body, alive and vital. Was this indeed air? Still vibrating, I looked at Sabazius. He was smiling at me, just a faint smile, a far-away smile from deep inside his face.

'Now you are *alive* … ' he whispered.

16 ❊ *A test of will*

Late that evening I walked with Sabazius through Hyde Park. It was a bitterly cold night, frosty, with an abundance of stars overhead. He talked to me of what I had learned and experienced, asked me questions, corrected what I did not fully understand, adding details to clarify certain points, then he said:

'How do you feel in yourself?'

'I feel fine,' I replied. 'In fact, I've never felt better.'

'Do you feel strong?'

'Yes.'

'How strong is your will?'

'I have no way of gauging its strength.'

'Then you must find out.'

'How can I do that?'

'By pitting it against mine,' said Sabazius. 'When a man wishes to find out the strength of his will – that is, a man who has just acquired will – he must wrestle with a Man of Will.'

'What do you mean by wrestle?'

'Become entangled.'

'Physically?'

'I don't understand what you mean?'

'Using your body as a weapon,' I replied. 'Brute force.'

He stopped, frowned at me. 'If we were animals,' he said slowly, 'then our wrestling would be unconscious; but we are not animals, we are men, and as men we will wrestle through will, not flesh.'

'You will have to teach me.'

'It is impossible for me to teach you to wrestle through will,' replied Sabazius. 'That is something you must teach yourself.'

'Where does one start?'

'One starts through confrontation. When a Man of Will is confronted by an enemy who has will, all he can do is defend himself. Retaliation mustn't become part of his code.'

'Can't he practise using his will in case he meets such a man?'

'That is to indulge in power. A Man of Feeling does not indulge in power for any reason. His will-reaction is but a token, a defence, not an attack.'

'So his will is only a shield, not a weapon?'

'Yes.'

'But you will have to attack me so that I can defend myself. Isn't that breaking the rules?'

'It would be if I intended to kill you, to send you to a roarless death, but as your teacher I have sanction to "challenge" your will, to activate its strength and present it with problems.'

'Is that why Men of Feeling and Men of Power stay clear of each other?'

'It is indeed. If a Man of Power attacks a Man of Feeling, he knows that the other has tremendous resources of will with which to defend himself, and if the defence is equal to the attack, then the Man of Power loses all he has to the other. However, if there is a flaw in the Man of Feeling, if he but for a moment forgets that his role is one of defence and slips into retaliation, then he immediately changes into a Man of Power, and the end result is that he becomes the ally of his attacker, a replica of what he fights.'

'Does the fight continue?'

'No, it stops immediately, for Men of Power have no quarrel one with the other, they are equal in intent, bound by the same flaw.'

'Or "law"?' I said.

'Indeed.'

'But surely the Man of Feeling who slips in such a manner retains his basic nature ... that of a Man of Feeling?'

'Of course he does, but because he is "conscious", because he is "awake" to the flaw which has presented itself, he knows that it is impossible to eradicate that flaw except through death and return. You must understand that the nature of a Man of Feeling, and of a Man of Power, is only different with regard to the question of "use".'

'It seems unfair that such a man should be penalized for one little mistake.'

'The balance between one and the other is very delicate,'

replied Sabazius. 'When the flaw of "use" appears in a Man of Feeling, it means that his system of functioning has been overcome by the cancer of power. In ordinary men, men who are asleep, the realization of a flaw means that consciousness is approaching, but in a Man of Feeling it points to consciousness receding. Very few Men of Power who decide to continue die sane.'

'Can they then decide not to continue?'

'A Man of Feeling who realizes that he has changed into a Man of Power can surrender himself consciously to universe in the moment of realization; but generally he does not, for the very flaw which changed him makes him *hope* for escape, and to hope in such a manner is to fall back into desire, to activate the cancer of conscious demolition.'

'Then to wrestle with you through will is to face such a danger!'

'At this point, no,' said Sabazius. 'You are not yet fully conscious, therefore you are not bound by the Law of Power. So if you have a flaw, that is, a flaw lying on the surface of your evolved nature, it can be dealt with at this stage; but if you have a *deep* flaw, one which escapes my notice, and yours, then depending on where it is situated in being, you will eventually have to face it, for such a flaw will grow as you grow, multiply as you multiply.'

'What happends to a Man of Feeling who surrenders to universe?'

'He enters a roarless death. Such a decision points to a strong will contained in balance, an almost perfect balance, for only such a will could reject the impossible hope of escape other Men of Power entertain.'

'Why is that?'

'Because the very act of surrender is enough to cancel out the flaw.'

'What ... '

'No more,' said Sabazius. 'You now know enough to defend yourself.'

Unbuttoning his coat, he took it off and laid it on the grass, then, stripping off the rest of his clothes, he folded them neatly and placed them on the coat.

I stood staring at him in amazement.

'What's the matter?' he asked.

'Aren't you cold?'

'No.'

'But it's freezing!'

'My will is not frozen,' he replied. Smiling at me, he said: 'Hold your hands six inches from my skin.'

'Like this?'

Sabazius did not answer, he just stood there looking at me, and then I felt the heat radiating from his body in waves.

'How do you do it?' I asked.

'I am not doing anything,' he said. 'It is my will *reacting*, that's all. There should never be any need to *use* will.'

Before I could reply, he threw himself to the ground, curled into a tight ball and rolled off into the darkness. I stood listening. There was the faint sound of something moving around me in a wide circle. Was he still rolling?

'Where are you, Alexis?' I shouted.

'I'm here.'

'Where?'

'Here.'

'I can't see you.'

'I'm behind you.'

'You can't be,' I replied, staring into the blackness, 'your voice is coming from directly in front of me.'

'Turn around, see for yourself.'

When I turned, Sabazius was not only behind me, he was standing within one foot of me. His body, wet with melted frost, glistened and sparkled, reflecting the far-off lights of Park Lane.

'Take your clothes off,' he said.

'But I don't know how ... '

His chuckling stopped me short. 'When you are naked,' he said, 'lay your hands on your Will Stone. Your will must react to the Law of Regulation.'

Only half convinced, I slowly undressed, folding and placing each item as I had seen Sabazius do. When I turned towards him again, my body was shivering uncontrollably.

'What are you waiting for?' he asked.

Laying my hands on the pendant as I had been shown, I tried to sense heat.

Reaching forward, Sabazius rapped me on the forehead with a knuckle. 'Allow will to activate,' he said sharply. 'You are trying to will your will into action, that is impossible.'

I relaxed.

The moment I allowed my body to go limp, the biting cold of the air lost its edge. I had noticed this very fact years before, but had never considered it of importance. Slowly, the temperature of my skin built up, until I felt as if I were wrapped in a robe of heat.

'Are you ready?' asked Sabazius.

I nodded.

Crouching, he raised both palms towards me, then, forming his mouth into a circle, he drew in a whistling breath of night air. The whistle grew in intensity, changing into an ultra high-pitched whine which attacked my ears like a giant hornet. I staggered back, covering my ears with my hands, but I could not eliminate that sound. How could I defend myself against an intangible? What was the secret of defence?

Running as hard as I could, I tried to place distance between us. If I could get out of range even for a few seconds, I might think of something.

The sound, however, did not diminish. It followed me, caressed me viciously inside and out. That was when the battle really started, for I suddenly realized that I could fight back by 'projecting' a line-of-will at Sabazius. I could knock him off his feet, even disable him if I so desired. The distinction between defence and attack arose in my mind. If I threw will at him, that would be attack, so the reverse of throwing or hurtling will was to retain it; but how could the retention of will shield me from the sound?

Standing naked in that black coldness, it dawned on me that the word 'allow' was closely linked with defence. Had I not *allowed* my body to generate heat! That had to be the key. Taking a deep breath, I relaxed as completely as possible, then, turning to where I thought Sabazius to be, I allowed will to activate in my defence.

The sound stopped immediately.

'Have you mastered will so soon?' said a voice.

I turned abruptly. 'Where are you, Alexis?'

In that very moment the sound returned, doubled, trebled in

strength. I spun this way and that to escape it, but was firmly caught. I had been tricked out of my 'allowing' by the voice.

'Stop it!' I cried out.

I was now huddled on the grass, lost and self-pitying like a child. No human being could stand against such an onslaught ...

The sound's frequency dropped, wavered uncertainly, melted into silence. Sabazius walked out of the darkness towards me. He seemed taller, heavier in build, almost ... I hesitated over the word 'evil'.

'Is it over, Alexis?' I asked.

He walked straight by me without a look.

'Alexis!' I shouted after him.

I think that's when my courage came back. A curious anger flooded me, not emotional anger, a clinical anger, a detached anger which convinced me momentarily that I could stand against Sabazius, or any other man who attempted to destroy me without cause. I had already proved to myself that the will I *was* could cancel out an attack. So if I paid no attention to his tricks, drew myself into a concentrated whole, then nothing would be able to touch or penetrate me.

'Now what are you thinking?' said the voice.

Ignoring Sabazius, or at least what sounded like Sabazius, I placed both hands on my will-stone and stood still with my eyes closed.

'Have you lost your tongue?'

A faint quiver ran through my hands.

'That ornament won't save you from attack,' said the voice. 'Its power is only in your imagination, and the strength you think you're getting from it is illusion. I am your strength, and if I wish, I can withdraw my strength from you.'

It was obviously another of his tricks. He was trying to break my will by attacking it verbally at its source.

'Like this,' said the voice.

There was a tugging sensation in my head and chest, as if something were attempting to drag will, my will, out of me like a tooth. Surely it could not possibly be true that the strength of will I thought myself to have belonged to Sabazius!

'No!' I said inwardly.

His laughter reverberated around me.

How could such a laugh belong to a Man of Feeling? From out of some vague centre in my head came a thought, a disturbing, terrifying thought. It was just possible that Sabazius was a Man of Power, had always been a Man of Power ... Maybe that was why he was so friendly with the Turk, and the little lean-faced man. He had even admitted to seeing the Turk kill someone with his bare hands. If my thoughts had foundation, then this was no mere test, it was Sabazius attempting to make me his slave, to make me slip into retaliation.

'Did you feel your will slipping away?' asked the voice.

Whatever he was trying to do now, he first had had to teach me to be a Man of Feeling, for only out of a Man of Feeling could spring a Man of Power. So what I knew of self was probably true; in fact, I knew from direct experience that it was true, that I could summon self to my assistance, throw myself out into universe, claim protection from ... But I had no memory of the self who had saved me! I had blacked out, returned to consciousness with Sabazius leaning over me. Was nothing sure? Was there no certainty in me at all?

'I am preparing to attack you again,' said the voice, and the breath which carried that voice brushed against my face.

Doubt took hold of me, fear raced in my blood.

'Hadn't you better strengthen your will?'

Sabazius mocking me, telling me yet again that my will was as nothing against his power.

And yet ... and yet something else ... a faint whispering in my heart, a small voice urging me to stand firm, to face the attacker, to cast out fear and turn inward, grasp the mainspring of my being ...

The Am-breath.

Mind-shattering sound directed at me from Sabazius, Sabazius the Man of Power who had tried to seduce me with truth itself. I would *not* retaliate. I would not give in. I would not be trapped into a roarless death; not by Sabazius or any other living creature, not by angels or gods, voices pleasant or unpleasant, sounds terrifying or sweet. I would stand *in* truth, not outside of it; face Elsewhere made manifest, not prostitute my will to the cancer of power ...

'AaaaaaaaaaaaMmmmmmmmmmmmmm ...'

Utter silence.

My attacker silenced.

Universe in silence.

When I opened my eyes, Sabazius was standing a few yards away from me, his face was expressionless. We stood looking at each other for almost a minute, then he said:

'I could detect no flaw in you.'

Was this another trick? Was the battle still raging in spite of the Am-breath?

'There is one more thing to be done,' said Sabazius.

'Now?' I asked feebly.

He smiled at me. 'You have nothing to fear,' he replied. 'You came through with remarkable courage. All that remains now is for you to "become" what you are in a total sense, the total of the moment.'

'A Man of Feeling?'

'Maybe.'

'Can something still go wrong?'

'Something can always go wrong.'

We returned to the spot where our clothes were. As I put them on, I felt the first tingle of the night air touch my skin: will was regulating itself. I marvelled at it.

'When They come,' said Sabazius, 'you must on no account move.'

'When who comes?'

'I would not know how to tell you. Who is there who can describe They who come …?'

I felt apprehensive. 'What do I have to do?'

'Absolutely nothing,' he answered. 'You will soon know what I mean.'

Dressed in the clothes of Peter Derwent, I watched Sabazius ease on his coat. When he was ready, he made me stand straight and still, then, having measured out some seven or eight yards, he walked around me a number of times, stopping on four occasions to utter a word I did not understand. Having completed this task, he approached me and pointed to the north.

'What do you see?' he asked.

I looked carefully, but could not detect anything.

'Allow your will to focus,' he instructed.

Remembering what I had learned about the bisecting point

of will, I again looked carefully, and immediately saw a pin-point of light. 'There's something there now,' I said.

Turning me to each major point of the compass, he asked me what I could see, and each time, on focusing will, I saw the same or a similar light.

'Now listen to what I have to say,' said Sabazius. 'When I leave you, close your eyes and will the lights to come to you; in other words, "allow" them to approach. You will not have to open your eyes to know that they have drawn nearer, you will just know. For no reason whatsoever must you open your physical eyes, if you do you will be dead before your body falls. Such things cannot be looked upon by man in any ordinary sense. When you know that all four lights are near to you, pronounce the Am-breath and hold it. You will discover immediately that breathing is no longer necessary.'

'What will happen?'

'I have no way of telling. If the lights find you acceptable, they will enter you; if they do not, well ... anything could happen.'

'Where will you be?'

'I will be in myself, buried deep, safe.'

'What ... '

'There is no time left,' said Sabazius urgently. 'Close your eyes, and only open them if you wish to die!'

With that warning firmly in mind, I obeyed. The sound of Sabazius walking from me faded into silence, a silence inter-rupted faintly by the far-off sounds of the city, dull, dumb sounds.

A moment of panic. What would happen to me if the lights did not find me acceptable? Would I die in some strange, terri-fying manner? Be reduced to a lunatic, a mindless vegetable? I drew breath twice to summon the lights, and twice my courage failed me. It even entered my mind to run away, run towards the safety of the city where ordinary people walked and talked, laughed and cried their way to wherever they were going. Where was I going? Then I remembered Sabazius, Sabazius who had spent so much time training me for this very moment, Sabazius who had said that if I became a Man of Feeling, our work together would be glorious. That was when I faced the problem, or rather my decision, squarely. If I was to become a

Man of Feeling, someone capable of assisting Sabazius, then it meant *all* of Peter Derwent being realized.

Drawing a long, cool breath of night air, I resigned myself to whatever lay ahead.

A crisp stillness.

Something in me trembled, moved, shifted out of sync.

All avenues of escape cancelled.

Suddenly, inexplicably, I knew the lights were within the circle Sabazius had created. Caught in that stillness I opened myself to the lights, opened myself and pronounced the Am-breath.

That something shifted in me again.

A whispering, rushing wind articulating wordlessly. A voice, yet not a voice, instructing. The *ever-comprehending act of will*, the purpose of that will, the beauty of that will, the meaning of it within reach ...

Part Two:
BATTLE

17 ❊ Wanting and not wanting

The days immediately following my experience in Hyde Park were ecstatic. I seemed to flow on a stream of tight energy, controlled in my inner being by my continual awareness of the relatedness of things. As a Man of Feeling, my systems of functioning were all-of-a-piece, and this afforded me a certainty of action and direction. I was, however, conscious of Sabazius watching me closely, for often when I turned around his eyes were fixed on me in a glassy stare. Try as I might, I was unable to return this look for any length of time, as my eyes involuntarily dropped away. Even my heightened state was intensified, sometimes dramatically by those looks. But this always depended on how long I was able to sustain my looking at him. Although curious, I was unable to question him concerning this form of looking. Ten, eleven, twelve days passed, then one morning I awoke to find the world a dismal, frightening place devoid of warmth and love. My Sheath of Vision had split. No matter how I tried, it would not re-form. What catastrophe had taken place during the hours of sleep?

As always, under such circumstances, Sabazius disappeared for almost one week. He had a talent for not being available when I needed him most. So I was left to my own devices, and my devices turned nasty on me. What I saw, heard, felt and attempted to do was reduced to a blank, energyless desert, a flat, dried up place of the spirit where I resided like a lunatic. A lunatic with enough savvy to realize his own lunacy. I telephoned Sabazius in despair and found that he had returned.

'What's the matter?' he asked.

In a garble of words I tried to explain what had happened to me.

'What do you expect me to do?' was his reply.

'Can't you help me?'

He laughed loudly into the receiver, and said, 'Who's there?'

Not knowing what to make of his reaction I said nothing.

'Who's there?' he said again.

'You know damned fine who's here,' I said emptily.

'You've got the wrong number, caller,' he said, imitating the voice of a female operator. 'Try another line.'

'Please stop playing games,' I said.

'What you require is on the middle floor, madam,' replied Sabazius, becoming a departmental salesman. 'You'll find it half-way up the building.'

'What are you trying to say to me?' I almost shouted.

Bzzzzzzzzzz.

I looked at the piece of black plastic in my hand in unbelief. He had hung up. When I put it down it rang immediately.

'Yes?' I said.

He talked fast and seriously, and seemed to be telling me exactly what to do, for my christian name came up twice; but as the whole thing was in indecipherable Greek, it remained totally meaningless.

'Can't you say what you've got to say in English? I can't follow your Greek!'

Silence.

Sabazius was still there, I could hear his breath in the receiver. That was when I decided to hang up. I put the 'phone down and turned, but it rang in the same instant. I stood looking at it. It kept on ringing. I lifted it and listened. An ear-piercing whistle ricocheted me across the room. I tried to crawl back and put the receiver on its pedestal, but found that I could hardly move. His whistling went on and on, inside and outside of me, just as it had the night he attacked me in the park. And then it stopped, and a voice was saying over and over again. 'Hello, hello, hello, hello, hello, hello ...'

'Go away!' I shouted.

'Hello, hello, hello, hello ...'

It took me a long time to raise the courage to approach that telephone of mine when the voiced ceased. I stalked it carefully, as if it were alive and able to bite, and finally pushed it back into place. When my trembling eased, I made coffee and sat down to consider every aspect of my behaviour up until the Sheath split. As I could find nothing of significance there, I tried to work out what Sabazius had been rambling on about. 'What

156

you require is on the middle floor, madam' kept jumping into my head. What had he meant by that? Why could he not have said something straight and to the point? I lay down on the sofa and closed my eyes, hoping that I might fall asleep and wake up reorientated. And still that sentence ran through my mind. Unable to make head nor tail of it, I tried to remember what being a Man of Feeling had felt like. Maybe remembering would trigger it off again. I reconstructed my experience, the experience I had thought would never fade.

Twelve days of extraordinary vision. Everything lined with colour, vibratingly alive, whole. Summoned in the early hours from inside myself by a clap of thunder, a call to awake and listen, to watch and see, to comprehend and appreciate. Static stillness. Awake in the morning to be bathed in a soft, yet alive calmness, a never-broken stream of conscious joy.

And then dereliction. The empty nothing of ordinariness. Being incapable of answering the question I asked of myself, I slowly drifted off into sleep. When I awoke it was dark and Sabazius was standing at the window looking at the sky. He said nothing.

'What time is it?' I asked.

'About ten o'clock.'

'Have you been here long?'

'Long enough to watch you dream.'

'I don't remember dreaming.'

'You don't really remember much about anything,' he answered sarcastically. 'You keep on thinking you've arrived at something, when in actual fact you've only just taken your first step towards *nothing*.'

I did not understand what he meant by that, and said, 'I'm sorry.'

'Being sorry won't produce the roar that will take you through your death!' His voice was hard and emotionless. 'You're still far too worried about feeling happy or sad, up or down, full or empty. Can't you learn just to accept your feelings, to flow with them until it does not matter what you're feeling. When you realize that there is no difference, that all feeling is *you* happening, then maybe you'll gain enough strength to stay upright.'

He had said all of this with his back to me, then he turned

and looked at me in that funny, glassy way. My eyes dropped.

'Look at me!' he demanded.

I tried to look at him, but could not.

He turned back to the window. 'Do you see that sky,' he said, nodding at it. 'It's not unlike the inside of your head.'

When I looked out of the window, the sky was black and heavy with rain clouds, lit up on the underside by the orange city lights.

'There are three things to be seen there,' he went on. 'The first two are visible, and the third is invisible. The clouds are black before a storm, and their bellies are on fire from what's going on underneath. That's why I say that you are like that sky, because your head keeps on getting filled with storms, and your storms look like the end of the world because your body is still on fire.'

'I don't understand,' I said.

'Of course you don't understand,' said Sabazius. 'How can you expect to understand when that's what you're like inside?'

'I don't want to be like that.'

'And that's where the subtle twist comes in,' he went on. 'It's your wanting and your not wanting that causes the mess. You need to feel happy, because if you don't feel happy, then you feel sad, so your fear of feeling sad drives your happiness away, and your fear of losing your happiness makes sadness all there is.' He paused to look at me, then directed my attention back to the window. 'You can't see the rain in these clouds,' he said, 'because the clouds are the rain you're trying to see, and you can't feel the happiness inside yourself, because the happiness you're looking for *is* yourself.' I seemed to be back at square one. 'You really are protected,' he said with a touch of astonishment. 'You've got no idea how lucky you are not to have been squashed flatter than a tomato. You've seen things ordinary men do not see, experienced things that would drive ordinary men out of their minds in an instant if they had half your pride; but for some reason you keep on surviving, keep bobbing up again for the next dish of cream!' He stood staring at me as if trying to work something out, then he said, his tone softer, 'Tell me what happened.'

'About a week ago,' I said quietly, 'I woke about seven in the morning with a blinding headache. Everything had gone into reverse. All my internal lights had gone out. I felt utterly deserted and alone. When I tried to get back into the Sheath, nothing happened. Even my Stone was useless. I worked at it for hours; but the more work I did the deeper I got into depression. I couldn't even eat because I felt sick. That's why I eventually telephoned you, I couldn't stand it any longer.'

'What happened then?'

'Well, I didn't understand what you were talking about, and got mad because I felt you were just playing games with me, just being clever for the sake of it.'

'Games?'

'What you require is on the middle floor, madam.'

'That is not a game.'

'Then you attacked me!'

'I did not attack you,' replied Sabazius. 'I was trying to clear your systems of a blockage.'

'You scared me out of my wits!'

'Then I did clear your systems.'

'How?'

'You recaptured your lost fear,' said Sabazius. 'I saw your fear dwindle over those first few days. That's always a bad sign.'

'Why didn't you tell me?'

'Because you would not have been able to manufacture fear out of pride. Fear has to grow in you like a tree, be looked after like a tree.'

'Why should a man have to be fearful?'

'If a Man of Feeling has no fear, then he has no respect, and if he has no respect, no true feeling of awe for the *ever-comprehending act of will*, then he slowly loses his grip on what he is ... a Man of Feeling ... and turns into a Man of Power.'

What he said shut me up instantly.

'How do you feel?'

'Terrified!' I said.

Sabazius laughed, switched on the table light and said, 'I'll make coffee and we'll talk.' He returned with coffee and biscuits and sat down beside me on the sofa. I waited for him to start, but he said nothing.

'What did you mean,' I asked, 'when you said that my body was still on fire?'

'I was pointing at your *need* for things,' he replied. 'Your need to be happy is the fire which consumes your happiness. All need is a fire.'

'Why is need a fire?'

'Because out of need comes desire,' said Sabazius, 'and desire is an ever-whirling wheel casting off new needs.' He passed me one of his curious cigarettes and lit it for me. 'But there is another fire,' he then said, 'and this other fire has the power to consume the first fire.'

'What is the nature of the second fire?' I asked, feeling that unless I actually asked the question he would leave it hanging unanswered.

'The other fire is your Will,' replied Sabazius.

'So will can eat desire.'

Sabazius nodded slowly. 'This is what is not understood in the world. Man thinks that his desire, that which springs from his need, is an Act of Will; but that is not true. Will does not desire anything, for Will is what a man is, it is his Being realized.'

I thought about what he had said.

'What are you thinking?' he asked.

'I was trying to work out the place of decision in this,' I said, 'for if a man's will is his Being, and Being desires nothing, then all decisions must spring out of something else.'

He waited for me to continue.

'But ... '

'Yes?'

'I don't know what that something is,' I said hopelessly.

'What did you say?'

'I ... '

'What?' he said quickly.

'I?' I said.

'What else is there?' said Sabazius. 'The function of 'I' in *Being* is to desire objective existence. To survive, man has therefore to continually sustain the objective world to reinforce his own separateness within it. As this is the substance of his *Identity*, it is his *Identity* which blinds him to the relatedness of all things. 'I', or *Identity*, or ego, is the foundation of his not-seeing.'

So when I'm in the Sheath of Vision,' I said excitedly, 'my *Identity* is momentarily stilled, or held in check.'

'Quite,' said Sabazius. 'That is why I have always stressed the necessity of the Sheath. Without a Sheath of Vision, a man cannot dissolve the difference between himself as a subject, and the world as an object. The world is made up of objects which are all intrinsically related, because at base they are of the same substance. But when a man's means of looking at the world changes, this difference, or gap between himself as subject and world as object, fades away.'

'So one is included in the other.'

'No. That is not possible,' he replied firmly. 'Subject and object are for ever distinct from one another, and because of this they cannot merge and create a third principle. What happens is that they obliterate each other into *nothing*. If they became some*thing* else, then they would be but another object bound in universe.'

'The fire that eats the fire!'

'The fire of Will gobbles up the fire of desire.'

'What is the fire of Will?'

'Intelligence.'

I stared at him, then I said, 'But intelligence seems to belong to "I"?'

'That is the mistake,' he replied. 'The "I" of a man only *reflects* intelligent comprehension, it is not that comprehension in itself. The intelligent comprehension of Will, or *Being*, is the comprehension of Elsewhere. "I" is therefore only the instrument, not the originator. But because "I" has objective existence in universe, and can only recognize universe as a series of objects, it is bound through those objects by the string of Time, for Time is the duration of perception fed through the "I" instrument.'

'You seem to be saying that Time is perception?'

'Time is both perception, and that which is perceived. Time erupts out of subject viewing object,' qualified Sabazius. 'And *Identity* is only "matter" *Identifying* with all other matter of which it is an intrinsic part.'

My mouth literally fell open as the meaning of what he said slotted into place. 'So desire,' I said, almost unable to contain myself, 'is only the matter out of which the "I" instrument is composed trying to link itself with the basic substance of universe!'

'Exactly,' said Sabazius. 'This is what the relatedness of all things means. Matter is related to matter, and Will is related to Will. That is why it is possible to say that matter has Being, for it is Being *as* Will which holds matter together. That is why a man's body disintegrates at death, for when Will deserts matter it can no longer sustain Being in existence.'

On having said that, Sabazius got to his feet, switched off the table lamp, and asked me to stand in front of him. He then gripped my face in both hands and pressed at it with his palms. After a few minutes of this, he proceeded to massage my face gently, pushing the flesh upwards and away from my mouth, gathering it below the eyes, and from above the eyes, pushed it up yet again to the hairline.

'Keep your eyes closed and look into the middle distance,' he said, his thumbs pushing at me.

The moment I did this, rippling colours appeared, and a fan of bluish light moved up and out in time with his thumbs. And then a curious circle, indistinct but nonetheless visible, appeared, and at its centre the bluish light accumulated, and the outer edges of the light began to flicker with a deep, startling violet colour.

'Keep looking at the middle distance,' urged Sabazius.

The bluish centre then erupted with this same violet flickering, and slowly solidified until the blue was eaten up, and the circle itself faded. This left only a jagged, violet spot with fluctuating edges.

'Look only at the middle distance,' whispered Sabazius again.

The violet light evaporated suddenly, as if going back into itself, then it was nearer, and larger. Again it evaporated, and again it was nearer and larger.

Sabazius began to hum a deep, reverberating note to himself, his thumbs still working on my face. The violet light, or spot, kept jumping towards me, its outer edges bubbling starkly against velvety blackness. And then suddenly I was reacting against it, and it hesitated, devolved into itself with the same jumping motion, and vanished.

Sabazius removed his hands.

I remained in this dark space, wondering if it would return. But whatever had taken place as his thumbs worked on me, whatever it was that had come jumping out of nowhere, no longer existed.

Sabazius switched on the lamp and asked me what I had seen. When this was done, he said, 'Why did the violet light go away?'

'I seemed to fight it,' I said.

'Why did you fight it?'

'Because I had the feeling that if it came any nearer I would get swamped.'

'What would get swamped?' he asked.

What he was getting at dawned on me immediately.

Sabazius chuckled to himself and shook his head. 'You look as though you understand,' he said, motioning me to sit down, 'but in reality you do not understand anything.'

'You seem to be saying that men and women should try to lose their sense of identity?'

'Not quite, but something like that.'

'Why?'

'What is making you ask the question?'

'I suppose it's my sense of identity, my fear of losing my individuality that's making me ask it.'

'Just so,' said Sabazius. 'And this is the problem all human beings face, the problem of not being able to see what they are because of "I". As long as a man or woman believes that there is something to "know", some object called "self" to know, then they are still the prisoner of "I" and subject to the idea of a private identity.'

'Then why ask me to call on self?'

'Because such a call is not to an *identity* out there somewhere, it is to *all that you are* in any given moment of time.'

'My history?'

'Exactly.'

'I knew that all along.'

'But only understood it. Now do you understand?'

I smiled at him.

'What you have to grasp is that when a man or woman enters Being, even temporarily, they are linked with the unimaginable forces of universe.'

'The lights,' I said, remembering.

'Indeed, the lights,' he said back.

'And the Sheath is the linking factor.'

'Correct. When an awake human being enters the Sheath he or she is no longer able to "think" as an autonomous "I", for perception has been momentarily gathered up into itself, and the individual has ceased to exist.'

'Is Being then a form of matter?'

'Yes, but it is a very high form; it is matter *realized* in mind. Later, when you are ready for such things, I will show you how matter interacts with matter, how it penetrates all the way into mind, or psyche. But what you need to learn now is that when a man enters Being he is at once linked to unimaginable forces in universe, forces which respond to him through the ordinary everyday happenings, events and circumstances of his life. He is no longer alone; he is part of what *matters*, if you take my point.'

Allowing my eyes to drop from his face, I looked at the carpet. Was I ever going to penetrate what he was trying to show me? How could one comprehend something without first understanding it? I sat rock still and tried to appreciate what he had just told me about Being, identity and self.

'You have a problem?'

'I *am* a problem,' I said quite spontaneously. 'I don't really understand any of this. None of it. I'm flying by the seat of my pants.'

'At least you can fly,' he replied.

18 ❀ *The sea of blue glass*

After two weeks of intense work, during which I acquired and lost the Sheath of Vision a number of times, Sabazius intimated that I was about to embark on a new aspect of the work, an aspect which would at first drag almost all the energy I had out of me in a rush, but later, when I began to function properly, supply me with energy. I was about to learn, he said, how to project myself into other levels of Being, the result of which would be a deeper appreciation of my intrinsic nature, and an eventual integration of my higher systems, many of which I had not yet touched.

'How does one enter those new levels?' I asked.

'By getting to know the subtle twists and turnings of your history,' he replied. 'Part of your history has come together because the Four Lights manufactured out of your *intent* a vehicle capable of carrying you further. You are now much more flexible, more able to enter the small vortices which are everywhere. Creative people know a little of this,' he then said. 'They know how to enter into themselves and travel on the fantasy level; but what they do not generally know is that these fantasy levels are much more than imaginative figments, but are actual territories, vast stretches of internal universe where anything can happen. However, sometimes these people do slip through, and because they are totally unprepared for what they experience, they often find it very difficult to get back out again. Try as they might to find the door out, they compulsively create out of aberrated will further stretches of territory between themselves and that door. What I am saying to you,' added Sabazius seriously, 'is that this territory is dangerous if your systems of operation are not carefully prepared and tuned to deal with it. So be warned.'

He then instructed me to pay strict attention to my dreams, writing down everything I could remember the following morning, or, as was sometimes the case, if I awoke immediately after a dream, to put it on paper that very minute. However, I was to write down only what I could remember visually. For to do otherwise was to unwittingly add interpretation to a dream. Such additions would lead me astray. Reason alone could not break into those regions, he said emphatically, for the very purpose of a dream was to reveal to the dreamer that which he could not reveal to himself through reason. The sense of meaninglessness often felt after dreaming was 'reason' attempting to understand the impossible, that reason was incapable of real understanding. To laugh at that meaninglessness, said Sabazius, was to laugh at one's own history as reflected in dreams.

'Is this the territory which was available to me during the first twelve days?' I asked.

Sabazius shook his head. 'Not quite,' he said. 'That was the entrance to the territory. During the days after the lights visited you, when you closed your eyes there was a whole world vibrating on its own inside your head. You saw mountains and caverns and waterfalls solid enough to touch. It was almost as if you had entered a fairyland, and indeed you had, for could you not change the scenes at will, manipulate them in any way you wished? But during that time you were still consciously linked to this reality. You knew that all you had to do was open your eyes and it would vanish. What you are now approaching, however, is not the entrance, but what lies behind the entrance. When a man passes through the door of himself into himself, he cannot open his eyes and escape. When you move into this realm, it is to experience by choice and without possibility of escape the knots and shuttered sections of your Being. To re-enter a dream is very different from dreaming it in the first place. When you go in you take all of yourself with you, and that includes ego. When ego activates and starts to fight the dream content, it unknowingly fights itself, for the dream content is always pointing at the limited and limiting nature of ego. When this happens, shredding takes place. Shredding is simply ego smashing itself to pieces on ego. The purpose of this level is to open you up like a tin can and pour out your preserved nonsense. The secret of success is to bend and flow with what happens, to breathe in the truth of what you are and what you are not like fresh air. If you can learn to do that quickly, the shredding, if it is necessary at all, will be like a needle-prick.'

I was then told that I must think of each part of my dreams as myself. That if a monster appeared, then I had to realize immediately that I was that monster, and allow what was 'monstrous' in me to roar itself into oblivion. 'If you can approach any terrible vision in that way,' said Sabazius, 'you will immediately experience and know that aspect of yourself. You will not be subject to an object. If a beautiful angel with golden wings appears, know it to be yourself and none other.' And so my instruction went on, and my dreams were written down, and my knowledge of the territory mapped and charted. Everything was elucidated. He explained and explained until I was dizzy, then he explained what he had explained back to me again and again. There was neither reason nor excuse to inflict pain and suffering on oneself when knowledge was available, he said. To do so was idiocy. A path which included too much suffering was a path of ignorance. The ignorant walked on it, and the ignorant advocated it.

At the end of that week he told me it was time to start. I lay down on the sofa. He pulled the curtains, sprinkled a fine powder on my forehead from his little box, crossed my hands on top of my Will Stone like a dead man, and told me to close my eyes. He then reminded me of the method of entry, asked me to select one of my dreams, the first one to come into my head, and breathe towards it. Then he started to hum in that reverberating tone.

The dream I chose to enter was as follows: I was in a space-ship travelling somewhere in the universe. There were two others with me in the cabin. A man and a woman. Beyond the spaceship window, which was large and circular, lay the black of deep space. An almost purple blackness. Crystal stars could occasionally be seen. My two companions talked and pointed out of the window excitedly. I was at the controls, guiding my ship I know not where with apparent determination and knowledge. The scene changed suddenly and I was on another planet. My spaceship was already docked, and stood in the centre of what looked like an early settlers' township. There were people everywhere. Women were shopping, men carried tools on their backs and headed for places of work. An excited throng of men and women stood looking at my ship. The people I encountered as I walked through the town were friendly and smiling. They waved to me as I passed, but did not speak. Reaching the edge of the town, I walked towards the dry, dusty hills which surrounded it. The hills gave way to mountains, mountains of extraordinary presence. As I walked among them the light began to fail. Before long it was quite dark. The mountains, however, remained visible, for they had lighted up from within with deep reds and blues, rust browns, beautiful shades of green and amber.

It was then I noticed the ridge, a sharp-edged, sandy-coloured bank of fused rock. Above it lay that indescribable blackness. I started to climb the ridge. As I rose higher, I saw two children, a boy and a girl, clambering about with great pleasure on the ridge's edge. Sensing danger, I shouted to them and they climbed down. When I reached the edge of the ridge I lay full out on my stomach and looked over. As far as the eye could see lay a blue ocean of solidified glass. I stared at it in amazement. Huge waves, crested with foam, hung never-to-fall, icily suspended. And far off to each side the mountains, their internal colours flickering and dancing, rose splendidly. With great care I lowered myself down the rough bank of rock until my feet touched the edge of that sea. Satisfied that is was quite solid, I stepped out on to it. There was no suggestion of movement. The contrast between the thriving township and this incredible vision of ossified beauty astonished me. On what did I stand? I was looking at a storm; but the storm had been tamed, bound by something greater than it. Unafraid, yet wary, I ran my fingers across the back of a wave, felt its smooth, curving body, its quartz-like head. Would this sea ever awaken?

I was returned to the township in that moment. The people smiled and waved to me, and I wondered if any of them had ever travelled to the ridge and looked over. Did they know such a sea existed? What was the work they were doing that kept them so busy? As I turned from them, I found myself back in my ship and already underway. My two companions were again at the window pointing and exclaiming. Ignoring them, I grasped the controls firmly and adjusted the instruments. We had a long journey ahead of us.

As I once again moved into that dream landscape, I was

followed by the deep hum Sabazius was emitting. It moved round and through me like a wind. In what could be loosely called imagination, I was again in the spaceship with my two companions, and then standing in the township among the people who waved and smiled. As before, I walked out among the hills until I reached the mountains, climbed the ridge and shouted at the children. But as I looked over the edge of reality, stared at that sea, I knew the danger that faced me was not dream-like, but actual. If I did not hold the sea steady, it would turn into a raging holocaust of destruction. There was now no way to avoid standing on that glassy surface, no way to side-step the issue of my own depth. I was looking at myself, not at an aspect of myself. There were no monsters or angels here, just the basic energy of which such beings were made. I lowered myself cautiously over the ridge and felt that time-frozen ocean beneath my feet. I was now standing on and in myself simultaneously. If the stillness I felt evaporated, the sea would erupt. The knife edge of compulsion.

My vision was suddenly grasped and directed far beyond the sea, directed to the very limit of the horizon. I was looking into the face of creation, the natural element out of which creations were created. The horizon's limit was a limit set by me, I could not see beyond it because I would not see beyond it. Yet I could sense something moving out there. Allowing myself to flow out to that something, I cognized it as an entity, a huge being turning over, a horizonless eye watching me. The dimension of this being fluctuated as my senses focused and refocused. I knew that it knew, it knew that I did not know. Being incapable of holding such a being in mind, it broke apart into lesser beings, multiplied out of itself. For the sake of manageability I had fragmented wholeness. I stilled further, allowed my stillness to merge like the colours of the mountains. The lesser entities re-entered the main being, the wholeness of the main being spread out across the sea like an invisible mist, approached me as I approached it. I stepped back. The mountains dimmed. Indeed, this was not a place for children to play and gambol.

Knowing that I could not yet penetrate that horizon, I climbed back to the ridge. Through gradations of darkness and colour I could see light, sense the township and its activity. What a strange planet I was, full of ordinariness and icy mystery side by side. At one end of the scale of my being lay creative darkness, an inhabited darkness, and at the other a cheerful lightheartedness.

I was a travelling capability, fitted out with instruments of navigation and a big window through which to watch passing stars. I was a double companion to myself, a unity of Being moving where Will willed, and I was living, settling on the edge of a new land where continuous work was required. But sometimes I played on the edge of chaos like an unheeding child, frolicked on the edge of mystery.

As I merged with the dream images, became the dream instead of a dreamer, what lay about me melted away. I slipped silently across the black wastes of myself and re-entered Time, cognized cognition, heard the rich vibration articulated by Sabazius. As I mentally swept up, tidied up my journey, I saw the sea of blue glass as that beside which all beings camped, and of which they were ignorant. A mere glimpse of that ocean was enough to drive such perceivers towards madness. The distant entities intuited, felt in the bones by such campers, were the ancient gods, and the horizonless being out of which these gods sprang was the *absolute limit of mind*.

My head was throbbing like a drum, Sabazius got a damp cloth and wiped my forehead, then applied it to my face, wrists and hands. When my headache eased a little, he gave me some dry bread to eat, and a glass of milk. It was fifteen or twenty minutes before I found my voice.

'It was absolutely real,' I said.

'All reality is real,' said Sabazius. 'When you understand that, you'll be able to move from one reality to another with the blink of an eye.'

He placed a hand just below my ribcage and held it there for a few seconds. Apparently satisfied with my condition, he let me sit up.

'Am I okay?'

'You've lost less energy than I expected,' he said. 'Your dream must have been empty of superfluous detail.'

'Do you want me to describe what I saw?'

He laughed, shook his head. 'I have had dreams of my own, they were quite sufficient.'

Remembering, I said, 'What was the powder you sprinkled

on my forehead?'

'It was a few grains of my Will Stone,' he replied. 'It enabled me to keep track of you, to hold you steady.'

'Did you actually see what I saw?'

'No, I felt what you were feeling, that is enough.'

I then asked him if I should attempt to re-enter my dreams while on my own, but he said I was on no account to try such a thing until I had gone in a number of times under super-vision. He again stressed the dangers. If a man got locked in, he said, then he lived a history which could not expand, a history that could only reiterate the same message over and over again.

Without knowledge, practice and assistance, such a dreamer would drown in the sea of mind, become lost among the gods. I told him of the entities I had sensed, of the great horizonless Being.

'That is how it is,' he said calmly. 'The gods are ever on the move, restless to give up their secrets. But if a man accepts such secrets before he knows the nature of the gods, then his not knowing changes such secrets into further ignorance. There is nothing worse, nothing more dangerous than a man who believes that his secrets are devoid of lies, who does not know that true knowledge is knowledge of ignorance – one's own ignorance.'

I could make no reply to that statement.

'Everything you saw in your dream,' continued Sabazius, 'was as you now know through experience, yourself. Everything you encountered was your own history. A man can-not grow unless this takes place.'

'What you drummed into me about being what I saw was invaluable,' I said.

'When you know and understand that fully,' said Sabazius, 'you will be able to move further into the dream world and return safely. Some men have even reached the horizon where the gods are, mingled with them, talked with them, and returned with their knowledge enriched. But as I have said, there is danger here, a hole into which a man can fall. Knowledge which is not based on knowledge of one's own ignorance is not knowledge at all. To approach the gods is one thing, but to approach the gods believing that they are gods, that they are somehow separate and autonomous is to approach and enter one's own mistake. The knowledge acquired from such an encounter is power, and knowledge as power is a flaw. That is the substance of Men of Power. They return full of knowledge and attempt to manipulate the world of man, and then man himself. That is why I stressed that you should not look at the gods when overcome by fear. To look at them through the I-body is to tear your systems of functioning apart with your own hands.'

I sat in silence and thought about what he said. It was a very complex picture. There were gods on the horizon of the sea of mind that one could talk to and learn from, but at the same time these gods were what one was in oneself. The dream world was a world of objects as real as the material world, but the objects were symbols of something else. Both worlds were systems of knowledge and comprehension, but one's under-standing of those two worlds could only grow when based on knowledge of one's own ignorance. Man, it seemed, could tra-verse universes internally, and at the end of it all still fall short and die without a roar. As I considered this, an inexpressible anger began to choke me. The whole thing was so complicated and unfair, so outrageously designed. Why was man subjected to such intricate folly, to a *will* which denied him recognition of himself so expertly? Surely it could have been otherwise.

'What's the matter with you?' asked Sabazius.

'I'm not sure,' I said. 'I suddenly feel very violent, as if some-thing in me is in rebellion against the whole majestic mess.'

'A great number of people have felt that.'

'I feel so helpless. I'm confronted by something so big, so incomprehensible that I can't grasp it.'

'So?'

'So I just have to go on, and on and on ... '

'That is reason talking,' said Sabazius quietly. 'Reason drives itself mad when it realizes that there is no end to reasoning.'

My feeling of anger gained strength even as he talked. What was the use of attempting to comprehend such worlds, of try-ing to move through them when every step might plunge you into some unimaginable disaster. I could see no purpose or sense in it. Could it not be that the whole thing was just imag-ination, that it did not, on any level of reality, exist at all. That dreams were just dreams, objects just objects, men just men.

Could that not be it? Maybe Sabazius was some kind of lunatic after all, a clever illusionist who spun webs before the eyes of weaker-willed men, a man who could draw them deeper and deeper into his own aberration, his own sophisticated stupidity. Was this the kind of man I wished to be?

'Look at me,' said Sabazius.

'I don't want to look at you,' I said forcefully.

Going over to the window he pulled the curtains. 'I want to show you something,' he said softly.

My sense of rebellion exploded, jerked me up from the sofa. 'I don't want any more of it right this minute,' I shouted, and I was surprised by the harshness of my own voice. 'I want time to think things out, to –'

I had always known that Sabazius was strong, but I had never suspected just how strong. He grabbed me by the collar and literally lifted me off my feet. Ignoring the insults I was throwing at him, he pushed me bodily across the room and into the bathroom. 'If you will not look at me,' he roared, 'then maybe you will look at yourself!' When I tried to turn my head away, his fingers twisted it back and held it steady. 'What do you see, eh? Tell me what you see?' I tried to close my eyes, but he rammed a fist into my backbone and ground them open. I saw a half-crazed face staring at me from the mirror. 'Take a good look at Peter Derwent,' demanded Sabazius. 'That is the man who has experienced the Four Lights, the man who has seen the Violet Spot and experienced the Sheath of Vision. Does he look like that kind of man to you? Would you believe that that man was capable of anything?'

A spasm ran through my body.

'Answer me!' he roared.

'Nnnno … ' I managed to say.

'Then where is the man who has experienced such things?'

I dropped my eyes.

'Where is he now?' asked Sabazius savagely. 'Tell me where he is and I will talk to him!'

A knot of emotion gathered in my throat and chest. Why was I in such a state? What was it that had suddenly thrown everything out of gear?

Sabazius placed a finger under my chin and made me look at myself again. 'No fear and full of pride,' he said with disgust.

'If a god walked into this little room right this minute, you would probably ask him for his autograph!'

I was fighting my tears.

Sabazius whirled me around and held my face in that strange grip. 'Who is this man who can't cry?' he asked. 'Why don't you tell him to go away?' And then he said something which broke me completely. 'Come out of your face, Peter. Come out and talk to me.'

At first, my weeping was locked inside, a kind of physical weeping that drew my shoulders together and sent shudders down through my body in spasms. And then my tears burst out, leapt out from my eyes, and I began to moan out my sorrow and despair, my sheer inability to understand or know what truth really was. Sabazius gathered me into his arms like a child, and like a child he lifted me from the floor, carried me through to the lounge. He laid me on the sofa, knelt beside me, placed a hand on my forehead. I quietened slightly, became aware of his hand's warmth, its size and strength. Then up out of my body came another, and yet another seizure of pain. Pain trying to release itself, trying to find complete expression through my body and mind. Sabazius took his hand from my forehead and placed it on my chest, pressed down as if trying to push out of me what I did not have the strength to drag out of myself. These pains, or spasms, kept coming to the surface for almost an hour, and all the while Sabazius gazed fixedly at his hand and applied that pressure. When I eventually quietened, and my body stilled, he sat back on his haunches and looked at me. I was unable to apeak.

'Well,' he said softly, his face breaking into a smile. 'That's got rid of some of your arrogance.'

I nodded weakly, closed my eyes. In the darkness of my mind I sensed my earlier thoughts gone from me for ever. It now no longer mattered that I did not understand everything, or that there was so much to understand. The demands that I had considered unjust, I now realized, were of my own making. I was my own demand. When I questioned something, I was the question, and when I answered it, I was the answer. The gods were situated on the outer horizon of my creativity, and my creative task, unimaginable in its compexity, stupendous in its simplicity, was to be myself. No more and no less.

19 ❋ *The nature of belief*

'I want you to sit in that old chair and allow your hands to dangle over the edge,' said Sabazius one afternoon. 'Let them hang lifelessly, try to feel their weight, their thickness, what they are made of.'

I did as requested.

'Now enter into your hands and feel the secret tensions,' he said, watching what I was doing closely. 'When you think your hands are completely relaxed, let their weight drop towards the floor even more.'

When I did this, tiny parts of my hands eased of which I had not previously been aware.

'Each time you feel that your hands are as relaxed as they possibly can be, allow more weight to accumulate, this will slowly untie the muscle knots.'

It was amazing. Each time I did this, my hands seemed to grow limper internally, become heavier. After a few minutes, a tingling sensation started up, and within five, my hands, even though I was looking at them directly, no longer existed in a feeling sense. I knew I existed right down to my wrists, but from there, well, there was nothing.

Sabazius questioned me on how my hands felt, and being satisfied with my answer, told me to lift my hands up and see how they felt then. When I raised them from the chair they were completely normal, and all natural sensation was there instantly.

'Where did your hands go?' asked Sabazius.

'I thought they had gone numb,' I said.

'If your circulation had been cut off in any way,' he replied, 'then they would have been numb, and when you lifted them, they would have remained numb; but what happens here is something else.'

Sabazius then explained this 'something else' as the body

falling asleep, or being cut off from sense distraction. But there was one intrinsic difference, for if the body was put to sleep in this manner, then consciousness remained unimpaired, so allowing the person who had mastered the art of body sleep while awake to move, or travel without resistance. To illustrate this point, he reminded me that when we had travelled together to the Rhodope Mountains he himself had cut my bond with my body, drawing us both out on the one energy circuit. That was why he had linked fingers with me.

'So when I master this,' I said excitedly, 'I'll be able to travel on my own to other parts of the world!'

'Yes, if you have something to do there,' he replied, insinuating that there generally had to be a purpose for such travel. And then he said, 'What you need to understand, Peter, is that there are many levels on which a man can travel. When I took you to Rhodope Mountains, that was to let you feel the first level; but what we're tackling now is much more important. I remember telling you that almost anyone with a little training can move on the first level; but to move into the other levels requires greater and greater degrees of Will. If a man does not perfect Will, he'll never get beyond stage one. Now there is a reason for this. As one moves into the other levels, the matter you are travelling through becomes fine, it is composed of even subtler forms of energy, and as that energy is refined Will, it necessitates that your energy of Will be of an equivalent nature. If any man attempts to enter level two without first raising the level of his Being to the required pitch, he will meet as powerful a resistance as he did when first trying to enter level one.'

'Is this tied up with my dream work?' I asked.

'Indeed it is. The more you enter your dreams in a dynamic way, and comprehend them, and have all the rubbish gutted out of your systems, the more refined your Will will become. The dream world is like a simulator. It teaches you the correct attitude to have by presenting your attitudes in visual form. It shows you how to think clearly by visually presenting your thoughts with all their inner discrepancies on the surface. When a man dreams, his history is played back like a roll of cleverly edited film, and each frame contains some aspect of the man's character which requires his attention.

'What about repeat dreams?'

'What you term a repeat dream is just an aspect he has totally ignored, an aspect probably relayed to him in many ways, and as a kind of last resort played back in its original form to attract his attention and focus his feelings. To ignore such dreams, is to stagnate like a pool of water cut off from a fresh spring.'

'What – '

'We could talk about this all day,' said Sabazius, 'but we have work to do. I want you to practise putting your body to sleep section by section until you can switch off all physical awareness with a blink.'

'Won't that take weeks to perfect?'

'It may take a few days; but your Will is strong enough to do it in half an hour if you really work at it. You'll be surprised how quickly such a thing can be mastered when you keep out of awake-dream.'

And so I started. I worked firstly on my hands, putting them through the process faster and faster, and then turned my attention to my feet, ankles, legs and arms. With instruction from Sabazius, I worked on my hands and arms simultaneously. Within two hours, I could switch off two-thirds of my body, and by ten that evening, had twice accomplished a complete switch off. What got me about the whole thing was the curious non-feeling, the I'm-not-here-yet-here feeling due to being completely conscious. I could see my body, but not feel one iota of it. And yet, when I wanted to move, it immediately responded. The subtle trick Sabazius had taught me was to simply do everything on the out-breath. I was to allow physical feeling to escape as I breathed out, just as the air escaped from my lungs. When this was done properly, thoughts ceased to appear, and as my attention to physical sensation was cut by half, so also was the physical sensation itself. Eventually, out-breath after out-breath, it disappeared altogether. From then on, Sabazius told me, everything I attempted to do which required a high level of concentration had to be done on the out-breath. When he was satisfied that I understood the principle involved, he then said that I had to conserve my energies for a few days, and work hard on myself that I might enter level two. When I asked him how this was to be accomplished he amazed me by saying that level two could only be entered through prayer.

'What exactly do you mean by prayer?' I said.

He smiled at me. 'I'm not asking you to paint yourself with treacle, I'm only asking you to do what you've already done – what you did when experiencing the burning of self. Prayer is "opening yourself up" through wordless realization. It is sensing the state of your Being through Will.' And then he said something which made me look up. 'Prayers are wordless thoughts, whole thoughts dropped into universe. When such thoughts spin away from you, Intelligences answer. But don't try to play with this,' he warned, 'for such Intelligences cannot be fooled. They can see you as you cannot see yourself. To attempt such prayer is to immediately know where you stand with yourself. If you are really honest, then prayer opens you up automatically, but if you are not being honest, if your Being is clouded, then it will close you like a clam. That is why speaking to the sky is generally such a nonsense, for the person praying in such a fashion fools himself with the sound of his own voice. He gets caught up in his intonation and choice of words, and ego closes the door of communication between himself and the Intelligences who are all around. True prayer has never been composed of words, it has been composed of man's Being comprehending itself through regulated systems of functioning, or freed Will. When a man faces himself squarely, no matter what he discovers, he begins to shine internally. As Will develops in him, his Being radiates energy, and this energy attracts passing Intelligences. When the energy level of a man is sufficiently high, a singular Intelligence will then take on the task of helping, or showing that man how to refine his Being further. And eventually, when the man's being has reached the necessary level, the Intelligence which has adopted him will use that energy to manifest itself either through sound, vision, or both. So in a curious sense, such men answer their own prayers, for unless they open themselves in an intrinsic manner, the Intelligences which govern universe would not notice them, and the help which must inevitably come, could only be channelled through systems of functioning refined by the emergence of a strong Will.'

'Which means that at all times,' I said, having understood

what he was saying to me, 'the ultimate responsibility is one's own.'

'Would you have it any other way?' asked Sabazius. 'Would you prefer to be tossed about at the whim of a faceless god?'

I shook my head.

'But this is where one must carefully differentiate between the Central Station of Command,' added Sabazius, 'which is intelligence centred in Being, and that of usurping ego. Ego, which is only the body identifying with matter, continually demands the *right* to make its own decisions. But the moment it is faced with real individuality – the Will of man comprehending itself – it crumbles; that is, it loses power over the man, and the man's eye becomes single.'

'You mean his direction and purpose is set?'

'Yes, I mean that, but I also mean that when he goes into himself he sees only one eye, not two.'

'The eye of the Awakener?'

'Quite.'

What Sabazius had just said opened up the reason for my seeing one eye as opposed to two. At first I had seen two eyes, symbolizing the duality of my nature and thinking, but after a while only one eye had appeared, symbolizing the Central Station of Command.

'When ego prays,' continued Sabazius, 'it demands this and that; but when Being prays, it *allows*. Prayer, when filtered through identification with matter is a half-hearted thing, a kind of duty which many men, because they can feel a tiny tug from Being, adhere to. But such prayer in itself is a waste of time, for it is bound in Time as subject to an object. Prayer is expansion, not limitation. It is breathing out, not breathing in. When a man learns to pray, he opens up a path which runs through all the levels. And as each level is opened, the man is opened. So it could be said that the man and the levels are one and the same. To enter a new level, does not mean that one travels somewhere, it means that your Being has produced knowledge. When a man with such knowledge prays, he spirals through the levels of Being already opened, and comes eye-to-eye with his *act* of Will. As he is the eye which beholds the eye, as the act of Will is his act, he ceases to be subject to himself as an object.' Sabazius stopped at this point, looked at me keenly, waited. The rate of my breathing had changed, and I found myself sucking in air, drawing it in as if to fill my whole body. Then he said, 'Only a "whole breath" can be breathed out properly.'

'It's like yawning,' I said.

'That's why we yawn. A whole breath causes stillness to appear. When a man yawns, or feels a yawn coming on, he slips momentarily from the I-body and feels his Being. For a moment, the world is different, not so important, not so real.'

'Just through yawning?' I said.

'To yawn is to open yourself up,' he replied. 'to become vulnerable. When a man yawns he has an overwhelming desire to close his eyes, to disappear into himself, to allow himself to be caught out-of-Time. Conversations, business meetings, almost everything man does stops when people start to yawn. That's why it's infectious – Being triggers off Being.'

'I always thought of it as a lack of oxygen.'

'A lack of what?'

'Oxygen.'

'You mean energy,' said Sabazius. 'What man calls oxygen, is energy. When he breathes in he takes in energy, just as he takes in the energy of matter visually; but when he breathes out, he breathes out toxins. He does not lose energy through breathing out, he loses his energy through *looking out,* through identifying with matter. The vital energies necessary to spiral through the levels of Being are at all times being poured out through his senses because of useless involvement with the external. When his energies reach danger level, Being demands a whole-breath, a breath that will carry the man to the edge of no-Time. This is why I have stressed the need to get to know your body. As you *are* your body, what your body needs must be known. And this is where we hit what at first appears to be a contradiction. For a man to realize Being, he must first enter into a close relationship with his body. Unless he becomes dynamically aware of his physical being, his Being-existence cannot be realized. But this must not be done as a mere act of identification. To merely identify with one's body is not to be aware of it, for true awareness is observation without evaluation.

'True awareness just *happens,* and so also does correct

breathing. The body knows how to breathe properly and completely, it is we who stop it. To say that breathing is involuntary is true; but to breathe as man breathes is to deny that truth. Man is full of conflicts because of dual perception; but when his eye becomes single, his conflicts wither. A whole-breath cancels out *Identification-conflicts*, draws man's idea of body and mind as separate things together, and allows true seeing and looking to erupt.

'During our first few weeks together, I forced you into an awareness of your body, demanded that you feel your feelings and know your knowing. I turned your thinking around so that you thought of yourself as *being a hand*, not just as *having a hand*. You slowly evolved from that point to the still dualistic "I am" of Being, and from there to the Word of Being – Am. This is where people get lost and confused. They either live in their bodies, identifying with matter through the I-body, or they live in their heads and turn into an I-body fantasy, an existence-theory locked in matter through verbal conflict. Now the man who lives almost totally in his body, loses the ingredient of mind to realize Being, and the man who lives in his head as an existence-theory loses the ingredient of body to realize Being, for Being is both subject and object of existence.

'Some men, however, realize theoretically that there is no difference, that the body/mind idea equals Being; but they almost always fall into the trap of *Identifying* with the body primarily because they are sick of verbal fantasy, and end up denying the body's mind which they *say* they are simultaneously. When they talk of awareness, they are not referring to Being realized, or the dualistic conflict stilled, but merely to evaluated feeling, feelings *Identified* within the body itself. That is a vicious circle. Such men are stuck because they only understand their own statements, but do not comprehend them in wholeness. What they do not know, and seldom realize, is that when body and mind are put together, they do not produce a third principle, a some*thing* else, they cancel each other out as Being timelessly observed.'

'But still Being *in existence*,' I said.

'Indeed. This is why a man must work his way through the levels of Being, through the levels of Time, through the levels of matter until, as I have said to you, he comes eye-to-eye with the *ever-comprehending act of Will,* his Being in existence without conflict. Then the man's Will is truly free.'

The sense of finality I got from what he said made me sit looking at him for some time, then I said, 'That raises a problem for me, Alexis. If my Will is the Will of Elsewhere, then I am Elsewhere. Is that correct?'

'Yes.'

'The Elsewhere is ... '

A laugh slowly rolled out of Sabazius. 'Why can't you say it?' he asked. 'Do you find it difficult?'

'The words won't form,' I said.

'Think it in, not through.'

I thought about it carefully and gave up.

'What's the matter?' asked Sabazius.

'If Am is Elsewhere,' I said, finding a way to articulate my question, 'then I ought to be able to say logically that Elsewhere is Am ... but I can't, because I sense a mistake.'

Sabazius clapped his hands together, beamed at me. 'Your systems are being true to you,' he said. 'Answer your own question.'

I applied myself to it a second time, hit the blank spot in my mind and rolled back. Sabazius said nothing. I got up and walked around the room, looked out of the window, lay down on the carpet and closed my eyes. Sabazius laughed quietly at my dilemma. The answer was there, just out of sight ... but how to ...

'The out-breath,' Sabazius reminded me.

Centring myself, I filled my lungs, and with great deliberation allowed the air to escape slowly, focusing simultaneously all my non-thinking attention on the problem.

Almost.

Energy bubbled up at my body Centre.

A third attempt.

The proposition is not reversible because ... because ... because ...because ... IT DOES NOT HAVE TO BE! I burst out laughing and sat up.

'Well?' asked Sabazius.

'If Am is Elsewhere,' I said in a rush, 'then Elsewhere does not have to be the Am I am.'

'Why?'

'Because oneness cannot be changed into a dualistic concept.'

'Did you think that out?'

'No. I breathed it out.'

'What is the difference?'

'To think is to evaluate, to breathe is to comprehend.'

'What is Will?'

'Comprehension.'

'What is Elsewhere?'

'The *ever-comprehending act of Will*.'

'What is Am?'

'The Will of Being.'

'What is the difference between your Being and my Being?'

'There is no difference.'

'What does that mean?'

'It does not *mean* any*thing*.'

'Look at me,' said Sabazius.

When I looked at him his gaze reverted to that glassy stare, that inconceivable *look* which I generally could not return. This time it was different. Our 'looks' merged, became one look, one flow of energy. I no longer existed as Peter Derwent, and Sabazius was no longer Alexis Sabazius.

Sabazius closed his eyes momentarily and the circuit was broken. He then said, 'Love is the perfect Will of Being.'

'And knowledge,' I said.

'True knowledge,' added Sabazius, 'is an act of love.'

I was now sitting before him straight-backed and attentive. Leaning forward, he gently pressed my eyes closed. 'Look at love,' he said.

The Violet Spot hung before my inner eye fully formed. As I observed it, it went into itself, evaporated, reappeared closer and larger with a characteristic jump. 'On the out-breath,' I heard Sabazius say. Stark, clear and jagged it came. The centre of my Violet Spot was not violet, but rather sky blue. Each time I breathed my attention out, the blueness became lighter, more delicate. Then in the centre of that blueness appeared a huge eye, the eye of The Awakener, and my looking fixed itself on a tiny speck of light, a seeming reflection on the eye's surface. That was when I made my final concerted effort, an effort not based on force of Will, but on the comprehension of Will, the allowingness of the out-breath. Like a spark of light I travelled towards the light. The tiny speck of light grew enormously, resembled a distant planet, a planet towards which I was speeding. A million images sped by on every side. I was travelling through a tunnel of images at fantastic speed. And then suddenly I was suspended some way off from the planet, viewing it for what it really was. From my position in the depths of nowhere, I saw what can only be described as a throne, a throne high up, and from this throne, or golden light, fell a tube of translucent blue. The tube contained mighty beings, winged beings ascending and descending simultaneously. There was a continual flow of those beings, a never-ending stream passing from and to, to and from. As my out-breath terminated, I was withdrawn from this awe-inspiring scene, drawn back through the tube into my little world of internal darkness. And there I sat, knowing, yet not knowing what I had witnessed, understanding, yet not understanding what I understood. I continued to sit long after the vision had ceased, immersed in wonder, stunned by beauty. What manner of universe was this in which I found myself? How was it possible to see such ... Words failed, fell away into themselves.

I opened my eyes.

Sabazius smiled at me.

That was when I remembered how my systems had filled up with energy. As I entered into the out-breath, every atom of my body had begun to vibrate, and as this vibration quickened, mounted higher and higher until it reached my head, I had sped out to that distant point, or, to be more precise, sped into the centre of my Centre. When I had gathered my senses about me again, I told Sabazius of what I had seen. He nodded with interest, but did not reply.

'Angels?' I said.

'Could be,' he said back.

'They had wings.'

'Probably.'

'Either they had wings, or they hadn't,' I said.

'Not necessarily.'

Feeling confused, I said, 'I saw angels ascending and descending from a golden throne. They were in a kind of blue tube, going up and down at the one ...'

'You saw what you had to see,' he said. 'Everyone sees what they have to see.'

'What do you mean?'

'I mean that you interpreted what you saw, changed it into angels and thrones. Two men from different parts of the world could experience the same experience, but they would interpret and see it in their own way. See it as "this" or "that". Remember always that you are what you see. This is what interpretation means. So if you are "this", then you see "this"; and if you are "that", then you see "that".

When I thought about what he had said, it began to open up immediately. Was it not for this very reason that I had 'known', yet not 'known', 'understood' yet not 'understood'. Against my fact-seeking and accepting mind, I faced what had happened. What I had seen had not been seen, it had been invented and planted on the surface of actuality as a wish-negative.

Sabazius looked at me, sucked at his mouth as if trying to determine something, then he said, 'When a man dies, he enters into what he believes. This is why we say that we believe "in" things, for to believe is to enter *into our beliefs*. What we believe shapes our lives, what we see is interpreted through our beliefs. Dreams and visions are important for they show us what kind of beliefs we are made of. To believe in something, anything, is to put a fragment of the universe in our pocket and think we have the key to understanding all of it. That is the dream from which we must wake. The whole universe is a beautiful dream to us, for we are dreaming the universe, not seeing it.'

I looked towards the window, looked out at the night sky, wondered what to 'awaken' really meant.

185

20 ❧ The asking of questions

'Keep your back absolutely straight,' urged Sabazius, pushing his hand gently into the hollow of my spine, 'and look up into your head as far as your eyes will allow.' He waited until he was sure I had done this, then he said, 'Now breathe out slowly, and watch.'

There was almost immediately a flicker of blue, not unlike that which my Centre gave off, but not so intense or flower shaped. This blueness moved about, kind of bubbled, then dropped slightly, making room for the horizon of darkness above it. After a few seconds of looking, the darkness was filled with tiny specks of brilliant yellow light, dancing particles punctuated with larger spots of dark blue. Above this lay more darkness, and as I watched, small curls of whitish cloud appeared, wind-blown clouds reflecting on their turning, twisting upper surfaces a dazzling light. Try as I might, however, I could not entice this light into view.

'Well?' asked Sabazius.

'There was something very bright up there,' I said.

He ignored what I said and told me to repeat the exercise, only this time, when I was at the apex of my looking, I was to double down into my Centre. This, he said, was one of the quickest methods of centring; but it had to be used with care, as one should not allow consciousness to follow vision with the same rapidity. If I dropped myself into my Centre without restraint, I could very well suffer from dizziness and displacement for days afterwards.

With this in mind, I closed my eyes a second time and looked up. Roughly the same thing happened, but when I reached the second darkness, and the first gleaming rays appeared – they seemed to come from behind the crown of my head – I noticed distinct changes on the lower levels. The moment I dropped my eyes, however, what seemed to be forming melted clean away, and it took me some minutes to learn the technique of not looking directly at the lower levels. The formations would only remain, and intensify, when my looking was somewhere between them and the fanning arms of light higher up.

This change on the lower level took the form of an exceptionally bright, almost neon-like green area. Being now aware of it, rather than watching it, I saw this green produce out of itself shapes not unlike letters and numbers; but I could in no way retain what I saw in detail, for the moment my concentration focused on that area they vanished. Having re-established steady awareness, I then saw a mass of patterns emerge from this central patch, like the multicoloured patterns on a Persian rug. These patterns were geometrically perfect, and changed kaleidoscopically from one intricate weave of symbols to another every few seconds. My concentration was suddenly broken by a blister of intense light from above. I looked up instantly and the light vanished.

'Go down,' said Sabazius.

Almost reluctantly, I swivelled my eyes down and looked into my Centre, then, with great care lowered consciousness as directed. At first, there was just the flowering blue I knew so well, but as I settled, I became aware of a silvery radiance buried deep and apparently behind my Centre, just as the rays of light had come from behind and above my head. I looked deeper still. The edge of this silvery area appeared slowly, then, like the neon-green symbols and patterns it was snatched away as I attempted to look at it directly.

'What did you see?' asked Sabazius.

'There was something that looked like a cave lying behind my Centre,' I said, trying to hold the image memory offered. I laughed, smiled awkwardly. 'It looked as if it were filled with precious metal, or stones.'

'Good,' said Sabazius, obviously pleased with what I had observed. 'You have seen the treasure cave.'

'What is it?' I asked.

'I have told you ... it is a treasure cave.'

'It's true that it looked like a treasure cave,' I said, 'but what is the treasure?'

'Don't you know?'

I thought about it, said that I had no idea.

Sabazius looked at me long and steadily, then he said, 'Without the contents of that cave you could not live for one second. Everyone has a treasure cave.'

It took me but a second to realize what he meant by that. 'Then it must be the energy of my energy Centre,' I said. And then I added, 'Is it?'

Sabazius nodded. 'You caught a glimpse of the substance which keeps your internal universe turning. Tiny particles of that substance are at this very moment feeding your systems, travelling to your cells and nerves. It is because there is more of this substance travelling around your system as a whole that you can see what others cannot see, do what others cannot do. But tiny particles of that energy are not enough for a Man of Feeling to survive on. If such a man wishes to function properly, then he must eventually enter the cave and carry off the treasure.'

'You make it sound like robbery.'

'It is a kind of robbery,' he replied 'but it is a very strange type of robbery.'

Not being able to make anything of what he said, I asked him how it was possible to enter the cave when it kept disappearing the moment one looked at it.

'That is the key,' said Sabazius. 'It is only when you walk away from the treasure cave that you can enter it. If a man seeks to enter, he will find nothing.'

'Why is that?'

'Because when an ordinary man looks, ego also looks, and when the ego of an ordinary man looks he *desires to see what he sees*. That is why the cave vanishes without trace. If ego were allowed to look directly at the seat of energy, it would burn up in an instant, and the man would be consumed. So one has to learn how to observe what is in the cave without desiring to look. The first step of this not-looking is the curious tangential awareness which you described. When that is mastered, and you have learned the meaning of empty looking, experienced it, then the cave will empty out its contents without fuss or bother.'

'What happens then?'

'Such things cannot be talked about clearly,' he replied, passing me one of his Turkish cigarettes, 'they can only be hinted at. The treasure cave is full of gifts, full of wonders; but these gifts carry a high price with them. The moment a man receives them, no matter in what degree, he has to live with extreme diligence. All Men of Feeling who have completed their training have secured the treasures of the cave. And it is this which makes them different from other men.' He paused, looked thoughtful. 'But there is something else here, something very important. If a man who has not properly prepared his systems is flooded with the cave's treasure, then he more often than not will totally break down and disintegrate.'

'But surely such a man would not be given the treasure in the first place?' I said.

Sabazius cast me a warning glance. 'Not quite. It is possible that the cave will unload its treasure on a half-prepared man because he has perfected empty-looking; but he must be prepared on many other levels as well. What I am saying to you is this: approach the cave certainly, but do not attempt to enter it until your systems say "Go".'

'But isn't there a danger that I might stumble into the cave?' I said worriedly.

'Yes, there is,' he replied; 'but it is that very fact which, if handled properly, will perfect your systems, because it will firstly perfect your fear. At this very moment many things are happening in you. Particles of energy from the cave are seeping into your systems, changing them, preparing them to carry the full load, the full responsibility for such power. Your attitudes are being shaped, your Will strengthened, your comprehension deepened. These changes are bringing about a refined intellectual faculty, a purified logic. When all of these things are in balance, and ego is under control, then you will be ready to enter the cave. But if you make a mistake and enter the cave before you are ready, then you will bring down on your head an unimaginable catastrophe. You will want to die, but death will flee from you. You will try to hide in the far reaches of the universe, but the finger of that power will seek you out like a wild animal. That is why your fear must be as perfect as your comprehension, for perfect fear is wisdom.'

I asked another question.

'You're on an information hunt,' said Sabazius.

'I'm sorry,' I said.

He laughed. 'Don't worry about it too much. A man must ask questions, for unless he asks questions he cannot come to the realization that questions are useless. Somewhere along the line, if he is really serious, not just playing word games for the sake of it, he hits on the final question, the questioning of questioning itself, and when that happens he has a chance to approach true knowledge. Most people prefer new knowledge. They screw themselves into language until their systems explode. New knowledge can lead a man to the very exit of universe, but it cannot open the door, for there is no door, just as there is no exit.'

'I'm full of questions,' I said hopelessly. 'Answers don't satisfy me most of the time – they only produce more questions for me to consider.'

Sabazius smiled in agreement. 'A man can have what he thinks is a perfect understanding, and he can have vision after vision to confirm that what he understands to be true is true, but what he cannot understand is why he continues to merely understand over and over again what he understands without ever escaping from the suspicion that there is something missing.'

Falling straight into the trap, I said, 'What is missing in the man's understanding?'

'If I told you that,' replied Sabazius, trying not to laugh out loud, 'then you would understand, and what was missing would still be missing. Do you understand?'

I stared at him.

'All questions contain their own answers. All questions are symbols which have to be penetrated. All questions when answered are not answered. To go beyond questions is to go beyond answers. To go beyond answers is to penetrate all questions.' He became very still, watched me unblinkingly. 'That is what the comprehension of Will means,' he then said. 'Such words cannot be understood, they can only be comprehended when a man enters them as an actuality. If a man hears or reads such words and thinks that he has understood them, then he has not recognized the difference between his understanding and his comprehension. It is possible to sometimes comprehend something yet not understand that you have not merely "understood". Understanding is the searchlight of man's mind, comprehension is the darkness of consciousness itself. To enter the darkness is to have access to light unimaginable.' He watched my face, looked at it as if studying the very pores of my skin, then he said, 'I want you to go back down into your Centre the way I showed you, and when you get there, I want you to create an imaginary ball of your questions, and your answers, and allow it to fall into the treasure cave. If you can do this, and open yourself up in wordless prayer, your systems will dance.'

Sitting erect in my chair, my hands lying palm upwards on my knees, I again looked up into that dark region. There was at first only a flurry of unrecognizable shapes and colours, but after a few minutes, the territory I had been in before began to unfold. The bubbling blue was followed by darkness, the darkness lighted up by clusters of yellow stars, the stars replaced by that horizon on which clouds curled and twisted. When thin beams of bright light shot out from above and behind, I doubled down into my Centre and allowed consciousness to follow slowly. The big, blue flower of energy I knew so well crept up and around, enveloped me soothingly. However, when I attempted to hold consciousness steady, it wavered, followed the direction of my eyes, which momentarily would not remain still, and before I could rectify the situation I was back in my head looking into the middle distance.

It is really quite impossible to describe what it is one does while in the energy Centre, or when attempting to re-approach it. Words cannot quite catch or contain the subtle changes of direction and movement which the mind makes and takes. It is an invisible mystery which has to be experienced to be understood, and the understanding one has of it is a memory which only activates truly when the experience is repeated. The only thing that can really be said is that the supposed operator does absolutely nothing, and because of this, everything happens. So, armed with nothing, I went back down into my Centre. Having reached the bottom of the shaft, exhaled and held my breath for a few seconds so as to close the petals of blue around me, I waited in stillness. After many minutes I became aware of a small bright-edged hole. The edge of this hole sparkled like a ring caught in sunlight. I fastened my attention on the ring's light, held it steady, and immediately it came into focus and jumped nearer. This surprised me a little, and as my attention moved with its movement, it fell back. I again focused on the ring of light. This time it expanded and jumped towards me without my concentration breaking. On the next out-breath it jumped nearer still, and in the middle of the next breath I found myself travelling through the ring, being able to see its huge contours as I passed.

I was in another world. Confronted by a stretch of blue sky in which a solitary star hung, I breathed towards it, entered it, and there exploded before my inner eye a vast landscape of incredible beauty and delicacy. In the centre of this landscape lay a lake, a lake of blue water touched by an invisible sun. It took but a moment to fasten on a crystal-bright wavelet, and in what I like to think of as 'the twinkling of an eye', I was through it and suspended above the cave of gems. This time the cave and its contents were completely in view. Rainbow colours flooded up on the tips of silver needles. I was looking into the treasure cave of a million fairytales. Yet to say that I was looking 'at' anything is untrue. I was not looking directly into it, but rather at a point of no-thing just above it. The most over-powering aspect of this diamond-deep-dream was the silence. It rested like black soup between the spikes of silver-blue, floated threateningly around the sea of gems as the cave's walls. I allowed this stillness to press in on me, and as stillness met stillness, and merged, what I thought myself to be melted clean away.

Questions.

Fashioning I know not how all the questions I had ever asked, and the questions which had sprung out of all the answers I had ever been given into a ball, I let it slip away from me. It moved down among the silver needles like an ink-spot, rose and fell like a black balloon caught on an updraught, and like a balloon deflated itself on the spikes. In the moment my image-ball of questions vanished, the spikes reached up towards me, penetrated me, and I was carried high up into another darkness. One hundred thousand years passed in but a second as I hung there. A million million beings lived their history, spun through their private universe, breathed away their lives with a sigh. Gaseous planets formed, solidified, trembled, flashed like roman candles in the depths of nowhere and became as nothing. And then suddenly there was again one man looking, and that man was thrust upwards, pushed back into his world of black and white, negative and positive, up and down. I opened my eyes. The room was just as before, although slightly yellowish around the edges. The curtains moved as the wind changed direction and forced its way through the narrow slip of the open window. The clock ticked, and clicked. Where was this place? What was I doing here?

As Sabazius had left while I journeyed, I went through to the kitchen and splashed cold water on my face and wrists. Drying myself, I walked back into the lounge and turned the radio on. A popular show rattled out its wares and I turned it off again. Going over to the window, I looked out at the adjacent houses. Lower down, just visible above frosted glass, a woman was washing her hair. When she bent forward, the pink of her back and shoulders was dispersed unevenly. I stared at her convoluted shape for some seconds. My eyes moved slowly and deliberately down the full length of the building. On the street, a woman was smacking her little boy across the legs. She was holding him on tiptoe with her left hand, and the child dangled screaming, his one free arm hanging limp like his head. Not far from her a fat man in a camel coat was squeezing himself behind the driving wheel of a large, sleek car: two girls, dressed in the clothes of another era, laughed and pointed at him in derision. I surveyed the scene unemotionally, took it in as one lump. Turning from the window, I put the radio back on and switched to the Third programme. Some fairly heavy music was being played. I did not recognize it. I stood in the centre of the lounge and looked at it the way I had looked out of the window. The music broke into two sections, two sections which I could hear separately yet simultaneously. Background was divorced from foreground, became another band of music related to but independent of the melody. I was literally listening with two ears.

My feelings too had changed. I was neither excited nor depressed, happy nor sad. Yet some kind of emotion was flowing through my systems. There was a subtle feeling attached to the way I could hear and see, a feeling which contained no concern for what was heard or seen. But this 'lack of concern' which I sensed was in no way a negative emptiness, for I was acutely conscious of myself as a total being as I stood there. That was it. The feeling I sensed was that of my own totality. I was quite simply 'alive', and knew it. As with the music, the room's colours became independent of the objects in that I could sense them by themselves, yet my sensing of them in this manner in no way made them into 'objects'. With no sense of logical progression I realized what I was doing. I was seeing and looking *out* of my own totality, not *through* interpretive involvement. Factual seeing was therefore a fallacy. We continually rearranged what we saw and heard to suit and 'fit in with' our preconceived factual notions – what we believed to be there whether it was there or not. This was why we asked so many questions. Our questions, on the whole, were meaningless, for we seldom had any intention of becoming activated through the answers. Only dire necessity could move us to accept the facts of existence, penetrate our systems and allow us to see truly. To see this in itself was to blast a hole in perception, to allow the first struggling rays of light free entry. Our senses were guarded by sentinels of belief, censored by comfortable prejudice. I laughed suddenly, realized of what my Sheath of Vision was composed – honesty. When I was honest with myself I could see, when I was dishonest I was blind. It was that simple.

21 ❋ *An experience of death*

The following morning, after a profound sleep, I went walking by the Thames with Sabazius. We had coffee and cake at the Festival Hall around ten. I was in excellent spirits. The morning had started dull, but as we sat in the spacious, first-floor coffee lounge looking out at the grey concrete, the sun burst upon London. A rather lonely nature-amputated tree I had been looking at came alive instantly. Even the concrete looked different. I breathed out slowly and allowed the difference to register.

'Would you like to meet my cat?' asked Sabazius suddenly.

I smiled at him, remembered how he had had me crawling about the floor of his flat in Johannesburg. 'I thought you were never going to invite me to your place,' I said, mocking him gently. 'Is it the flat you said I wouldn't like?'

'Yes.'

The pale green of the tree's leaves had now separated itself from its organic base, and was suspended fractionally.

'I have arranged for you to meet some people later this afternoon,' added Sabazius. 'You know most of them.'

Something inside me shifted. I said, 'Are we going to do some work together?'

'Yes.'

'The last cat you introduced me to had only one ear,' I said. 'What's missing on this one?'

Sabazius laughed quietly. 'This cat is quite complete,' he replied, 'it could even be described as beautiful.' He sipped at his coffee. 'We have three hours. Is there anything in particular you would like to do?'

At first I could not think of anything, then I said, 'Yes, there is something I would like to do. I would like to walk up to Westminster and look at the Rodin statues.'

So that is what we did. As we walked slowly along the

Embankment, in silence, enjoying the warmth of a sun which had decided to stay out, I noticed time and time again movements and separations of colour. I did not think about or consider what I saw. Aware of, but not involved in what was happening, my attention moved from the external world to a part of my body. My larynx seemed to have solidified, become a curious, vibrating organ. When I breathed down and into this organ, the sense of solidity expanded and engulfed my neck. There was also a feeling of steadiness, a growing sense of balance, and a straightening physically. I watched what was happening in me with great interest. As my physical body uncurled itself, opened itself up, my mental attitude changed accordingly. It was like taking deep breaths with one's mind.

'Will the Turk be there?' I asked.

'Yes.'

A feeling, a pictureless memory of the factory. A distant cracking sound from my spine as knotted bones separated and resettled, took up new positions. I had a momentary picture of a collapsed puppet being pulled straight.

'Is there anything important I should know about this afternoon?' I said, glancing at Sabazius. 'Anything I have to do?'

'Not really,' he replied. 'Just be there completely, that's all.'

We walked on in silence, reached Westminster Bridge and wound our way toward the little space of green where the statues stood like frozen history. I had stumbled on these solid men by accident many months before. I had looked at them from every angle, attempted to see what the artist saw, then realized that what the artist had seen was what I was looking at. The statues contained no meaning, they were meaning. But something else had struck me that day, and Sabazius had confirmed this something when talking of art as an expression of intelligence. The statues *as* meaning changed meaningfully depending on where one stood, because where one stood automatically backgrounded them with a different substance, or depth. Each background caused one's focus to change, and as focus changed, so also did the statues. So at any given angle, or moment, the whole scene changed and rechanged, shuffled itself like a pack of cards, presented a new momentary image. When confronted, not just as statues, as something which one focused on by themselves, they merged with their background, slid from sight, touched off an experience which was perhaps the artist's own experience. It was some time afterwards that the significance of that realization dawned on me, and that was that only true art carried the viewer beyond himself or herself, and in doing so allowed a 'seeing' to crystallize. Rodin had not made statues, he had built a doorway through illusion.

The flat Sabazius had moved into was as small as he had described it to be. It contained little furniture. There was a single bed, a reasonably comfortable chair, a small, hardwood table, a tablelamp with a rose-splattered shade, and an open grate in which a fire had been burning. On the floor, like a faded and forgotten oil painting, lay a large square of worn Indian carpet. There were no pictures on the walls. Yet although small to look at, the room felt big and expansive, probably because of its exceptionally high ceiling.

'What made you think I wouldn't like it?' I asked.

'If you had seen it then, you wouldn't have,' he replied.

I looked around slowly. 'I would have considered it empty and without taste,' I said, trying to remember how I once viewed things. Pointing at the little rosebud shade, I said, 'And that would have made me laugh.'

Opening the door of his only cupboard, Sabazius lit the gas on a two-burner stove and filled the kettle. Behind the stove hung a few pans and general cooking utensils.

'Where's your cat?' I asked.

Sabazius looked towards the window. 'If you whistle she'll come,' he said.

I pushed the bottom sash up and leaned out. The garden, a small square of dull green grass and a few bushes, stared back. On all sides, was an incredibly high wall. I whistled. A minute passed, but no cat appeared. I watched the top of the wall carefully, expecting him or her to suddenly jump into view, but nothing happened. I whistled more loudly. When I was convinced that the cat must be out of earshot, I closed the window and turned, only to find it sitting behind me with a more than apt expression on its face. Sabazius did not say anything, but I knew he was laughing inside.

'Hello cat,' I said.

'It's a she,' said Sabazius.

'And she *is* beautiful,' I said.

Sabazius placed two cups of coffee on the little table. 'She came to me the day after I arrived here. Just walked in the open window and settled down.'

Sitting on my haunches, I ran a palm down her silky fur. She raised her back end, stretched, looked away from me. 'Have you given her a name?'

He shook his head. 'I don't have to give her a name, she already has one.'

As there was no other chair available, I sat down on the bed. Cat immediately jumped onto my lap. I stroked her gently and sipped at my coffee, then lay out on the bed. Cat now sat on my chest, facing me, paws tucked neatly under her body, her eyes almost closed. Curious things continued to happen to me physiologically. Muscles seemed to be stretching of their own accord, taking up new positions. Audible cracking sounds could be heard as bones did likewise. Peter Derwent as body was reorganizing himself. My brain, too, was undergoing some kind of restructuring process. It was as if tiny electrical charges were coursing across its entire surface. It was like having half a dozen ants at large in your hair. I scratched at my head but it made no difference. Sabazius, like a wound-up-toy continued to talk. I could hear every word, understood everything he said, but knew that he was not talking for the benefit of my learning anything, but almost as if to buy time, time to allow what was happening in me to happen as if it were not happening. Although amazed by what was going on, I found myself accepting it without question, able to ride it out unthinkingly. Anyway, I could still see the room, and Sabazius, and the little rosebud shade. I could see the square of Indian carpet, the cooker, my empty coffee cup and the ceiling. I could see the cat, the window, the big high wall and the green postage stamp of grass. Everything was just as usual, except that I could see them all simultaneously. That did not bother me. If there was any one thing I had learned in the months (or was it years?) with Sabazius, it was to accept as 'natural' the seemingly unnatural movements of my own psyche.

The people Sabazius had said would come that afternoon arrived one by one within minutes of each other. They took up what looked like positions around the room. I knew most of them by sight. The Turk sat sweating near the window. The little lean-faced man who had projected pains at me sat with his back against the cupboard door, and the girl I had thought threatened by him, a tall, angular creature, sat on the floor behind Sabazius with her legs drawn up to her chin. Three others, two men and an elderly woman, stationed themselves at equal intervals. Sabazius, wedged in his little chair, did not move. Although conversation did take place, it was not of a 'nattering' variety, but concerned the positioning of each individual. I said nothing. At one point there was some kind of uncertainty about where the elderly woman should sit, not I suspected because she was elderly, but because of what she was in herself. Sabazius looked at the woman for some seconds, then pointed to a new position. She moved to it immediately, and for some reason, laughed. But as from that moment there was absolute silence.

No one seemed to consider the cat now fast asleep on my chest a problem, so I closed my eyes and forgot about it. I felt comfortable, but not sleepy. I could quite easily say that the time 'ticked by', but that would be singularly untrue as Sabazius did not own a clock. There was just a rich, easy silence. My body, still happily reorganizing itself, jerked a little from time to time, but it did not bother myself or the cat unduly. It was rather like a body-blink. I just lay there breathing in, and out, in and out. Eventually, the sound of my breathing became the gentle wash of a huge sea, a tidal movement. There was no reason to start reasoning, no purpose to make me purposeful. The room, and those it contained, existed without existing.

After what could have been a few seconds, or hours, my eyes opened wide. As there was no 'expectation' in me concerning what I *should* see, what I did see was not the room, or its contents, but a superimposed projection. In other words, what I 'needed' to see was there. Funnily enough, it was another room, but different in every way from the one in which I lay. It was a big room, large and airy, filled with warm light. I was standing at its exact centre waiting for something to happen. No one else was present. Then suddenly the most extraordinary thing took place – I was shot three times in rapid succession. I felt the bullets tear into my middle, disrupt my life processes. I fell forward on to my face knowing that I was about to die. As I lay there, chin on the carpet, blood spurting from my mouth, I knew I had only seconds of life available. Drawing what was categorically my last breath, I breathed it out in a long stream of blood, and as consciousness flickered, approached its non-moment, all that I was enveloped it and held it steady. Slowly, inexplicably, that breath moved out, and out, and out, and as it moved, flowed from my body as a red river, what I *was* followed it.

I was dead.

But in a rushing, roaring stillness the dead me popped through death and appeared somewhere else. Suddenly, I was standing in warm sunlight in an English country village. I looked around me dumbfounded, There were cottages with neat little gardens, flowering trees and privet hedges. But not a sound. Joyous that I had somehow escaped oblivion, I started down one of the narrow roads, energetically headed for what I sensed was the village square or centre. When I reached it, something very odd was going on. A huge screen had been erected, and in front of this screen, on little wooden chairs, sat some forty or fifty people, They paid no attention to me, for their attention was riveted on the screen. When I looked at the screen to see what was so interesting, so captivating, I was confronted by some kind of documentary. A dull voice was mumbling something I could not hear properly, but knew myself to know. A little uncertain as to what I should do at that point, I stood there for a few minutes, then, becoming bored, moved off across the village square. Not far away, I came across three men. They were standing close together. When I reached them, it became obvious that one of them was ill, for the other two were supporting him anxiously. I asked them what was the matter. The man who was being supported answered. He said: 'I'm moving to another level, but I'm having difficulty.' Having said that, his face became contorted as he tried to push himself through to this level. 'You're being silly,' I said. 'You can't push your way through. Just let it happen.' To help him in this, I directed energy at him. The man's face relaxed. Those supporting him slowly took their hands away. He remained firm and steady. 'Let it happen,' I said softly. 'Ride it like the wind.' The moment I said these words my eyes opened. It was the kind of instant wakefulness one sometimes experiences during sleep. One minute you are dead to the world, the next, alert and watching.

'Well,' said Sabazius. 'How do you feel?'

'I'm not quite sure,' I replied. 'Everything is incredibly sharp; but I'm puzzled somehow, not sure in here ...' I placed a hand where the cat had been. 'I feel as if I'm on the verge of understanding something, but can't quite make it out.'

'Don't try to make it,' said Sabazius, 'just let it happen.'

'You've just told me to do what I told the other chap to do,' I said quickly. 'He was in difficulty too.'

'What happened to him?'

'He was able to stand on his own after he stopped pushing.'

'Why was he pushing?'

'He said he was trying to get to a new level.'

'Did he get there?'

'I don't know. The moment he relaxed and was able to support his own weight I came back here.'

'Where were you?'

I laughed nervously, hesitated. 'I was dead and wandering about in an English country village. It was a beautiful place, full of flowers and trees. A very green place.' I laughed again. 'When I reached the village square there was some kind of picture show going on. About fifty people were watching a documentary.'

'Did you watch it?'

'Only for a few minutes, but I got bored.'

'Why?'

'Again I'm not quite sure. I had a strong impression of knowing what the documentary was about, of what the voice was going to say. So I walked away.'

'You walked across the village square?'

'Yes. That was when I spotted the three men. The one in the centre was being supported by the other two. I thought he was in some kind of pain, so I went over to help.'

'And you did help.'

'So it seems. His face relaxed and he was able to stand on his own.'

'What's the matter?' asked Sabazius.

'Where has everyone gone?'

'They left the moment you broke through.'

'Then you all knew what was happening?'

'We knew what was happening, but we did not know what form it would take. There are many forms. There is a form for every single human being in existence.'

'So nothing is fixed?'

'The levels are fixed, but not the manner in which we arrive. We each bear a unique history.'

'That's comforting.'

'Why?'

'Because it's ... democratic.' I added quickly, 'We aren't captive to a fixed ideology.'

He laughed. 'You mean God is not a Catholic?'

'Not even a Christian as far as I can see.'

We laughed together, enjoying the joke. And then he said something that carried me back into my past, back to the time when I had known neither him nor his strange, relentless ways. He said: 'This is the *second* emptiness, Peter.'

I nodded slowly, appreciating the subtlety of what he was saying. 'Empty vessels make the most noise,' I said, quoting him.

'Opinions plucked out of thin air.'

'The hard facts.'

'The hard facts which never ever deliver up the heart of the matter.'

I thought back to these days and marvelled that I had managed to hold on to my life at all, that I had found sufficient reason to cloud the fact that our lives and the planet we inhabited were just too peculiar to think about for any length of time. Who could explain what it was all about? Our scientific and philosophical disciplines had been trying to fathom how it had all come about for centuries, but were none the wiser. There was an emptiness at the beginning of things, an inexplicable space that was not a space, a time that was not time, a possible God that was not any kind of God known to the religious mind. No matter how hard we tried we could not fathom that emptiness. Why? Because it was beyond our thinking capacity to penetrate the non-objective with objective reasoning. We were at a loss over that one. How explain our existence without postulating that matter was somehow intelligent, that at some depth or level or dimension of its own nature the hard stuff of universe was not only not hard, but aware? How deal with that? How explain the hard fact that complex systems were somehow compelled to become more complex and thin out into objective consciousness with a subjective base? I had been around that block many a time, and when on the point of giving in to the terrible emptiness of heart such thinking could generate, Alexis Sabazius had walked into my life with his relentless and often infuriating Socratic dialogues and offered me a glimpse of unimaginable beauty. Rescued from my own sterility by his deeply evolved sense of purpose, I had slowly and painfully learned to open myself up to what existed in the expectation that what existed would respond. And it had responded. Whatever 'it' was, it was willing to communicate even with the likes of me.

22 ❋ The fire which consumes fire

We sat on either side of his open fire that evening smoking Sabazius's curious Turkish cigarettes. Cat sat on the windowsill watching the darkness. The atmosphere was peaceful. For but a second, I thought I saw an old man facing me. Moving the upturned wastebin I was sitting on back a little, I leaned against the wooden bedrail. The fire was very hot. Sometime later I got up and opened the window. The fire's heat was incredible. That was when I looked at it properly, tried to determine what he was burning. It did not look like coal or any of the new-fangled substances. Shielding my face, I looked at it more closely.

'What are you doing?' asked Sabazius.

'I was just wondering what kind of fuel you were using,' I replied. 'It looks like bits of ordinary stone.'

'It is stone.'

'Ordinary stone?'

'To me it is just stone,' he said innocently. 'I dug it out of the garden.'

'But surely stone can't burn like that.'

'Maybe the stone isn't burning.'

I again looked at the fire. 'Then what's causing the heat?' I asked.

'It's just a trick,' he replied. 'I learned it many years ago.'

I had noticed nothing unusual when he lit the fire. He had gone through the usual process of cleaning it out, emptying the waste pan and sweeping the hearth. His actions had looked perfectly normal.

'Why don't the stones explode?'

'Because the heat is not external to the stone, it is coming from the stones themselves.'

'How did you light it?'

'It's very simple, really,' said Sabazius with a straight face.

'All one has to do is enter one of the stones and trigger off its energy. When that is done, the energy of that stone communicates itself to the others. But the stones must be of the same nature, or composition. An alien stone could very well start an explosion, an explosion without end.'

'Why have you lit such a fire?' I then asked.

'Because you are ready for it,' he replied. 'This fire is very special. It is the fire I once told you about, the fire which consumes fire. The moment a man begins to wake up, he requires a special Stone; but when a man's eyes open fully, he must give back the little gift given to him by the earth. His systems will not move into full functioning until that is done. When the gift is returned, the man's Will is natural Will – it is free. Wherever that man travels, Will is available. Such a man is not visited by death as other men are, for he has already penetrated the symbol of death. By knowing the fire which consumes fire, he no longer claims Will as his own, just as he no longer claims Intelligence as his own, and his freed Will extinguishes the gap between himself as himself, and matter as matter. But he can only enter such freedom by entering the fire which consumes fire. This is the secret that man has lost. He discovered fire, was given the gift of a greater fire by a passing god, but was so preoccupied with the first fire that he lost the second. Instead of seeking to rediscover the fire which consumes fire, he ran away from it thinking its demands too great. He has now come to believe that the fire gobbles up evil men, and has completely forgotten that the fire gobbles up the evil *of* man. Having projected the fire-symbol outside of himself, from his own bowel into the bowels of the earth, and through perceiving it as a symbol of destruction instead of a symbol of life, he has reversed truth, and in reversing it destroyed his Will-to-Will. Helpless, he seeks forgiveness; but not for what he thinks. It is not the bric-a-brac of evil which weighs him down, but his stubborn insistence to live on the surface of reality. He is willing to look "at the mirror", but not into it. He sees the world reflected in the mirror, sees himself in that world, but will not admit to it being only a reflection. As an "I", he refuses to penetrate the reflected illusion. Such a man is not recognizable as a man ... he has no face. To build a face, he needs to build a bridge across the "gap" in his seeing, then walk across that bridge in the full knowledge that he will not return as an "I". When the gap in his seeing vanishes, when he looks into the mirror instead of at it, then and then only can he claim to see. But this claim can only be made when he penetrates the symbol of death and enters the fire which consumes fire. There is no other way.'

'What do I have to do?' I asked.

'Nothing, as yet,' said Sabazius, glancing at the fire. 'You must wait until the fire signals you to act. If you recognize that signal, then you can deliver up your Will Stone. But not before. If you were to throw your Stone on the fire now, you would perish. The fire would reach out and take you, gobble you up. The "I" of a man cannot make that decision, it must come about naturally.'

'I'm frightened.'

'I should damn well think so,' said Sabazius softly.

Looking at the gleaming surface of the fire, I said, 'Do you mind if I make some coffee?'

'Help yourself.'

Just moving across the room helped to still my trembling. If I had remained seated, it would have probably overwhelmed me. Having put the kettle on, I went over to the window, pushed the sash up a little further and looked out. Cat immediately leapt from the sill into the darkness. I could see neither the wall nor the garden; but I could hear Cat moving about some six feet below. I called to her and the sounds stopped momentarily. Just looking out into that darkness made me consider my own position. If I climbed on to the windowsill and jumped, would it not be much the same as I was about to do ... to enter the fire! The signal Sabazius had mentioned would only say 'jump', it would not articulate what I was jumping into. Taking a deep breath, I turned back to my task of making coffee.

'She's gone hunting,' said Sabazius.

I smiled and said, 'Her leaping into the darkness like that made me think of my own position.'

'In what way?'

'Leaping blind.'

'Don't be an idiot,' he said evenly. 'Cat can only leap into the darkness because she is not blind. To her darkness is light. She does not even leap because she sees, there is no "because" in her seeing. Her "seeing" and her "leaping" are the same. She does not differentiate because she has no need to ... and neither will you.'

Handing him his cup of black, unsweetened coffee, I said, 'I never learn, do I.'

'You don't learn because you try to learn standing on your head in a bucket of water,' he replied dryly. 'When you learn to stop doing that, then you'll learn.'

The image he had painted forced me to laugh at myself. Was I really that ridiculous? 'You've been very patient with me,' I said.

Sabazius shook his head. 'No, I have been impatient with you, that is why you are here. If I had been patient, you would still be there. A true Man of Feeling has no patience with patience, for all it generally means is that he has to continually walk around in circles when his objective is but one step away. What man thinks of as patience is often an excuse which carries him further into illusion, allows him to continue dreaming when he ought to be awake, to lie down when he should be standing firmly on his own two feet. That is what to look at, rather than into the mirror means. It means to face one's self squarely and stand firm. In your vision of death you were supporting yourself with patience, making a battle out of something that was not a battle, allowing yourself to push and strain when all you had to do was let the energy of Will carry you to the new level. Man's first enemy is himself, that is why he fights with other men. When he stops fighting himself the world will be at peace.'

'What a peace that would be,' I said.

'Indeed,' replied Sabazius. 'It would be peace beyond "understanding", for it would be founded on man's comprehension of himself as man. Such a peace has no formula. It cannot be built or constructed out of "desire for peace", for desire will use any old brick lying about. Desire is filled up with determination, but it has little discretion; it is surrounded on every side with good intentions, but it does not know how to love. Love cancels out war because it is empty of conflict, it "allows", because it does not have to make allowances.'

I sat on the edge of the little table and looked at him. He

207

looked back at me fearlessly. After almost a minute of this looking I dropped my eyes and sipped at my coffee. It was not easy to look into the face of love. 'I've stopped trembling,' I said.

Sabazius did not reply.

Cat dropped into the room, stood looking at us both stiffly, started to clean herself. I watched her moisten a paw, clean her face with it, set up a rhythm. She looked so self-contained. Putting my coffee down, I shuffled towards her on hands and knees. She watched me with great interest. When I was little more than two feet away I stopped, and remembering what Sabazius had taught me, offered her the side of my face. She moved in, curved, brushed my cheek with the length of her body, took a few steps and turned clockwise to face me. Stretching our heads forward on our necks, we allowed the tips of our noses to touch. A fleeting exploration. She again turned clockwise, walked away. At a distance of five feet she swung suddenly and flattened herself to the floor, her hind quarters trembling. The look in her eye said she was going to charge. Placing my chin on the floor I kept my eyes on her eyes. Her back end came up slowly, her tail stiffened, the trembling containing itself in rapidity. And then she threw herself at me. Knowing instinctively that there was no seriousness in her attack, I remained still. Her body flew by with the silence of an owl, the precision of a hawk. Lifting my belly from the floor I waited. Cat crawled all the way up under me until her head was just below my chin. I nuzzled the top of her head with my nose.

'Marvellous!' exclaimed Sabazius. 'I did not know which was cat and which was man.'

Raising myself further from the floor, I stretched my fingers, allowed my spine to curve down naturally and pushed my head up and back as far as it would go. When I reached the apex of this movement, I closed my eyes slowly and let my breath escape in a hissing stream.

'Bravo!' he shouted.

The next set of movements happened of their own accord. My body gathered itself up and became balanced on my forearms. My feet left the floor as my legs curved up behind me, arched themselves over my head.

'A scorpion,' said Sabazius with delight.

I remained in this strange position for some minutes without strain, then my body slowly unwound itself. Cat had not moved a muscle during all of this. When complete recognition of what I had done came to the surface of my mind, and I realized that my movements defied what I thought my body capable of, the spell broke. Getting up, I moved back to the fire and sat down.

'You're full of surprises,' he chuckled.

'I'm not really sure what happened,' I said hesitantly.

'You hit the perfect rhythm of your body,' he replied, 'triggered it off through playing with the cat. All the tension fell out of you, and your body danced.'

'I feel very light.'

Sabazius laughed. 'Tension and gravity are in partnership,' he said, winking at me. 'When tension evaporates, the organs of the body float, and when the inside floats, so does the outside.'

I looked at the fire. 'It's getting hotter,' I said.

'Is it?'

'Don't you feel it?'

'My feeling of the fire is different from yours,' he replied, 'because unlike you I am already in the fire. You have yet to enter.'

'I haven't noticed any kind of signal.'

'If you are waiting for something unusual to happen, you may very well miss the signal.'

Leaning against the bedrail, I said, 'How many people live in this house?'

'Up until yesterday there were five of us,' said Sabazius; 'but today there is just myself. The others decided to move out.'

'Why?'

'They each said they couldn't stand the silence, that it got on their nerves.'

'I could feel it the moment I entered the building.'

'Yes, it is getting strong,' he said, smiling at me; 'and it will be even stronger after tonight.'

I did not ask him what he meant by that; it seemed self-evident. I sat down again on my little upturned wastebin and stared at the fire. What would happen? How would the fire signal its readiness? How *could* a fire signal anything? As a statement, it did not make sense. I smiled to myself, acknowledged once again that my view of the universe had changed somewhat, that I now accepted universe as being somehow conscious in its own right. Conscious? No, not conscious. Not conscious in our terms; more in the sense of being aware, but not in any personal sense. That had always been my problem with Christianity – Christians worshipped a personal God, a divine personality full of gigantic human flaws. Their God was capable of anger, jealousy, hatred and even murder, yet they spoke of this God as the God of love. Through his followers this God had persecuted the innocent and sown deep and lasting conflict throughout the world. In fact there was hardly a minute in the whole of human history when this God had not vengefully demanded unthinking obedience, and the myth of human creation revealed this state of affairs to have been generic. Treated unfairly from the very moment of their creation, our supposed first parents had been denied proper consciousness of self and world. And so now with the whole human race, the Dark God of the Christian imagination continued to block the possibility of our waking up out of awake-dream. Condemned to remain asleep on the face of reality by way of divine fiat, we were discouraged from pursuing the facts of existence to their natural conclusion.

The fire changed colour suddenly, flared and fell back into itself. I needed no prompting. Squatting down before it, my Will Stone held in my right hand, I waited, knowing intuitively that the moment had not yet arrived. Then I saw it – a tiny black hole at the fire's heart. As I watched, it expanded slowly. When it reached the size of a man's fist, I bent forward and dropped my Will Stone into it. It remained visible for some seconds, then vanished without trace. As the hole contracted, the fire's energy withdrew into the stones, and when it dissolved, the fire was no more. I sat looking at the stones for some time. They looked so ordinary, so grey, so incapable of the beauty and intensity they had just generated.

Sabazius produced a canvas bag and handed it to me. 'What you have to do now is remove the stones one by one. Focus your attention on each stone, enter the stone and let it speak to you. When the stone has said all it has to say, when you have its secret, place it carefully in the bag. Do not drop them.'

He indicated that I should start.

Choosing a stone at random, I lifted it from the pile and held it tightly, entered its coolness, listened for its voice, but heard nothing. Convinced that this particular stone had no message for me, I reached out to put it in the bag. As I pulled the canvas carrier open the stone's message came through loud and clear. I withdrew my hand and took a deep breath. The stone had not actually spoken, I had just been overcome by the deep significance of my own action – *impatience*. Not quite knowing why, I held the next stone to my forehead, closed my eyes and was rewarded with the meaning of that word in my own life. Picture after picture came up, frozen frames of impatient reference, the uncensored truth relayed visually, unmistakenly. When the circle completed itself and the last picture had became the first, I put the stone into the carrier and reached for another.

The second stone's secret came through right away, its path smoothed by the first. When I passed it to my brow, I witnessed my own arrogance stretching ahead like cats eyes on the centre of a dark road. I began to cry softly as the images piled up, not the whimpering tears of hopelessness, but of acceptance. To have cried for myself would have been to supply yet another frame. And so the story unfolded itself. Each stone ground me like a mill wheel, opened me up like a surgeon's knife. I had entered the fire which consumed fire. Like the room, I was burning up. As the last stone came to rest among its neighbours, I flared internally into a composite picture of what had been revealed. What I had thought myself to be curled up at the edges like a burning photograph, blackened, crumpled and disintegrated. From ashes to ashes. Ordinariness was exquisite when seen through a 'cleared eye'. What man saw as ordinary, unworthy of his attention, was by its very nature extraordinary. This was where the nectar of life lay, where the secret energy of existence was embedded.

Our familiar world was what we knew least well, what we rejected with unseeing eyes. As we censored it second by second, we censored our own natures, amputated ourselves from life, and withered towards death. We were judge, victim and penalty combined. We died ignominiously by our own hands. Caught up in self-pity we sought forgiveness, and in our very next breath could not *give for* lack of love. How petty we were, how intolerably intolerable. But if we gave up trying to escape our natures, responded to ourselves as adults capable of response, looked fearlessly at what we were and what we did, then the emptying would start, and the first flicker of life would erupt. How astonished the world would be when the fire which consumed fire spread throughout its cities, licked at the feet of its believing and unbelieving hordes, gobbled up its very idea of truth. What a battle that would be, how strange that its weapons should be shaped like tears, its armour openness! Was there enough courage in the world to ignite such a vision, to accept it? I knew there was, because I had.

'Now you have to bury them in the garden,' said Sabazius.

Unable to speak, I followed him to the back door. As we rounded the corner of the house, Cat leapt from the window and darted into the darkness before us. When we reached the centre of the lawn, she was standing stiffly, her tail straight up. After only a few seconds of deliberation, she trotted to the far south corner of the garden and started to dig. She removed some soil, looked back at me as if to say 'Will that do?', and wandered off. Sabazius sat down on the lawn and sank into himself without trace. How quickly it had all happened. Going over to the little hole Cat had dug, I put the carrier bag to one side and applied my fingers to the soil. It was soft and rich. As I enlarged the hole, the thick darkness began to lift. I looked up and around. I could see the rest of the garden quite clearly, make out the topmost part of the wall, the lower windows of the building. But it was not because of light, it was because the darkness had thinned into itself, become transparent. I looked at Sabazius. There was not a flicker of physical movement in him. I could see his shape, his shape was the shape of a man, but there was no man present. I turned back to my digging. When the hole was deep enough, I took the stones out of the bag and placed them in the hole one by one, then, pushing the soil back in, I packed it tight by treading it in with my feet. The little stone gifted to me by the earth had been returned, the circle was complete. Lifting the carrier I walked over to where Sabazius sat. When I touched him he got to his feet.

'It's almost dawn,' I said. 'If we wait awhile we'll hear the birds singing.'

23 ✳ *The courage to find courage*

Although we had been up all night, the idea of sleep did not
occur to us. My burying of the stones seemed to supply us with
mutual energy, so we sat talking until nine o'clock. Sabazius
then suggested that we have breakfast out as he had nothing in
the house. As we left the building, I had the feeling that an
important milestone had been passed. I felt lighthearted.
Sabazius, too, was in a cheerful mood, and this lifted my
spirits higher, for it signified that the work we had been
engaged in had been satisfactory. After breakfast we took a
taxi back to the centre of London. But as from that moment
Sabazius ceased to speak. When I spoke to him, he simply
grunted yes or no, and as we left the taxi and headed slowly
towards Oxford Circus, his unease registered on me forcefully.

'What's the matter?' I asked.

Giving me a strange look, he said: 'Can't you feel it?'

'All I feel is your unease.'

'You're so perceptive on some levels,' he replied, continuing
to look at me, 'but on others you're as dead as driftwood.'

I took a deep breath.

'A Man of Feeling has to be on guard at all times,' he said in
a flat, disinterested voice. 'He has to live continually on the
edge of himself, be awake to every subtle change internally and
externally.'

In spite of myself, I could not hide the anger I felt. And yet
behind my anger lay a profound respect for what this man said
and did. If he posed a question, then the question was real, and
if he made a statement, then his statement was grounded on
accurate observation. Yet I was still angry. Something within
me was still capable of jumping out of focus, of carrying me
along with it into anger, fear or hopelessness. Concerned by
what I could detect in myself, I watched my anger grow and
incorporate into itself the trust and respect I had for Sabazius.

And then suddenly the focus of my emotions shifted; but not enough to remove my anger. Was it possible to be angry, yet not angry simultaneously? To be involved in an emotion, yet capable of standing alongside it critically? It was. I was doing just that.

'Do you know what I'm talking about?' asked Sabazius.

'I think so.'

'I thought you would say that,' he retorted.

'You're making me very angry,' I said.

'I'm doing no such thing.'

'You damn well are!'

Sabazius gave a little laugh. 'I'm not concerned about your anger,' he said. 'I'm concerned with what was going on before you got angry.'

'I'm afraid I missed that,' I said sharply.

'That's exactly it. You are still afraid. You have not yet got courage.'

We walked on in silence for some minutes before I replied. 'Everything seemed fine until we got into that taxi. I was in a good mood, you were in a good mood, we were chatting and laughing ...'

'Then I spoiled it for you, I suppose.'

I wanted to shout 'Yes', but the word stuck in my throat. 'I don't know what you're getting at.'

'Of course you know.'

'I haven't the faintest notion.'

'Nonsense.'

A niggling sensation in my mind, a verbal blankness nudging me, accusing me.

'What did you mean when you said that I did not have any courage?'

Glancing at me with exaggerated astonishment, Sabazius said: 'Do you no longer understand the English language?'

Sighing, I remained silent.

We continued up Oxford Street at a smart pace. And then suddenly he linked his arm through mine and held onto it. Within seconds we were getting odd glances. When my discomfort was noticeable, he stopped before a display of evening gowns and pointed at them enthusiastically. The expression on his face was one of awe. A couple of young girls giggled as they passed. When I tried to remove my arm from his he applied pressure.

'What's the matter?' he asked.

'You know damned fine what's the matter.'

'Why are you whispering?'

'Because I feel very uncomfortable.'

'Why?'

I stood very straight and stared into the window, but all I could see was our reflection. It was not enough to know that what Sabazius was doing was intentional, that it had some kind of purpose, for no one else knew.

'Why are you doing this?' I asked.

'Why does a man do anything?' he replied casually. 'If we were not doing this we would be doing something else.'

'Then let's try something else.'

'I prefer this.'

'I don't.'

'Then change it. Do something else.'

I again tried to remove my arm, but the pressure he applied made me give up instantly. 'I can't do something else with you hanging onto me like this!'

He smiled at me as if I had said something funny. 'Then why don't you strike me? If you strike me hard enough I'll have to let you go.'

'I don't want to strike you.'

'Then you will have to put up with what I want.'

With a gentle push from his hip he started us walking again. As we moved slowly along the pavement I tried desperately to rationalize the situation. What did it matter what people thought. It should not matter. But for some deep reason it did matter. My body was trembling involuntarily. My throat was tight. I knew there was a little gap in my being where such things were of no consequence, but I could not find it. When we turned off Oxford Street and reached the entrance to my flat I heaved a sigh of relief. It was short-lived. Sabazius dragged me on towards the corner of the next street. And then he stopped and said:

'How do you feel?'

'Dreadful.'

'Why?'

'I've almost lost control of my body.'

'What is it doing?'

'It's shaking.'

'Can't you stop it?'

'No,' I said crisply.

'Why is your body shaking?' asked Sabazius.

I blurted out that I was afraid of what other people thought. That I did not have the courage to let them think whatever they wanted to think. And then I asked him again what had gone wrong earlier.

'That's for you to find out,' he replied.

'But everything seemed to be going so well.'

'Everything did go well.'

'Then why do I feel like this now?'

'Because you're an idiot.' Letting go of my arm he pushed his hands into the pockets of his coat. 'You still believe in going up and down emotionally, of going forwards and backwards, of going in and out. When you stop believing in your belief concerning these things, you'll be okay.'

'Easier said than done.'

'Nothing of the sort,' he replied emphatically. 'It is because we prefer acts backed by thought that we hardly ever act. Man is impotent to act without thought. All of his acts are physical thoughts thrown out into the world. He does not act, he reacts. He always does something *because* of something else. He is continually being led by the nose, for his Being has come to think that thought must govern action. Men think that they move about in the world, but they are mistaken. The difference between a man and his world is that the world moves, whereas man *makes moves*. The movements of man have nothing to do with movement, they only have to do with fear. It is fear that makes man move. Fear drives him, feeds him, clothes him, and eventually destroys him.' He paused and looked at me sadly. 'There is an age coming, Peter, in which men will appear to do the right thing, but he will do even the right thing because of fear, and his fear will sterilize the good he does. Doing the right thing is not enough. One must learn to do it without fear. It was fear that made your body shake, and your body will shake for eternity unless you lose your fear.'

'But ... '

'Let's have a beer.'

In all the time I had known him he had never once suggested going into a pub. But that's where we landed, in an empty bar still sweet from the freshener sprayed into the stale air. Sabazius ordered two pints of beer and carried them to a nearby table. When we were seated, he wished me good health and downed half of his beer like a professional. I took a couple of mouthfuls and placed my mug on the table. I was just about to say something when he again lifted his pint glass and put it to his lips. When he put it down it was empty. I smiled and took another sip. He got up immediately and came back with two more pints. His second pint disappeared in three short bursts. I finished my first and started on my second.

It was like drinking with a marine. As fast as I drank my pints he replaced them. And never a word passed between us. As our alcoholic competition progressed the bar slowly filled up. There was the usual bunch of business people, a few lone drinkers staring into newspapers, a sprinkling of tradesmen. And still the beers kept coming. I now had three untouched pints lying before me. Within an hour the pub was jammed tight with people. The hum of their voices sounded distant and muffled. As he downed each pint of beer, Sabazius looked at me and smiled. My breathing steadily became deeper and rougher. And yet in a curious way I was enjoying myself. There was a sense of release, a sense of being allowed to indulge myself. I would never have attempted such a thing on my own.

And then suddenly Sabazius appeared to get drunk. He began to smile a lot and talk to those standing around our table. I watched him in amazement. His almost perfect English began to break down slightly, and every so often he would substitute a Greek word for the word he had apparently forgotten. In spite of not believing that he was really drunk, I found myself suggesting appropriate words and phrases as he struggled to express himself. As his inability to communicate developed, others began to assist him in a similar fashion. He was fast becoming an endearing foreigner, an endearing drunk foreigner. But what astonished me the most was his ability to mouth meaningless sentences as if they really mattered. He got involved in a conversation about race-horses that went on and on, and then incomprehensibly it was politics and the cost of living. Everyone seemed fascinated. They nodded and smiled at him whether they understood or not.

But the big moment was when he got to his feet and proposed a toast in Greek. He stood uncertainly, pint glass in hand, and let out a torrent of his native language. A number of people clapped. Maybe it was because of the strange expression on his face. But clap they did, and he bowed to them. As I looked at him standing there, a feeling of icy coldness enveloped me. I tried to fight it, but it was useless. And then everything became stationary, frozen like an unusual picture postcard. I knew it was not just the drink, for in the midst of that sea of immobile faces and bodies Sabazius turned and looked at me. His face cracked into laughter, a terrifying laugh which rippled visibly through the air as a pink substance, the substance of derision itself.

I awoke four hours later feeling like a dried-up prune. I was in my own lounge, on the sofa, with a blanket over me – I stank of vomit.

I thought of calling out for Sabazius, but knew instinctively that he had dumped me and gone off. Probably in disgust, I thought. A strong feeling of despair drove me back into sleep. When I next came to it was seven o'clock in the evening. I lay looking at the ceiling in a state of numbed exhaustion.

When my body began to respond a little, I got up, made myself a strong coffee and ran a bath. I took the coffee and some dry bread into the bathroom with me. What bliss it would be to let the soreness of my head out through my pores. As I lay soaking in about a foot of steaming water, what Sabazius had said about my not having courage came home to roost. Was it really true? Did I not have any courage at all? I comforted myself with the thought that I must have had something like courage to have come this far. Surely it was not possible to take on such a task without guts. But what were guts? When it was obvious that I could not answer that question, I drank some coffee and chewed at the bread. I felt empty of emotion, drained of sensibility. The only thing I was sure of was that I was a fool. With that kindly thought uppermost in my mind, I lay back until my face was just above water level.

Sabazius had said that it was not my anger he had been pointing at, but something I had not noticed before my anger appeared. I tried to determine what that could have been by going over everything from the moment we finished breakfast. Something had happened when we left that cafe. But what? All we had done was walk along the street and hail a taxi. I had not even said anything. But as from the moment we got into the taxi, Sabazius had switched off. Something must have happened. A word, a gesture, an expression could have intimated that I had fallen into some trap or other. I sighed and allowed my attention to fasten on the water's warmth. What was the use of beating my brains out when I could not think of anything to think about? Within a few seconds, however, I was again circling around the problem, trying to identify the moment in which that invisible something had happened. Before I could stop myself, self-pity welled up and changed into anger. I had come full circle.

It was there, yet it was not there. It was a mirror in which a face could be seen, but in which no face was being seen. I knew suddenly that I was approaching what Sabazius had been getting at, for the emotion in my system was the same emotion I had felt when he reproached me. 'Can't you feel it?' he had said, and in that same moment I had felt it. I lay very still until the realization, the full meaning and implication of his statement and my reaction came together. When I saw clearly what had happened my anger evaporated and turned into shame. There had not been anything to feel until I reacted with the feeling that there was something to feel. Yes, I had fallen into a trap, and the trap had been my own fear of falling into traps. All he had had to do was suggest that something was wrong, and in that same second I had manufactured guilt around the illusion. You're an idiot. You're an idiot. You're an idiot.

Courage. I did not have courage because I was full of fear. Fear and self-pity stalked my systems like wild animals. I could not stand still, I could only *make* moves. My burying of the stones had been a farce, for I had not possessed the will to overcome my fear in the first place. As these thoughts etched themselves into my mind, I experienced an inversion of the very thing I had discovered. The self-pity which lay in my systems of functioning actualized into real self-pity, and I fell to pitying myself for being self-pitying. There was no way out of it. It did not matter which way I turned, there was only guilt, and then more guilt. The guilt for being afraid. The guilt for having no courage. The guilt for being Peter Derwent. As I faced this guilt, the muscular structure of my body collapsed. There would be no triumphant roar as I passed through death, – just fear.

In a state of deep inertia I allowed the water to close around my face. I had reached the end of my journey. It was all over. When I next saw Sabazius I would tell him that I had discovered my true nature. I was a coward, a person not warranting his time, effort and love. How strange it was that he had chosen the wrong man on which to lavish such care and attention. All these months of work, and all for nothing. With my mind firmly made up I tried to move, tried to bring myself up out of the water; but my body would not move. Something was holding me under the water with a strength I could not break. Panic. I was not going to die in some distant future, I was already dying, silently, there and then, murdering myself without as much as a twitch. Only one thought appeared in my mind, a very curious thought: *Tears are meaningless to a drowning man.* Paralysed by the compulsion towards paralysis, I waited. There was nothing I could do but die, die dumbfounded at my own stupidity.

But I did not die. When I came to I was lying on the floor beside the bath. There was no memory in me of how I had escaped. Shivering uncontrollably I stumbled through to the bedroom, pulled off the top cover and wrapped it around my body. With every step I remembered the numb terror I had experienced. My shivering intensified. Pushing a wad of blanket into my mouth I got myself into the lounge and switched on the electric fire. There was nothing to do but sit and wait for the shivering to stop. As I sat there, my arms folded in tight against my body, I tried to face the fact that I had almost died. I found it an incredible thought. It was one thing to get depressed, it was quite another to involuntarily attempt suicide. For almost twenty minutes I stared into the fire's reflector, felt rather than thought, allowed what had happened to present itself without words. Stillness. The sound of electricity expanding rolled wire. The tiny dump-dump of glass bending before the wind. And then the sudden revelation that I had not killed myself burst upon me and brought me back to my senses. Just as something had held me under the water, so also had something plucked me out of it, something stronger than my despair, bigger than my fear.

When the heat of the fire got through and I stopped shivering, I went back to the bathroom and stood on the spot where I had awakened. In an attempt to break open the puzzle, I imagined myself back in the bath and unable to move. As a result of this, I remembered my odd thought about tears being meaningless to a drowning man, and also that I had made the decision to break with Sabazius. But I drew a complete blank on what had physically lifted me out of the bath. Shaking my head I returned to the lounge and dressed. With clothes on I felt much better. I sat down on the sofa. What a funny world it was. Ever since I met Sabazius that world had been whirling in the opposite direction. My whole life had become an oddity since I met him. I smiled. My smile melted away as the enormity of what I had experienced hit home. I was taken aback by how blasé I had been. For the first time I faced the fact that I had not really come to grips with anything, that I had sailed through the most extraordinary experiences with only a flutter of realization. I had accepted everything on some basic level, a level totally inadequate to deal with such phenomena. According to everything sensible they ought not to have taken place; but they had taken place, and I knew they were going to continue until the day I really did die.

Then there was the question of 'warmth'. In the early days my work with Sabazius had been canopied by a sense of *loving warmth*, an appreciation of the presence of things. My attempts to *see* had revealed an essential quality in things which far outstripped any imaginative idea concerning unity. But through some trick of the ego I had lost contact with that essential quality, managed somehow to sweep it out of sight even in the midst of seeing itself. There was now an emptiness in me, a longing to be filled up with that quiddity of vision which transformed the psyche and allowed it to lean in the direction of universal harmony. Maybe this was what Sabazius had been getting at when he accused me of not having courage. He had probably detected this emptiness in me, watched me wander about alone and blind inside a multi-coloured landscape of meaning and revelation. I could *see*, but I did not want to accept the nature of what I could see. So instead I ran away into anger and self-pity, buried myself inside the empty bag of my ego and peered out hoping that the whole damned thing would vanish and not return. Yet in spite of this I had not died. Something had lifted me out of that bath. Even when unconscious something had been looking after my interests.

That's when I decided to pray. It was a strange thing for me to consider doing, but as Sabazius had said, prayer was not to paint oneself with treacle, it was to open oneself up *wordlessly*. Sitting very still, I closed my eyes and focused my attention, not on my mental horizon, but on my feelings. What did it matter what appeared on the mind's horizon. Mental pictures were very interesting, but at the end of the day what one was left with was a sense of self, a sense of one's history which made one either happy or sad. If there was no human warmth in there, in your heart, then in spite of everything experienced you weren't worth a toss. That's when I acknowledged that the heat in me was mostly emotional heat, the heat of self-satisfaction, arrogance and anger. I was all puffed up inside because of what I believed myself to have accomplished, yet could be brought low through the merest suggestion of failure. Which rather suggested that part of me was still infantile, still undeveloped, and that I had better be careful or the whole house of cards might come crashing down about my head. With that realization I opened myself up, emptied myself of words and began to surrender my heart, not just my head, to that which ever comprehends and responds.

24 ✻ *Fantasy of the superman*

Sabazius held his coffee cup in both hands and sipped at it. Every so often he would nod his head and smile vaguely to himself as some part of my narrative confirmed his suspicion of where I had been. When the description of my night's work was complete, he replaced his cup on the saucer and asked me what I made of it all.

'I feel as if I'm part of a force which is working on itself,' I said, not fully understanding my own statement. 'It's almost as if I'm tailoring myself for a new suit.'

'That's a good description,' he replied. And then he said: 'But you're puzzled about something.'

'The puzzle is that I don't understand what I've just said. I can sense its meaning, but it won't open up.'

'That's only because you've personalized the puzzle. If you can depersonalize it, not own it as yours in particular, but as a something which belongs to human beings, then it will soon come into focus.'

When I tried to do this I hit a blank wall. There was something intrinsically wrong with the manner in which I was trying to depersonalize my experience. And then suddenly I noticed, almost out of the corner of my intellectual eye, the kind of mistake I was making. When I attempted to depersonalize my experience, making it belong to all men and not myself in particular, I kept falling into the trap of sensing humanity as an incomprehensibly large group of beings *individually* united. So in actual fact my supposed depersonalization was actually a supra-personalization, a kind of gigantic individual outside of myself. I described my problem to Sabazius immediately.

'Follow that through,' he said.

'The supra-personalization bit?'

'Yes.'

He was now staring at me hard as if to drill what he could see into my head. 'I suppose I end up with a kind of supra-image of man as a collective individual,' I said, virtually repeating myself.

'A supra what?' asked Sabazius.

'A supra-image.'

'Of what?'

'Man.'

'So what do you end up with?'

I laughed nervously. 'A supra-man I suppose.'

'A what?'

That was when I saw what he was getting at. 'A superman,' I said in astonishment.

'And that is why man as he is will never understand the force which is trying to refine him,' replied Sabazius with glee. 'He keeps getting side-tracked into the "idea of a superman", a single entity in which all power and knowledge resides. This is the flaw which turns him towards power. It's also the flaw which turns him into a Man of Power when he gains knowledge about himself but falls back upon his intellect for support. But whether he has knowledge of himself or not hardly matters here, for all men inadvertently seek *knowledge as power*, whereas Men and Women of Feeling seek knowledge as *freedom*. This is why the world is in such a mess, the nature of power is bondage. Human beings who seek power seek it for only one reason, to exercise it, to make their whims concrete. Knowledge as freedom, on the other hand, leads to love in action, to an insightful penetration of the nature of power. Few people realize that love is perfect power, that it constitutes the freedom to *move* without first making moves. It isn't concerned with the "location" of power as an individual, or a projected God as superman, it is only concerned with the breaking down of barriers through intelligible communication. Intelligibility is the corner-stone of real knowledge, real love, real freedom and real power. Supermen, whether phantoms of the mind or phantoms of the flesh, are never intelligible. What they demand of others is always shrouded in dark and mysterious words, in incomprehensible logics which lead into labyrinths of subtle confusion and conflict. Knowledge as power, whatever its intention, always heads toward a "superman conception". It can't really do anything else, for its conceptions are governed by an *Identity*-complex which cannot conceive of itself as anything other than singular. Even the projected super-God of man is held in this trap. He is the *one* true God, and there is none other like Him. Knowledge as freedom, however, has no truck with this conception, for the *Identity*-complex no longer rules. There is therefore no singularity of intention, no axe to grind, no personal conception of things containing the superman seed.

'To really understand this, a man must eventually wake up to the fact that the huge, interdimensional territory of consciousness is not personal, that is, that it does not belong to any one individual. Consciousness is not contained in man, man is contained within consciousness as Form. Consciousness is the matrix of Being, Being is the matrix of Form, Form is the matrix of Perception, and Perception is the matrix of *Identity*. To deal effectively with *Identity* and its dream of supra-individuality, a man must deal effectively with his Perceptions, and to deal effectively with his Perceptions, he must cognize the "emptiness of Form" meaningfully through an *act of seeing* in the moment. When this has been done he can experience his Being as the last boundary of Form, and from there be drawn into the fullness of consciousness as a whole. Such a man no longer thinks of himself as a self, therefore he is not influenced by gain or loss. As you very well know, the substance of the panic you felt when being pulled out into the fullness of consciousness, was your *Identity*, what's left of it, fragmenting into its unrecognized subsections. As full consciousness approached, it flew in all directions to escape fragmentation, and in doing just that fragmented itself to a new point of intensity. This is where the Central Station of Command comes in. The Central Station of Command in a developing human being is their ability to perceive consciousness and its Being content without interference from the ego. The term for this is "cohesive" perception. People totally unaware of the nature of consciousness are said to be governed by "adhesive" perception. Cohesive perception is "cognition without intent"; adhesive perception is "recognition with intent". An *act of seeing* is cohesive perception, an act of *interpreting what one sees* is adhesive perception. When a man learns to allow what he is to surface through feeling, the battle of adhesive perception grows less and less until, finally, he becomes properly conscious. This is the self which the conscious mind can neither understand nor approach, for by its very nature it must personalize the self at every step so that its dream of the superman can remain intact.'

'Then consciousness and the moment are one and the same thing.'

'Now you have it,' replied Sabazius. 'The moment is experienced as being full of meaning, for it is the meaning of Being breaking through the self-constructed conscious barrier. To be merely aware *of the moment* is to be unconscious, which is awake-dream, whereas to be aware *in the moment* is to be fully conscious. What a man terms his conscious mind is actually unconscious, for it is a self-created objective dream, and what he terms the unconscious mind is actually fully conscious, for it is the self observing the true nature of Form without comment. The conscious mind is composed of levels, or layers of thought kept active through constant memory-recognition, whereas the unconscious is composed of knowledge, the knowledge out of which thoughts *in accordance with reality* can appear. So when a man learns to allow what he is to erupt, knowledge of a direct nature replaces thought. A "cognitional act" takes place – an Act of Will – and the man begins to feelingly-know the nature of his own nature. It is at this point that the man's dream-image of himself begins to break up, and as the central core of this dream-image is his idea of himself as a "self" an *Identity*, he spends much of his time shuffling between panic and stillness, between the fear of *Identity* loss and the cognition of consciousness. As he gains true freedom through his cognitional knowledge of the self, his panic decreases, and when there is no more panic left in him, he fully cognizes his nature *as* consciousness and steps out of awake-dream.

'But what we have to double back to now is the fact that all men are capable of experiencing moments of true conscious-ness. And of course such moments complicate the game even further. What happens is this. Someone remembers a moment of true consciousness during an interesting conversation, and immediately falls into the trap of regurgitating that moment as a description. This regurgitation almost always takes place out of context, that is, it is unwittingly used to support some spurious theory or pet idea of the mind. Religious discussions in particular are full of such supports. What has to be seen, and seen clearly here, is that the person who remembers such a moment is at that very moment in a state of awake-dream. The result of such a state, no matter how hard the participants try, is always a dim and second-hand seeing which adds confusion to confusion. The faculties of such people get all mixed up. As the purpose of all interesting conversation is to be interesting, or appear interested, the energy of the game obscures the energy of the moment, and even the raising of this issue itself would change nothing. It would only make the conversation more interesting. Conversations in which the energy of the moment does erupt, however, clears the debris of interesting characteristics aside, and allows *penetration* to take place. In other words, an "act of communication" as opposed to mere conversation is established. Such moments are always initiated by people who are aware of the nature of their natures to one degree or another. This is the intrinsic difference between what can be termed "ordinary man" and "natural man". Natural men Listen and Speak, ordinary men Hear and Talk. Natural men, because they are vulnerable to what *is*, are at all times willing to risk revealing their true natures; ordinary men are caught up in the business of continually defending their manufactured natures. The life of an ordinary man has generally to fall about his *ears* before he can *see* this, and even then it is not certain that he will. And at the foundation of all of this lies conformation and confirmation.'

I sat looking into the bottom of my empty cup. How curious it was that we could not recognize the coded messages we kept on sending ourselves. We talked of cold-blooded-murderers, but seemed unable to make the connection with cold-blooded-talkers and cold-blooded-thinkers. In the name of objectivity we continually robbed ourselves of the capacity to 'listen', to feelingly enter the subtle interconnecting streams of language as a living force. Everything had to fit together, or be made to fit before it became acceptable. The pieces of the jig-saw were becoming smaller and smaller, more difficult to handle, more difficult to see, more difficult to touch. We had almost reached the point where we could no longer touch language, and because of this we were getting more and more *out of touch* with ourselves and others. Words were no longer seen to only 'contain meaning', they were believed to 'be meaningful.' The interdimensional quality of words was slowly burning up on the altar of facts. Language as a living force has been turned into a mere grocery-list with attendant values. The natural, lubricating energy of 'being human' was continually draining away into the icy pool of objective language. Most of us were walking refrigerators; some of us were deep-freezers. Our natures looked fresh and palatable, but the cellular structure of our inner being was deteriorating fast. Maybe this was why we were so interested in procreation, or at least in the act itself. It was the only avenue left to us through which we could *communicate* our essential natures. The hope we had in our children was therefore not one of physical immortality – the idea of merely living on for ever and ever – but one of entering into full conscious awareness by proxy. The immortality we thought ourselves to seek was really the immortality of the monent, the timeless experience of waking up out of awake-dream. And yet deep down we knew this, for every so often our frosted language thawed out sufficiently for it to become self-evident. Yet within seconds our realizations were parcelled up in neat time-language-sequences, translated into objective scannings and frozen into memory. And as there was no warmth in us, nothing which could melt these memories back into actual experience, these moments became more and more rare, and were finally extinguished altogether. It was then no longer a matter of the blind leading the blind, but of the dead leading the living towards death. In the hard light of objective day, the world, both alive and dead, saw such thinking as 'sheer dramatics', but in moments of stillness when the game gave out, when the computer of the conscious mind was alone, it thought otherwise.

Sabazius waited until my thoughts had completed themselves before adding the final touch to his argument. 'It is thought which separates man from man,' he said suddenly. 'He is so busy thinking about his thoughts, so busy *Identifying* with them, that he cannot penetrate the nature of consciousness. All he can do is *understand* his own thoughts and the

228

thoughts of others. The dimension of comprehension is missing. However, if for a split second he manages to penetrate consciousness itself, and continues to do so, then he slowly discovers that he has access to his own thoughts and the thoughts of others in a new way. Such thoughts then become available to him as images within himself. At first, because he is still groggy from awake-dream, he doesn't realize what is happening, doesn't pay any attention to those images, but as his moments of true consciousness grow, he grows, and as he grows into himself, knowledge as an *experience* comes into proper focus. It is for this reason that he must learn to "listen", for without listening the "art of speaking" is an impossibility. This is why man must become his history, gather up everything that he is and penetrate it from end to end. He has to learn to *read his own mind*, and close the book.'

25 ❋ *The cave of blue moonlight*

The amount of work Sabazius demanded of me over the next few weeks was daunting. I hardly had a minute to myself. When I asked him the reason for this, he said that I had to bring my systems up to the pitch required so that further penetration could take place. This was the law. A man worked hard and reached a particular density of Being, then he worked harder still, and reached another. So I worked. At first, I was so caught up in what I was doing, that I paid no attention to the slight trembling in my fingers, but when this trembling communicated itself to other parts of my body, and on occasions even awakened me from sleep, I began to wonder if I was pushing myself too hard.

Doubt.

As Sabazius had again taken off on one of his trips, the responsibility of what to do, or not do, was mine alone. Should I cut my programme of activity down, modify it in some way, or stop altogether? I pondered the alternatives. At the end of those hours I was only the more uncertain. Being unable to resolve the situation, I continued to work as hard as before, and took to having long walks in the evening as a kind of therapy. It was during one of those walks that I found the question I needed, a simple question which immediately mutated into a further question, and then into an answer. Why was I so bothered about my twitching body? Did it matter if I twitched? I stopped walking and addressed those questions to myself over and over again until they struck home. And then the answer came through. No, it did not matter if I twitched. I only *thought* it did. This was why I had taken to walking in the late evening. I did not wish to be *seen* twitching. Simple as this answer was, it was enough to break my pattern of behaviour and allow me to twitch without concern. And so I walked and twitched by day, twitched happily in the evening, and even twitched myself to sleep without further worry. By the time Sabazius returned, my disability had reduced itself to a tiny spasm in the left eye.

'Has anything of interest happened?' asked Sabazius.

I told him about the twitching.

'Is that all?'

'No, there is something else. When I closed my eyes to sleep a couple of nights ago I seemed to light up inside.'

'Describe the light.'

'It's kind of silvery-white.'

'Can you describe it further?'

'I get the impression that it's alive, and that I'm sitting inside some kind of cavern. The cavern itself is composed of the light.'

'How does it feel?'

'It feels gentle and silvery simultaneously.'

'How long does the light last?'

'Just a few minutes.'

'Then what happens?'

'I don't know. The next thing I know it's morning and I'm opening my eyes again.'

I had been astounded when it first happened. The day had been as usual, that is, I had completed my pattern of activity, which was centred around a three-hour period of silence, read a little, eaten a light meal, walked perhaps a couple of miles and back, and gone to bed around ten. But when I closed my eyes everything had been different. At first, the darkness had had an almost luminous intensity, and then the luminosity of the darkness had been transformed into the cavern of light. Everywhere silvery light. Sparkling moonlight without a moon.

'How do you feel first thing in the morning?'

'Quiet.'

'How quiet?'

'As quiet as it's possible to feel.'

'Any dreams?'

'Only one; but it didn't feel like a dream.'

'What did you see?'

'I saw three people standing near to one another. The one in the middle was stripped to the waist and had his back towards me. When he turned around he had three eyes. The eye in the middle was hooded and sort of half open.'

'Did this man say anything to you?'

'No.'

'Did you say anything to him?'

I shook my head. 'There was nothing to be said. His being there seemed to say everything.'

'And what did his being there say?'

I gave a short laugh and looked toward the ceiling. 'I don't know. And yet somehow I do know.'

'What are you looking for up there?' asked Sabazius.

Hesitating, I said: 'When you asked me that question my head went back of its own volition.'

'Really,' replied Sabazius. And then he said giving me a pointed look: 'The action of your body *was* the answer to my question.'

'In what way?'

'It does not matter.'

Knowing that it was useless to pursue the matter, I suggested that we have a meal out. He seemed to like the idea. We went round to a small Indian restaurant not far from the flat. As we waited for our meal to come, Sabazius asked me to describe the cavern of light again. I did so. He listened intently, then pointed out that I had added details to the second account which had not been in the first. I explained that I could see my mental picture of the cavern much more clearly in the dull light. Closing his eyes, he sat without moving for some minutes, then, with his eyes still closed he said: 'Cool, moist light radiating down from above. Noiseless light filling up the cavity of your heart.' He opened his eyes and looked at me. 'What are you going to do now that you've found the cave?'

'Remain in it?' I said.

'That would be just like you,' he snorted. 'You spend months working to enter the cave, and when you find it, what do you do? You curl up and go to sleep.'

'What is one supposed to do?' I asked.

'Ask the three-eyed man,' replied Sabazius. 'He'll tell you.'

We ate our curry in silence.

When we left the restaurant, he said that I was to go back to the flat and do some more work. When I felt that the work was complete, I was to go to bed immediately, and if the cavern of light appeared, I was to sense what lay behind my back. Before leaving me he added: 'But whatever you do, don't attempt to turn around.' With that said he gave me a pat on the back and was off. As I turned the key in my front door, I noticed that my hands were trembling again.

Preparation.

I undressed carefully, folded my clothes and laid them in a neat pile. After a few simple exercises (mainly to stretch the body), I stood erect in the middle of the lounge floor and regulated my breathing. When I had the impression that I was breathing in and out within the chest cavity alone, I splayed my legs a little further, moved my arms a few inches out from my body, and started to consciously send my breath in a downward direction. Within three or four minutes, my breath was flowing down through my arms and legs as a detectable sensation. Then came stage two. This entailed not only breathing down into the arms and legs, but also allowing the breath (at least what appeared to be the breath) to escape from the body out through the fingers and toes. Stage two also included breathing in through the fingers and toes imaginatively. Having successfully set up this internal rhythm, I moved on to stage three. Stage three was to exhale out through the top of the head, then inhale at the same point. On the completion of this circuit, I added the extra dimension of colour. This required one to visualize the breath coming in through the top of the head as gold in colour, and the breath coming in through the toes and fingertips as violet-blue in colour. Sabazius termed this kind of breathing the 'washing breath', and when teaching it to me said that if it were successfully executed, it *burnished the heart*. When the whole process was fitted together, it resulted in a bath of violet-blue energy rising up through the body and out through the top of the head, and a bath of golden energy cascading downwards and out through the fingers and toes.

After thirty minutes of such breathing, I pulled a thick cushion off the sofa, placed it on the floor, and sat down. The next part of the work was to centre myself on an imaginary threadline. Such a thread cannot really be imagined, for it is not actually seen. It had to be sought for as a 'feeling' with the full intensity of inner vision. The thread is not actually there to be found, it is merely a reduction of conscious interference to a point where *one feels like a thread*. And so I set about finding the thread, and having found it, moved into that delicately balanced space where consciousness scrutinizes consciousness without comment. This space cannot be described in adequate verbal terms. It is enough to say that it sounds like a *crackle of lightning*. My very first experience of this space had sent me rocketing to the surface like a bubble released from the depths of a pond, but as I approached it more and more, I slowly came to know it for what it was.

Centred.

Taking six deep breaths, I placed the palms of my hands together, and with the tips of my fingers touched my forehead, my lips, and my heart. This little ritual was simply a symbol of my intent. I then got up, replaced the cushion, and went to bed. In the same instant as I switched off the light, my internal vision exploded into a pattern of brilliant colours and designs. Flowers intermingling with signs. Neon flashes of numeral-like characters bursting with the vitality of suggested meaning. A firework display which numbed the conscious mind into utter silence. And then, suddenly, the cavern of light. Moist moonlight, cool as a midnight frost.

Time does not pass in the cavern of light, and neither is there any movement. The moist moonlight of the cavern does not stream down, it is fixed-light, held beyond steadiness, moist without being wet, cool without being cold. It is light, and coolness, and silence and knowing joined without seam. It simply IS. The only description applicable is that of a gigantic hood of light in which one sits without sitting. Who can truly say what the hood is, or what the hood is not. Only one thing is certain, it is not composed of mind. No tinkering thought machine can exist in such a place. Nor can it reach it. And yet something which is not mind is aware of the space, capable of moving without moving, of thinking without thinking. As directed by Sabazius, this 'something' appreciated the *other* space available, that which in ordinary terms can be described as *lying behind*. A snaking finger of vision, an immediate and abrupt withdrawal. Fear? No, not fear – dread. A dread knowledge of that which the mind even in its finest moment cannot contemplate. My breathing changed rhythm and I slowly emerged, slowly rose up to the surface of myself and

234

opened my eyes. The ordinary darkness of the room. An awareness of warm blankets and a breath of wind from the window. The creak of matter settling upon its atoms. And then sleep.

Sabazius arrived at eight-thirty. He sat near the kitchen window and watched me eat. Without looking at him, I said: 'I did as you asked.'

'And?'

'It was almost too much.'

'You still look quite healthy to me.'

Getting up, I took my dishes over to the sink and put them in the basin. 'I've got the feeling I'm going to get stuck at this point for some time.'

'Most people do.'

We looked at each other.

'Don't worry about it,' said Sabazius. 'It'll take as long as it takes. No longer.'

By ten o'clock we were sitting in St James Park. The sky was almost unmarked by cloud. Some twenty or thirty yards away, a young mother with a shiny new pram was standing quite still looking out across the pond. She seemed entranced by it. Not far away, to her right, two fat ducks were standing side by side staring in the same direction. A light breeze moved through them and touched my cheek.

'Isn't she beautiful,' said Sabazius suddenly.

I glanced at him in astonishment. 'I didn't think you noticed such things,' I said.

'Without guile,' he continued, 'and empty of malice.'

I looked at the woman with renewed interest. She had not moved. 'How can you tell?' I asked.

'Tell what?'

'That she is without guile and malice.'

'I did not say that.'

'You said she was without guile and malice. I heard you say it. In fact I saw you say it.'

He shook his head. 'I was referring to her frame of mind. If human beings could learn to talk to one another as if they were looking out across a beautiful pond with blue sky overhead, then their talking would be meaningful. But mostly they prefer the storm clouds and the roaring winds of the mind.'

The woman turned and pushed her pram towards us. As she passed, I noticed that a deep frown had replaced the previous smoothness of her face. She did not look at us, but I knew she was watching us out of the corner of her eye. Distrust. Wary calculation. I watched her every movement until she vanished from sight.

We sat absolutely still for almost two hours. During this period I totally forgot that Sabazius was with me. All I could see was the world and its beauty. The beauty of the trees. The beauty of the grass and the water and the sky and the light breeze stroking my skin. What was this beauty? It could arrest a man's attention, stop him in his tracks, make him stand absolutely still. When he caught sight of this beauty, was enveloped by it, all his conflicts ceased. For but a second or two he entered a new space, a space empty of ambition and intrigue. It was in such moments one saw the wistfulness, the longing for knowledge. How often I had noted human beings shake their heads at the end of such moments, turn back to their stark inner worlds with a shrug. They knew they did not know, but could not find the energy to pursue their not-knowing until they did. And that, really, was the crux of it all. To continually run after what one did know only heaped coals on existing fires, whereas to pursue what one did not know resulted in entirely new fires, new networks of sensibility. Men talked of their thirst for knowledge, but they talked through parched lips because they would not quench their true thirst. Man's true thirst was for true knowledge, not just new knowledge. And as true knowledge contained the essence of beauty, and he continually turned his back on such beauty with a shrug, he was for ever missing the point of the whole exercise – to become beautiful. True knowledge made human beings beautiful, new knowledge by itself dried them up until they were unrecognizable. Sabazius had been correct when he said that everything was composed of three principles. As I looked out across the pond I could see the three principles of knowledge quite clearly, or rather the three principles of knowledge that were available to man: New Knowledge, True Knowledge, and Dread Knowledge. New Knowledge pertained to how the world worked, True Knowledge pertained to what man was in his essential nature, and Dread Knowledge

236

pertained to the unimaginable darkness out of which light sprang. On the horizon of light itself hung a black sun, and out of this black sun emanated all things.

'Are you okay?' asked Sabazius.

When I looked at him he seemed to be far away at the end of a tunnel.

'You look strange,' I said.

'Not half as strange as you look,' he replied. 'I think I'd better get you home.'

'I saw ... '

He touched my lips with a finger. 'Leave it alone.'

When we reached Piccadilly he hailed a taxi and bundled me into it. Each time I tried to speak he stopped me with a look. And all the while that feeling grew, that feeling that I was not so much approaching a 'something', but that that 'something' was approaching me.

Part Three:
CHAOS

26 ❧ *The predator and the steps*

Suddenly and unexpectedly it was summer. A blue sky, unmarked by cloud stretched from horizon to horizon. Trees, previously shrouded by buildings, stepped out from among the shadows like brilliant green torches. I opened all the windows in the flat and allowed the warm air to circulate from room to room. Sabazius arrived just after eleven o'clock looking hot and dusty. We decided to take a couple of chairs down to the garden and spent the rest of the day there. As we trundled down the stairs with our bits and pieces, Sabazius laughed and said that I was making an old man work too hard.

What a glorious day it turned out to be. We talked and ate late into the afternoon oblivious of the honking traffic on the other side of the high, Victorian buildings. Sabazius softened visibly in the warm sunlight, and I wondered if he missed the almost tropical climate of his own country. As this thought formed in my mind, he gave me what I can only describe as an odd look, and started to talk about some work I had been engaged in. We discussed the ins and outs of the procedure, the subtle feelings which had to be translated into knowledge, and what one did with this knowledge once one had it. And then there was a lengthy silence during which we both closed our eyes.

Released from directed thinking, I observed the images and thoughts in my mind without attempting to give them order or meaning. Totally unrelated images flitting in and out of focus along with scraps of equally unrelated information. Much of this information was 'abstract' in quality, that is, it seldom clothed itself in words, or meanings, and gave me the impression of having been offered a suggestion at too low a frequency. It was almost as if one were looking into the circuit of memory, that curious hotchpotch land where one's history bubbled and heaved without rest. However, as I sank more deeply into myself, and approached sleep, this restless ocean of information gave way to a more peaceful area of consciousness. As the interference of non-verbal suggestion lessened, I switched from the sleep-track to the conscious dream-track. This allowed dream material to form freely, but with one major difference: the dreamer knew at all times that he was dreaming.

As if by magic I suddenly found myself crouching on a narrow ledge on the side of a mountain. An unimaginable drop beckoned only a few inches away. The ledge was actually a path, a twisting and turning path which ran at an angle of forty-five degrees down the side of a sun-bleached gorge. As I looked toward the mountain which formed the other side of this gorge, it blurred and danced out of focus. Turning my head, I stared hard at the path until my dizziness settled. That was when I decided that I did not much care for the dream I was experiencing and attempted to cancel it out. Closing my eyes, I visualized myself sitting in the garden at home, but when I opened them again the glittering canvas of rock and mountains was intact. Only the sky looked familiar. Realizing that the dream-form was not going to allow me to escape so easily, I took a careful look at the path both above and below, and made up my mind that a descent was more in keeping with my nerve. So I stood up, and began to inch my way downward.

To enter a dream in such a manner is not something one can play with. When teaching me the method, Sabazius had stressed two things: the first was that one should never remain static, for a dream image, if it had any validity at all, was a movement toward completion on some level of the psyche, and as such demanded that the dream-traveller take part in the dream to the best of his or her ability. It did not matter if one made mistakes – mistakes were the bread of life. The second thing was that one had never to forget that it was a dream. If that happened, then the dream was incapable of completing itself, and ended up repeating itself endlessly. This was what Sabazius called 'getting locked in'. It was therefore necessary to have an experienced traveller with you when you attempted dream-entry. With these things in mind, I moved slowly and carefully down the path.

It was a stark landscape. The gorge itself was so deep that it blackened into obscurity at many points. After only a few yards something happened which flattened me against the mountain side. Far above my head a whistling sound erupted, and as I looked up, a dark shape hurtled out of the sky and passed me with the speed of a bullet. An electric shock ran through my body. My eyes barely caught and translated this projectile as a large bird. Although I had not seen it clearly I had however a picture in my mind of a large predator with its wings folded tight into its body. When I looked down into the gorge, I was just in time to see a black dot curve up out of the gloom. This incident shook me quite a bit, and for a moment I fell into the paralysing belief that the alien landscape surrounding me was real. When this feeling passed, I took a few deep breaths and continued.

On reaching an outcrop of rock and rounding it, I found that the path broadened substantially and then narrowed again. Taking advantage of this, I stopped for a moment and wiped the perspiration from my face. Straight ahead, the path rose up and disappeared behind a second bluff of rock. Knowing that the only way to get out of this dream was to see it through to its conclusion, I pushed myself forward. As I came down the other side of that rock, some white marks partially obscured by a few dehydrated bushes attracted my attention. When I realized that they were crosses whitewashed onto the rock I felt a sudden excitement. People had been here, and these crosses had to signify something. Within a few minutes I knew what their significance was. Just beyond the crosses, up on the left, the path stopped abruptly before a flight of stone steps. The steps were smooth and well worn, and led, not simply up the mountain side, but into the mountain itself. Upward they spiralled into the mouth of a cave. Like a child confronted by a secret passage, I reached the steps and started to climb. But it was not to be. In the same moment I was whisked away and deposited at the middle level of consciousness. When I opened my eyes, it was to find Sabazius frowning at me.

'Where have you been?' he asked.

I described my journey.

He listened without looking at me, and then he said that I had been given a powerful sign in the shape of the predator.

'What about the steps?'

He shrugged, looked at me blankly. 'Could mean anything,' he said.

'But surely that was the highpoint of the journey!' I protested, remembering how I had felt when I saw it. 'I don't think such an image can be just pushed aside.'

Sabazius rolled his eyes in mock depair. Then he said: 'The steps will take care of themselves, but *you* will have to take care of the predator.'

Wanting to say something, yet knowing that it would only get me into trouble, I fell silent. Whatever the steps were would become evident eventually.

As it was still sunny and warm around five-thirty, I prepared some food and brought it down on a tray. Sabazius surveyed my efforts with interest. Picking up a neat egg sandwich he bit into it. 'You've got such a tidy mind,' he said. 'Even your sandwiches are tidy.'

'Isn't there enough?'

He smiled at what remained in his hand. 'Where I come from a man would slit your throat for offering him such meagre hospitality.'

'This is London,' I replied.

'Indeed it is.'

I nibbled at a sandwich, then I said: 'Do you miss Greece?'

'Why do you ask?'

'I sometimes get the impression that you think we're a bunch of stuffed-shirts.'

'Who is *we*?'

I smiled. 'Everyone who isn't Greek?'

'That is a silly statement,' said Sabazius. 'It smacks of sophisticated emptiness.'

'I was only joking.'

'No. You were annoyed. You were annoyed because I criticized your sandwiches. You thought I was criticizing the British unfairly, so you criticized the Greeks by criticizing me. When you asked me if I missed Greece, I knew by the tone of your voice that you weren't actually asking me if I missed it. That's why I asked you what you meant. And then you started talking about "stuffed-shirts", and in the next moment your sophistication got the better of you.'

Realizing that I had been firmly nailed on a rather subtle issue, I said: 'What exactly do you think of us?'

'I think you're a bunch of stuffed-shirts.'

I laughed outright. 'Who's being sophisticated now? You twisted that beautifully.'

'I didn't twist anything,' replied Sabazius. 'Your sophistication is born out of malicious wit, mine is born out of the necessity to keep your head above water. There is no humour in humour which downs another human being for the sake of it.'

The impact of his statement cut my reply short. Was it true? Was the cutting edge of my humour rooted in maliciousness? My eyes moved from side to side as I attempted to pin-point the influences which had produced that cutting edge. When it became clear to me that my training ground had been one of sharpening my intellectual wits off the subtle mental surfaces of bored minds, I could do nothing else but admit that he was right. It was a kind of quirk in my character which at one time had afforded me personality status, but which now signalled a return to awake-dream.

'Can you see it?' asked Sabazius.

'Yes, I can,' I replied.

Sabazius chuckled at my seriousness. 'It's not so easy to escape from one's idea of oneself,' he said, smiling at me. 'Especially when one likes the shape of the idea.'

'I thought I knew that.'

'You certainly think it, but thinking a thing is not knowing it. Even thinking that thinking a thing is not knowing it is not knowing it.'

'But it's impossible not to think about what one knows.'

Sabazius looked to the side for a moment as if someone had spoken to him, then he said: 'Thought is only the shadow of knowledge. It has shape and form, but no substance. It has length, width and height, but no depth. An experience of knowledge is an experience of depth. When knowledge flashes into the mind of a man, the mind of that man ceases momentarily as mind. In that moment the man *is* knowledge. An infinitesimal moment later he recognizes that he *has* knowledge, that is, that he has been modified through the experience. What this means is that his moment of cognition subtly rearranges the sum total of his recognition. He of course *feels* the difference. If he continues to seek himself *as* knowledge, then his recognition of knowledge grows proportionally, and his ability to convey what he recognizes follows suit, but if he

245

falls into the trap of merely seeking out his recognitions, then he ends up thinking around his moment of cognition, and his ability to convey his experience to others and himself withers and dies. That is to seek shadows, to fight with them, to be overpowered by them.'

I remained silent.

'Can't you think of anything to say?'

I shook my head.

Sabazius gave me a long look to cement my feelings in place, then he said, 'If you can stop yourself from merely trying to remember what you know, then the moment will deliver up what you know, which is what you ARE, and add a new dimension to it. You see, true knowledge is never static. True knowledge is an expression of the *ever-comprehending act of will*. To get stuck in the act of remembering is to automatically cancel out the energy of the moment. You may at first find it difficult to recognize what you're saying *as what you know*, but that is only because you have expressed what you know in a totally unique manner. Truth does not stand still, it's ever on the move, continually revealing itself in unexpected ways. In other words, truth gobbles up dogma through its act of ever expanding. The observable result of continuous acts of memory in a conversation is a dead rabbiting, an energyless mouthing of the shape of knowledge. This is knowledge without substance. Communications of this nature breed confusion, confrontation, condescension and cold aloofness. As a reaction, an act of memory can spin off in any direction whatsoever. There is no knowing where it will end up. An Act of Will, on the other hand, is a unique gift of knowledge applicable in any moment of time because it is a true *act*. Such an act penetrates the total content of memory and brings about a modification which is worthwhile and lasting.

'The basic problem with memory as an instrument of knowledge, is that the rememberer attempts to superimpose an experience of knowledge upon the present moment in the form of a re-built, or re-constructed image. Such images take two forms: either they are experiences of true knowledge robbed of their energy through continual acts of memory, or they are remembered acts of learning which contained no energy in the first place. What generally happens is that people who have had an experience of true knowledge in the moment, make the mistake of merely remembering that knowledge, and end up teaching others to teach others to remember what they themselves had forgotten as soon as they remembered it. All the great faiths and ideologies are composed of such remembered truths. It's no wonder that they are without energy, knowledge and direction. Their only hope of coming alive again is when some adherent short-circuits his or her way out of the self-created, energyless desert of belief, and points without wavering to the timeless moment. When that happens, the twin sisters of emotion and factuality can be replaced by feeling and actuality.'

'And yet there's a gap, isn't there,' I said, sensing that gap within myself. 'It isn't just a matter of switching over from one thing to another.'

'Indeed it isn't; but the gap which you're referring to is really an overlap, a kind of developmental overlap where beings in the process of changing from a grub into a butterfly can fall foul of a passing predator. There is nothing more vunlerable than something in the process of becoming something else. This is why human beings must develop a Central Station of Command, a stable "I" structure with the wit to watch out for such predators constantly. It isn't that one should be shielded against all forms of attack, but that one ought to learn how to construct natural systems of defence. The word camouflage is better. When a human being lights up inside, they have to guard that light with their life. If they don't, someone somewhere will attempt to extinguish it. Such people don't understand what they're doing, all they know is that an indeterminate "something" is irritating their perception. It isn't nice to be forced awake when one is enjoying a deep sleep. Anyway, when the Art of Disguise is mastered, and a man has learned to behave invisibly among his fellow men, then and only then can he risk revealing the nature of his nature, and even then only with great caution. You see it's no longer a matter of someone destroying him, but of the light within him destroying others because of its intensity and brightness. During the overlap stage, this light flickers in and out as the man flickers in and out of true consciousness, but when the man's ability to focus on his feelings becomes stable, then the light becomes stable, and as from that moment such a man is a walking bomb. During the focusing period a man's memory dims, that is, his idea of himself melts and reforms constantly, until finally the idea-self ceases to have independent life. However, as the man is still composed of flesh and blood, and has to interact with the world in as natural a manner as possible, he relies on his previously constructed stable "I" structure for communication purposes.'

I interrupted Sabazius at this point and asked him what the difference was between an ordinary 'I' structure and the stable 'I' structure of a Man of Feeling. For if the idea-self melted, then how was it possible to retain any form of 'I' structure?

'That is not a difficult question,' he replied. 'But it is a tricky one, so listen carefully. Memory is the final hurdle in the evolution of a human being. The light which springs out of the impenetrable darkness of actuality cannot find full expression until this is realized throughout the systems of all self-styled individual organisms. This light, or knowledge, expresses itself in the same moment as memory dims, for memory is the shutter of consciousness. All conflict is caused by the emotional tension lying between the ingredients of memory. You see, emotional tension, whatever its nature, is the fantasy relation-ship between facts and identity. Identity is triggered off as an off-shoot of perception. Perception in an unevolved organism can only supply that organism with facts, that is, a fragmented knowledge of the world. As the human psyche is a plastic medium, these facts register upon it as impressions, and out of these impressions come further fragments of fact. The more impressions there are on this medium, the surer the organism becomes that its factual seeing of the world is meaningful, and as this meaningfulness grows and multiplies through the relationship between the impressions themselves, the organism finally includes itself as an organism, and registers itself as an "objective fact" along with all the others. This is why I have called emotion and factuality twin sisters. Emotion is the energy of Being channelled off to support and sustain factual-mindedness, and factual-mindedness, in turn, supports and sustains the *prime fact* of individuality as adhesive recognition. Man perceives of himself as an isolated unit, as a "fact", because memory cannot conceive of him in any other way. A Man of Feeling on the other hand, because he has discovered that this is the case, is no longer subservient to the *fact of his existence*, therefore he can use the stable "I" structure without falling back into the belief that it is *actually* real. That is the answer to your question.

'Now I said that memory cannot "conceive" of man except as a fact. In this context the word "conceive" is of vital importance, for it points to the interaction between factuality and actuality. It is thought that the conscious mind of man "conceives" things, and that to conceive something is to "think", but that is a mistake, for thinking is only the rattling-of-perception-articulated, the relationship of facts tumbling out into the world because there happens to be a hole in the bucket. Conceiving, or conception, is something else altogether. When a man conceives something, that something is *born within him*, not thought up by him. In a moment of stilled memory he is literally impregnated with a modicum of true knowledge which, if it is allowed to grow and blossom, will eventually turn into an experience of *being* born again. In that moment, that timeless, objectless moment, actuality replaces factuality, and feeling replaces emotion. However, as it is impossible for the plastic surface of memory not to be "impressed" by such an experience, the man more often than not seeks out his memory of that modicum of knowledge, and in doing so, soon reduces it to an energyless objective fact. Most of the great energy symbols man has discovered within himself have died in such a manner. But if a man can regain entrance to that secret place where consciousness lights up as a whole, then he will become slowly aware of the nature and purpose of that space, and seek it out in place of his objective memory. The basic problem is of course that he generally does the opposite, and his ability to conceive true knowledge is snuffed out. So, the evolutionary urge toward unique expression is strangled, and the creative impetus of man's psyche reduced to an impotent *trying* which gets him nowhere. What I'm saying to you is this: every real movement toward real knowledge which has taken place has been due to an individual ceasing momentarily to be an individual. All the rest is emotional arithmetic. People involved in such arithmetic cannot cognize even the basic dimensions of their Being, and as such cannot construct the stable "I" structure necessary to start.'

249

'Unless they find a teacher.'

Sabazius shook his head from side to side, then he said: 'Such things cannot be taught, they can only be experienced.'

'But you're my teacher,' I said, 'and you yourself had a teacher.'

'That is nonsense.'

'But I can remember you saying that you learned from your teacher, and when you realized that you could teach yourself, you left him.'

Sabazius laughed at my words, poked me with a finger. 'Can't you see what you're saying? You've just mouthed the most important piece of knowledge imaginable, and yet you don't know it. The man I left was not my teacher, he was his own teacher. When I woke up to that fact, I was then my teacher.'

'Then what are we doing sitting in this garden talking to one another. Aren't you even now attempting to teach me that I am my own teacher?'

'No. You are attempting to teach yourself. Each and every experience you've had has come from within yourself. In such moments you have responded to what you are, taken the responsibility of *being* responsible. The moment you act in such a manner, your eyes open. I cannot open your eyes. Only you can do that.'

27 ❈ *Rememberers and realizers*

Sabazius cracked open the problem of 'teachers' later that evening by again drawing my attention to the role of memory in man. He said that there were two basic people inside all human beings: Rememberer and the Realizer. Rememberers had to be taught things, whereas Realizers taught themselves. This distinction, however, was not known to Rememberers, for it was one of the realizations only a *Realizer could realize*. This did not mean that Rememberers did not have realizations, it just meant that they were unable to recognize the nature of such realizations when they occurred. In the world at large, it was thought that to realize something was simply to draw a conclusion from data already stored in memory, but that was only rememberization juggling with memory content, realization was an Act of Will outside of memory, a coming to grips with reality on its own terms.

As all memories were secondhand, that is, not of the present moment, beings who relied on memory alone automatically amputated themselves from experiencing reality firsthand. Through the process of remembering, they could add, subtract, multiply and divide secondhand reality effectively, and indefinitely, but at no time could they penetrate it, for penetration necessitated the unshackling of the senses from memory interference. In Ordinary Man, memory governed the senses and interpreted reality in accordance with its particular bias, whereas in Natural Man, memory and the senses functioned separately. This did not mean that they were somehow locked off in separate compartments, it just meant that they functioned properly within the domain of consciousness.

The rate of psychical recovery, or growth in a human being, depended entirely on the realization of this fact *as an experience*. When an experience of knowledge took place in a human organism, a portion of energy in exact proportion to the density of that knowledge was released into the organism's systems of functioning. This energy, which was primal in substance, modified the organism's perception of reality, and so allowed for further penetration to take place. However, as the whole civilized world was involved in the education of the senses through memory, which resulted in a secondhand 'appreciation' of reality, this vital crystallization of knowledge was either halted for long periods of memory-time, or stopped altogether through the storage of data which, by its very form and nature, held the senses rigidly to memory content. This meant, in effect, that such beings were totally cut off from *being* the Intelligent Ground of their own natures. In other words they could not *be* natural. The psyche of an Ordinary Man was governed by the film-like quality of memory, whereas that of Natural Man was governed by *instant realization* based on cleared perception.

The pain, suffering and sorrow which Ordinary Man went through in his search for real reality was nothing more than his attempt to penetrate that reality with an instrument only capable of constructing life-like duplicates. So the task of Natural Man was not to teach ideas or philosophies, but to 'create conditions' wherein the psyches of others could experience the meaning of the moment, and not just moments of meaning. This situation only became complicated when individuals who had no real knowledge of their own natures, attempted to communicate what they knew in the form of teachings which demanded that the content of memory be switched this way or that. As to play with the content of memory was simply to play at 'I believe' or 'I do not believe', the end result was an energyless changing of psychic patterns for no other reason than that someone *thought* they should be changed. Men of Feeling were not interested in such games, they were only interested in the production of real knowledge as an experience. This also meant that a Man of Feeling could never congratulate himself when one of his pupils woke up, for he realized that it was always the pupil who awakened himself. Men of Feeling did not actually teach anything to anyone, they simply *exercised themselves in the world to continually enlarge their own knowing*. To be a Man of Feeling was therefore to be involved in a kind of *dance*, a series of movements which allowed the sacred nature of reality to burst into view.

There was then the question of what happened to memory when it was unhitched from the senses. It was some time before this puzzle unravelled itself for me. Memory, when it took up its proper role in consciousness, became an energized channel of communication. Having ceased to be a re-actor, that is, an *I*dentity and *I*dentifier, it turned into a 'synthesizer' governed by the meaning of the moment. This meant that the Rememberer was no more, in that instant, and that the Realizer was in charge.

Sabazius did not allow me to intellectualize this knowledge in any way whatsoever. We moved toward it in a halting and hesitating fashion, all the while paying strict attention to the fact that such knowledge could only be absorbed and actualized within a Realizer. By the time we reached the point concerning what happened to memory when it was no longer attached to the senses as a governing force, I knew without doubt that I had managed to penetrate the mystery. How did I know? I knew because I was captured in that state of physical and psychological rest which all beings seek, but cannot find because of the nature of their seeking. Unless one entered an ego-empty space, it was not possible to walk through the *door of realization* into the matrix of consciousness. At its best, memory was a thin veil lying between us and reality, but at its worst it was a solid wall of reinforced concrete. At our conscious best we could intellectually allow for the fact that memory and the ego-complex constituted some kind of barrier, but at our conscious worst we poured scorn on anything which even suggested that there was a 'something' beyond objective knowledge which could be meaningful in itself. Energy was seen as a something to be exploited, a means to an objective end, when in actuality energy was the beginning and the end, the very substance of knowledge itself.

This was why Sabazius kept on talking about the importance of art. To him, art was the narrow, overlapping passage between reality and what man thought of as real. When art worked, it carried the artist, the art, and the viewer of the art beyond the stultifying effects of artefact, and allowed a mode of perception to appear which defied intellectual scrutiny. Art, like human beings and truth, could not be termed 'good', it could only be termed 'real' or 'unreal'. Goodness was an artefact of the conscious mind beyond realistic attainment because of the nature of the conscious mind. There was simply no such thing as an 'objective' good. Reality, however, was ever attainable and available to those with the courage to seek it. And this was another thing that Sabazius had pointed at time and time again: that 'morality' was man's search for *more reality*, not a socially acceptable goodness. Morality, as it was consciously taught, was man's natural vision of reality reduced to the level of memory bric-a-brac. It was the real devoid of energy. The moral confusion in our world was a product of conscious confusion. As human beings sensed the approach of the real, their *idea of reality* melted into an unrecognizable mass, and as they were unwilling to let go of that mass and experience reality, the result was a foolish, and totally worthless attempt to rationalize the mass into yet another acceptable social form. As one box disintegrated, another formed. What had to be sought out with all serious-ness was what lay outside of the boxes. However, as this necessitated the seeker of reality to move into the space between the boxes and become that space, few ever made the attempt, or even realized that such an attempt ought to be made. And so humanity ran hither and thither in its endless conscious search for a glimpse, an experience of that reality which would spell out once and for all the meaning of the moment, indeed, the meaning of human existence, and the very act of searching in such a fashion bolted the door they wished to open.

The question was, when someone actually managed it, would it make any conscious difference? The answer to this question was *probably not*. Knowledge pertaining to the moment hardly ever made sense within the terms of manu-factured knowledge. Such knowledge was immediately censored *in time* by the conscious mind. The conscious mind was by its very nature always *behind the times*, or simply *behind time*. And according to Sabazius this was only the tip of the iceberg. The senses were governed, on the whole, by manufactured conscious attitudes, and one sense in particular, the sense of sight, was physiologically governed by conscious attitudes. In other words, the human eye had become an extension of mind. This meant that the mind itself was in a double-bind situation, being both that which censored, and that which was censored. So it was not the hypothetical soul of man which was mirrored in the human eye, but the conscious *Identity* with its attendant attitudinal traits. And so we talked of 'alive eyes', 'dead eyes', 'empty eyes' and 'innocent eyes'. The eyes of a human being usually portrayed and betrayed their exact psychical position in any moment. The complex personalities which looked out of the human eye were, for all to *see*, the complexes, or complexities of conscious intention, or tension. No wonder human beings diverted their eyes on so many occasions, or indeed took to covering them up in one way or another. How uncomfortable we felt if a *penetrating eye* appeared among us.

But there was more to it than this. Sabazius had always said that human beings were possessed by a multiplicity of personalities, not just one personality which expressed itself in different ways. What he meant by this came into focus when dealing with the formation of attitudes. Each personality was composed of a 'string of attitudes,' just as the idea of a conscious identity was composed of a 'string of personalities'. This meant that an angry personality was always angry, and a peaceful personality was always peaceful. An angry personality could not become peaceful, and a peaceful personality could not become angry. What happened was that one literally replaced the other like cards in a deck. Each personality, or 'attitude complex', constituted a 'frame of mind', and this frame could be slotted into place at any given moment. This slotting in and out took place as a re-action to environment allied to memory content. It signified nothing more than a mechanical activity. The conscious mind was composed of many such 'frames of mind' with the ability to slip in and out unnoticed because of one prime factor: *Identity* acted as a cementing force and gave the illusion of a continuous and meaningful process. So personality was only a 'string of attitudes' triggered into *being* under certain sets of circumstances. As long as a human organism remained under the dictatorial sway of such attitudinal frames, the possibility of finding the state of 'reflective rest' wherein this could be seen, or realized, was not available.

To bring about this state of 'reflective rest', the human organism had to find the means to detect what was going on within it as an organism second by second, and this meant that it had to find the courage, never mind the concept, to face the observable fact that it had no freedom of will. Will was comprehension, and it was obvious to any organism in which a modicum of intelligence had erupted, that comprehension was not available to man in his present condition. He could certainly understand things, but his understanding did not allow him to penetrate the nature of the things he understood. It was therefore not a matter of balancing this attitude against that attitude, or this supposed facet of personality against some other, it was a matter of *detaching the idea-self from the whole attitudinal framework*. If this was allowed to take place, consciousness itself came into the picture, and the conscious mind slowly gave up its *reactionary* habits. It was then, like its memory content, an energized medium of communication. The organism had then access to itself as an expression of the *ever-comprehending act of will*. This could not be translated as a religious experience, for it was essentially an experience of BEING REALITY, not just being in it.

The conscious mind, however, incapable as it was of comprehending the nature of this experimental process, simulated it as best it could through religious and philosophical 'appreciation', and in doing so, manufactured for itself a 'hybrid awareness' of reality which, although apparently exact in logical, psychological, religious or scientific terms, could not allow for the real nature of 'creative realization'. The end result of this could be seen in varying degrees throughout the works of the academic establishment, and seen clearly in certain philosophical systems where the adherents, robbed of their natural, feeling energies, headed inexorably toward a dehydrated reflection of themselves. In such cases, the idea-self tore itself apart in what appeared to be an emotionless paroxysm of despair. And it was no wonder, for what else could result from the contemplation of the mechanical framework of mind? A few escaped from this withering framework by plunging themselves into some emotionally loaded system where they could end their days fighting for what they did not believe in. Better to live a conscious lie than die whimpering on the attitudinal-spikes of conscious mechanicalness. All of it was doomed to failure for one simple and blatantly obvious reason: to seek ultimate knowledge through the conscious mind was to face the idea-self through the 'eyes' of the idea-self. Sabazius stressed this point emphatically, for it constituted the vicious, circle-like nature of limited idea-structures attempting what was outside of their ability to perform. Man could only face the unimaginable nature of his own nature when he felt it pulse within him as an expression of Will. Then and only then could he say that he knew what he knew to be real. Will was the foundation of real knowledge, and to be without it was to stumble about in the darkness of manufactured light.

And yet knowledge of a profoundly practical nature was available to man, that is, an inside knowledge which could straighten out the seemingly unanswerable intellectual problems he had surrounded himself with. What he sought so ardently through his logical processes alone, but could not 'realize' for himself or others, became automatically available when he woke up to the fact that he was asleep *on* the face of reality. But of course this was a difficult thing to wake up to, for it necessitated that the conscious mind, led by the ego itself, actually take a few faltering steps into the creative darkness of consciousness as a whole. As this creative darkness demanded a new form of seeing and level of awareness, the ego shrank from it like an animal from a burning brand, and reported back its own chaotic reaction *as the nature of the sphere entered*. This was the crux of the matter, the interpretive block which kept the human ego stranded on the time-side of consciousness.

Consciousness as a whole was the Fire which consumed Fire, the bright flame which burned up the dross of objective mind and allowed greater and greater visions of reality *as* knowledge to appear. All levels of psychic breakdown, in whatever degree they occurred, were primarily composed of conscious confusion in the face of this approaching reality, not an indication, as many thought, that consciousness in its vaster element was primitive and chaotic in substance. There was nothing primitive about consciousness as a whole. It was the most sophisticated and intelligent matrix imaginable. Had not the conscious mind itself erupted out of its depths? Until this was creatively seen, man would rip himself apart needlessly and attempt to patch himself up through the very insrument that was doing the ripping. This could not be side-stepped. Man was fully prepared in his ignorance and stupidity to destroy himself and all other living organisms in a holocaust of hatred built out of suspicion. He toyed daily with the idea of total destruction, and somewhere along the conscious line of his thoughts would find the incomprehensible 'reason' for actually doing it. This was the beast in man, that part of his manufactured nature which would release the forces of unimaginable catastrophe.

Good intentions, or ideas of the 'good', were not enough in and of themselves to bind the beast. Good intentions were just fantasy ideas, energyless hopes mouthed endlessly into the vacuum of human despair and need. Energy, visionary knowledge, and the ability to act effectively, rather than just react effectively, was what was required. No amount of talking, preaching, arguing or ideological activity would bring the beast to heel. Only the presence and acts of inspired human beings who had penetrated beyond the surface of their conscious psyches could do that. This was the challenge which faced man on every level of enquiry. If he turned his back on this challenge, then he would consciously usher in, indeed invite with open arms, the very disaster he wished to avoid. So it was time to give up the notion that others would somehow work out logical answers to our illogical behaviour, for our illogical behaviour was rooted in our over-dependence on logic and its attendant value systems. Man's fear of himself was an experience, and only an experience of something beyond fear could release him from its clutches. But what was it that had the power to cancel out fear, the power to answer unanswerable questions, the power to release and renew the battered, disillusioned, emotionally unstable conscious mind?

To talk of love was to be immediately accused of milky idealism, to have turned one's face away from the acid reality of human nature. And yet love was the answer, the answer we knew we were incapable of furnishing. Love had been interpreted out of existence, reduced to a gross, social tolerance which was the basis of the suspicion gnawing at our innards. Love, it was thought, was just another one of those ideal images in the conscious mind, the stuff of poets and novelists, the weak-minded hope of spiritual freaks devoid of *common* sense. Surely love had no real substance apart from biological attraction and aesthetic appreciation? Where was this love, this ultimate good we believed ourselves to possess but could not uncover? This was the kind of argument we used against the existence of love as an actuality, and the truth of the matter was, they were good arguments, for they confirmed the terrible fact that the conscious mind was incapable of real love, unable to manufacture out of its contents a force dynamic enough to deal with what it itself had created.

And yet the answer to all of this was simple, for love was not an excretion of the molasses-mind, it was the *act* of coming face to face with the breathtaking, all encompassing nature of Intelligence. Intellect could only juggle with love as an emotional idea, Intelligence was love in action. To love the world was to compassionately comprehend the nature and meaning of human failure. It was to penetrate beyond projected images, to have access to one's own nature as a profound experience. When this was realized as an experience, love would deliver itself up as wisdom.

'All I want you to do is walk across to the other side of that carpet.' He pointed at it and waited without looking at me. Not knowing what he was up to, or what I was supposed to be up to, I did as requested. When I turned to face him, he had seated himself at the far end of the room. 'You did that beautifully,' he said, smiling at me. 'You started out as an idiot, and managed to remain an idiot all the way through. That's the kind of consistency required to master the carpet.' Getting to his feet, he came across the room slowly, looked at the carpet for a few seconds, then, without hesitancy, walked towards where I stood. When he reached me, he said: 'Do you understand?'

'Yes.'

'Then do it.'

With considerable care, I traversed the carpet a second time.

'What have you learned?' asked Sabazius.

'That I can't walk across the carpet like you do.'

'Why is that?'

'It's because I'm seeing the carpet as a carpet, and myself as walker.'

He nodded as if in agreement. 'Please do it again.'

I walked across the carpet a third time.

'What have you learned this time?'

'I'm afraid of the carpet,' I said. 'I can sense the gap between it and me and I can't do a thing about it.'

'Why is that?'

'I don't know. I know what to do but I can't do it.'

'What did you realize when you felt that you could not do what you know?'

'Helpless.'

'And?'

'Afraid that I'd lost the knack of cancelling out the gap.'

'Have you lost the knack?'

'It would seem so.'

'Why do you think that is?'

'My fear?'

'Yes, it is your fear; but what is the foundation of your fear?'

'My knowledge of the gap.'

'Fine,' said Sabazius. He sat down on the edge of the carpet and indicated that I should do the same. 'We're now going to return to basics. The basic act of *seeing* always gets rusty around this point. Men of Feeling refer to this as "the balance which upsets balance". It's very simple, really. All that happens is that the seer, in spite of himself, starts to remember his acts of seeing, and his remembering stops him from actually seeing. Out of this reduction in energy springs clever thoughts, and before the seer knows where he is, he no longer knows where he is. All highly complicated mystical philosophies grew out of this impasse. Such philosophies are born out of the gap, for the gap is sensed with fear, and the fear demands that the gap be filled in with something meaningful. It doesn't matter whether the person concerned is aware of the nature of the gap or not. Fear is no respecter of persons. Even you, after all the experiences you've had, after all the work you've applied yourself to, still cannot find the stillness inherent in things at a moment's notice. You either have to work at it for hours, or be drawn into it by factors outside of yourself. There are two reasons for this. The first is that your seeing is not yet stabilized, and the second is that your experiences of seeing are now beginning to interfere with even the seeing you're capable of. What you have to understand all over again is that when you look at an object, the energy of your seeing moves out and into that object through identification, and when you think of yourself, that is, objectify yourself as an idea in the mind, the energy of your seeing is withdrawn from the physical object and enters the idea-object. In both cases the act of seeing is incomplete. An act of seeing can only be considered complete when the looker is one hundred percent aware of himself and the object at which he looks simultaneously. If this double-looking does not take place, then the looker either identifies with an object in place of himself, or he identifies himself *as* an object at the expense of what exists.

'Single-looking makes the looker vulnerable on many levels. The personalities, or mutually attracted strings of attitudes, can then hold sway over the whole organism. They can drag it this way and that at a moment's notice. Double-looking, on the other hand, allows the seer to see, and see the seer who sees. This kind of looking breaks the *idea* of a continuous self who sees, and allows the seer to observe what he previously thought was himself in its many aspects. As this ability to see develops, the seer can then penetrate any object to any depth. In other words, seeing strips away the ideas with which we surround objects, melts the factuality, and allows the actuality to surface. All objects are obscured by our ideas about them. To really know something, these ideas have to be laid aside. Now of course it is not believed by thinking men that this can be done. They contend that the object must ever remain an object, for they believe that an object is only an object because it is perceived as an object, a something "out there". But they only think this because they believe that a gap exists. The gap is a factuality, it cannot be disputed. Now this of course is perfectly true. To the ego there is a gap, indeed there has to be a gap, for if there is no gap, then the ego cannot exist in its own right. As men do not understand the nature of their own egos, they cannot make the mental jump necessary for seeing to take place, and as they consider any experience which suggests that the jump is taking place as an aberration, a mental deviation from what is considered "normal", the actuality of such an experience is made into a factual impossibility. So in a sense they are not really saying that it cannot happen, they are just saying that it *should not happen*. And within the terms of their logically constructed seeing, they are perfectly correct in their assessment.

'Seeing is seeing, and not-seeing is not-seeing. It is not possible to nearly see. Either one sees or one does not see. There's no half-way house. What man interprets as seeing is just the scanning backwards and forwards of his senses across the point where seeing is available. Sometimes odd sensations arise when a person touches that point, but odd sensations are not to see. To see is to see. Odd sensations are just moments of veiled panic as the ego notices out of the corner of its "I" that something is tugging at its seams. For an infinitesimal moment in time the *whole point* of existence is staring at the ego. This presents the ego with a terrible problem, for on the one hand there is nothing it desires more than knowing the meaning of its existence, while on the other it intuits from some other level of being that to know such a thing spells the end of itself as an ego. It knows that it will never be the same again if it relaxes its control over the organism and allows that knowledge entrance. And yet it's fascinated. It's fascinated by the idea of gaining that knowledge without selling itself to that knowledge, for to have such knowledge, no matter how little of it, would be to have power, the power over other egos who do not possess that knowledge. And so quite often, a man's ego will force him to experiment, to flirt with the meaning of his existence in the hope that even the meaning of existence can eventually be controlled by the logical processes. That, in a word, is the substance of what man calls "damnation". It is to dam up the meaning of existence and only allow it through in trickles. Under such circumstances, the ego is not concerned with the possibility of a full revelation, it is only concerned with *having enough* of that revelation to make it special in the "I"s of men. Other egos are of course at the same time denying that such knowledge has any factual existence, that the knowledge itself is only an idea in the mind of man. This means nothing in itself. It only means that some egos aggrandize themselves through denying such knowledge, and others aggrandize themselves through tinkering with it. The end of both parties is the same, a roarless death.

'A half second of seeing is greater than a quarter second of seeing, because a half second is twice as long as a quarter second. What does that mean? It simply means that more energy is available. Seeing equals energy. The human body is an energy generator greater than anything man has ever built or conceived of. It has the ability to supply an infinite amount of energy if and when an organism wakes up to the meaning of its existence through continuous acts of seeing. An act of seeing stirs this generator into action, and the energy supplied stirs acts of seeing into perception. When enough energy is available, the acts of seeing expand and carry the seer far beyond the normal confines of conscious recognition, and if the generator is not allowed to run down, the psyche eventually penetrates itself as energy. All this is possible if a human being will only stop for a moment and look at the world properly. It is, as you know, that simple, and it is this very simplicity which makes it so profound. This is why it is not understood. People only attempt to exercise their understanding in relationship to the difficult, not the simple. The simple is a waste of time – good solid logical fact-filled time. As existing is so difficult a thing to take part in, then the meaning of existence must be equally difficult to understand. If it is not, then it can't be worth having, for simple things offer no power to those who have them. That is roughly the reasoning of those who seek the meaning of existence, whether it be through religion or any of the sciences. Power, and being part of the process of power, is all important. And this is why you must not fall back into awake-dream, for if what you know remains locked up in your ego without the levelling quality of acts of seeing, then you'll turn into a Man of Power without even knowing that it's happening.'

As from that moment, Sabazius reduced the work I was involved in to a minimum, but stepped up the amount of time he spent with me. We walked a great deal, and as we walked, I looked at my looking. Amazement. Amazed at the world and amazed at my self. Empty. Empty of superfluous thoughts, ideas, notions, opinions and hopes. Alive. Alive to the wonder of *being* alive. Over the weeks that followed I fell in love with that carpet, in fact, I kind of fell in love with everything I looked at – especially fruit. The amount of energy communicated from a window or stall heaped with apples, bananas, oranges and grapefruit was astonishing; not to mention the added factor that I could tell at a glance whether they were old or fresh. Old fruit behaved differently when looked at. So when Sabazius announced that it was the Turk's birthday, and that we were going shopping for a load of fruit, I was more than pleased.

'Is there going to be a party?' I asked.

'But of course,' replied Sabazius, giving me a look of astonishment. 'The day a man is born is the most important day of his life.'

'Will there be many people there?'

'Quite a few.'

'When is the party to be held?'

'Tonight.'

'Where?'

'Guess,' said Sabazius.

'At the factory?'

'No.'

'At the Turk's house?'

'The Turk doesn't have a house. He stays at the factory.'

I laughed and said: 'Your room wouldn't hold more than half-a-dozen.'

'That's true,' he replied, 'but your flat would.'

I stared at him blankly for a few seconds before replying. 'You might have asked me,' I said.

'And what would have been your decision?' asked Sabazius.

'I would probably have said yes.'

'Only probably?'

'Okay, I would have said yes, but … '

'Don't start *butting*. The truth of the matter is that you would have said yes, that's all that really matters. Anyway, if I had told you about the party earlier, you would probably have got involved in thinking about it, and that would have messed up your looking.'

I closed my eyes for a second and allowed the tiny unit of irritation to melt away. It struggled for a moment, zipped this way and that, and then died.

'Does the Turk like curry?' I asked.

'What do you think?'

'Well, if he likes it, that could be my present,' I said. 'In fact, if you haven't already bought him something, it could be our present.'

'That is an acceptable idea,' he said.

It took three journeys to collect everything. Three because Sabazius had volunteered to set the whole thing up with a little help from myself. The sheer number of items astonished me. Fifteen pounds of chopped steak, five pounds of best kidney, eight large Spanish onions, six pounds of tomatoes, five green peppers, endless mushrooms, three fresh garlic clusters and a handful of special bark called Dalchenni. This was followed by one bottle of olive oil, ten pounds of potatoes, ten hard apples, ten bananas, five small tins of mandarine oranges, ten ordinary oranges and a few extra onions for slicing up. Next came the fish. Sabazius purchased six sizeable smoked mackerel. Packets and packets of long-grained rice then went into a plastic carrier along with an assortment of cheeses and three large lettuces. The lettuces, he informed me, were for laying the fish on. On top of this went a number of fresh lemons. The third journey was the heaviest. We staggered into the flat carrying two crates of wine surmounted by numerous loaves of bread. Paper plates and cups were wedged between the bottles.

'I've never seen so much stuff,' I said, looking around the kitchen. 'How long will it take to prepare?'

'It will take as long as it takes,' replied Sabazius.

We got down to the task of preparing the food around two that afternoon. Sabazius washed the meat and lamb's kidneys carefully, put them to one side, and poured equal portions of olive oil into three large aluminium pans. While he was doing this, I peeled and chopped the onions as finely as possible. Together we stripped the fussy, shell-like bindings from the garlic segments (ten segments to a pan), and reduced them to pieces the size of coarse sugar granules. Sabazius then heated the oil to a high temperature, and we dropped into each pan a tablespoonful of sweet Hungarian paprika, and the same of black pepper. Next came equal portions of garlic, ginger, green pepper and onions. Each item went in singly and was carefully stirred into this volatile mixture. When the onions were golden brown and the green peppers reduced in size and colour, we dropped in the meat and kidneys and stirred the whole concoction until everything was mixed with everything else. Turning the gas down to about half pressure, we clamped on the lids and prepared the rest of the vegetables during the half an hour it took to complete the first stage of cooking.

Going back to the kitchen table, we sat facing each other. There was a basin of tepid water between us. Sabazius carefully peeled the mushrooms and put them to one side. As we completed each of the vegetables, they were placed in a separate dish, or bowl, for easy handling later. Then we got down to the job of taking the bones out of the mackerel. While I was doing that, Sabazius washed the lettuces, split off the larger leaves and laid them on two china platters. He then helped me cut each of the fish into seven equal segments, and arranged them on the platters in a circular pattern. Pieces of chopped tomato, onions, and slices of lemon were added for decoration. When this was to his satisfaction, the platters were covered with clean dishtowels and placed at the bottom of the refrigerator. At a quarter past three, Sabazius removed the lids of the pans – they had been carefully stirred a number of times – and added the second lot of vegetables and spices. Into the pans went the tomatoes, the mushrooms, the green peppers and a carefully quantified amount of crushed chilli, roasted coriander and cumin, an expensive curry powder, and sticks of Dalchenni. This was followed by bay leaves and a finely chopped stalk of lemon grass which he produced from the inside pocket of his jacket. When the contents of the three pans had again been carefully stirred, I helped Sabazius drain off a portion of the liquid that had accrued in each one (keeping the lids on generates a substantial amount of meat and vegetable juice), and this was used to curry the potatoes. Sliced and laid out in an overlapping pattern in an oven-proof dish, the potatoes were cooked later – about half an hour before it was time to eat. Turning the gas down, we replaced the lids.

'All we have to do now is clean this place up,' I said. 'Would you like a glass of wine?'

'Not yet', replied Sabazius, 'there will be more than enough wine later.'

The Turk arrived at seven with three friends. He was wearing a dark suit, an almost white shirt, and a black bow tie. The tie hung limply on his shirt-front like a dead crow. The rest of the guests piled in at five- and ten-minute intervals. It was all rather a shock to my system. At first, I tried to do the right thing and answer the door each time the bell rang, but within half an hour I was too busy pouring wine to bother. This resulted in the door being left open. Sabazius appeared from time to time, talked a little to some of the guests, and returned to the kitchen. By nine o'clock the place was humming.

It was like a dream. It was also not at all what I had expected. And yet, what had I expected? I looked at the Turk. He was perched on the edge of an armchair, the palms of his hands resting on his knees like a Japanese wrestler. My eyes strayed around the room. Who were these people? Were they really friends of the Turk, or were they just playing out a role like myself, putting up with a few hours in the Turk's company to please him? He didn't look terribly pleased. He was talking to a young, dark-haired girl, his face devoid of expression, the bulk of his body held stationary, indeed, balanced curiously on the edge of that chair. I looked at him steadily for a few seconds, then, lifting a paper cup, I filled it to the brim with red wine and downed half of it.

When it was time to serve the curry, I cleared the table, covered it with a green tablecloth and placed my wooden carving board on top. Sabazius carried in the pans and deposited them. I then helped him to bring in the rice, the platters of smoked mackerel, and the side dishes of fruit and chopped onion. The bread, cheese and other titbits were put on a side table. Everyone was very appreciative. As was his way, Sabazius would not allow anyone to touch the curry. He dished it up carefully onto the paper plates, and handed each plate over with a nod. When everyone was served, apart from Sabazius, myself and the Turk, he went into the kitchen and came back with one of my best dinner plates and a white bowl. He filled the bowl with rice, and ladled a more than generous portion of curry onto the plate. 'This is for the Turk,' he said, pushing the dishes towards me. 'Don't drop them.'

With this warning firmly in mind, I made my way over to the Turk, and with what I thought of as dignity, delivered his birthday meal. He accepted the dishes without comment. It was the girl who pointed out that I had come without cutlery. Knowing the Turk's volatile nature, I immediately ferreted out a tray and loaded it up with everything I thought he might need, including a bottle of wine. It was not that I was still afraid of the Turk, his throwing me out of the factory was long since by and understood, it was just that I had no liking for the man or the way he went about things. Apart from the girl, who had been with him since he arrived, no one else had even attempted to speak to him, and I got the feeling they were of the same mind as myself. He nodded his approval at the tray's contents, helped himself to cutlery and fruit, and allowed me to top up his glass. I smiled at the girl as if to say 'You won't catch me out this time,' but she did, for she addressed me suddenly in

Greek, and I found myself stumbling out a reply as best I could.

'I'm afraid you've hit me on a weak spot,' I said, reverting to English. 'My Greek isn't too hot.'

'It sounds fine to me,' she replied.

'Are you Greek?' I asked.

The girl laughed and shook her head. 'No, I'm German, but my mother was Greek.'

'Do you speak German?' asked the girl.

'Yes.'

'French?'

'Yes.'

She paused. 'Turkish?'

'Not a word. Do you?'

'Yes, I learned it from the Turk. He's a very good teacher.'

I looked at the Turk, surprised to hear someone praising him, but he was too busy eating to bother with us. 'I don't know your name,' I said.

'It's Alix.'

'I'm Peter Derwent.'

'Yes, I know,' said Alix. 'I've heard all about you.'

'That makes me feel a little uncomfortable,' I said. 'I hardly know anyone here.'

'Why don't you get some food and join us?'

'Okay,' I said.

I went back to the table to find Sabazius waiting for me. He handed me a plate of curry. 'Is the Turk happy?' he asked.

'Seems to be.'

'And the girl?'

'Yes, she's fine. She's very talkative.'

Sabazius looked at the pan nearest to him, picked up a paper plate and handed it to me. 'For me, please,' he said.

His request caught me off guard, then it dawned on me that he simply wanted to be served as he had served. Putting down my own plate, I attended to his and gave it back. He tasted it immediately, then he said: 'I don't know the girl.'

'She speaks Greek,' I replied.

'What does that mean?' asked Sabazius.

I laughed. 'I'm not quite sure. I just thought it might be significant.'

He stared at me. 'She's a stranger.'

'She isn't a stranger to the Turk,' I said. 'He's known her long enough to teach her Turkish.'

Sabazius said something under his breath which I did not catch.

'Is anything wrong?'

'I don't know.'

'Her name is Alix.'

'So?'

'Thought it might trigger something off.'

He gave me a cool look.

'I'll find out what I can,' I said.

As I turned from the table, he said: 'Be careful, Peter. Her eyes are too bright.'

I felt trouble as I walked towards Alix and the Turk. What had Sabazius meant? When I reached them I looked straight at Alix, but her eyes looked perfectly normal. That was when I noticed that the Turk had relaxed back into his chair. His plate looked as if it had been licked. I sat down on the floor and tasted the curry. It was very hot. Alix filled her glass with wine and placed it in front of me. 'You're neglecting yourself,' she said. 'I see I'll have to look after you.'

When the meal was over, I helped Sabazius gather up the plates and stack them in the kitchen. I wanted to talk to him about the girl, but he seemed distant and uncommunicative. Lifting the second crate of wine, he headed for the lounge. I stood in the kitchen for some seconds trying to make up my mind about something, but as I had no clear idea what it was I was trying to fathom, I gave up and decided to play it by ear. Alix, like Sabazius, virtually ignored me on my return. Like the Turk, she sat back into her chair and closed her eyes. I sat on the carpet and stared aimlessly at the others talking and drinking. I had only just decided to leave and join Sabazius when she said:

'Haven't you got any music?'

'Of course.'

I got to my feet. 'Classical?' I asked.

She gave me an annoyed look. 'Where are your records?'

We passed within inches of Sabazius, but he did not react. I showed Alix where the records were and watched her thumb through them. 'This should do the trick,' she said.

'Are your sure?'

'Yes.'

I fully expected the sound of pop music to disrupt the party, but no one seemed to notice. Turning the volume down to a comfortable level, I said: 'It may not be to everyone's taste.'

'What's taste?' asked Alix coldly.

Her tone made me frown. 'What's the matter?' I asked.

Looking at me with what I could only interpret as contempt, she said: 'Your wide-eyed innocence annoys me. It's phoney.'

'What on earth are you talking about?' I said.

She fixed me with a look. 'You're afraid.'

'Of what?'

Turning up the volume she started to dance.

'What am I afraid of?' I asked again.

'Well, for a start, you're afraid to dance.'

I glanced at the people nearest to us, but they were deep in conversation.

'Let's just say that I missed out on your kind of dancing.'

'Haven't you ever tried it?'

'A couple of times.'

'And?'

I smiled lamely. 'I wasn't terribly successful at it.'

Simulating my expression, Alix said: 'That must have been a blow.'

Perplexed and angered by her attitude, I said: 'What the hell do you want?'

'I want you to dance with me.'

'No, that isn't it,' I said. 'What you want is a little more subtle. You want me to dance *for* you.'

She stopped dancing. 'I think we both need a drink.'

I caught her by the arm and held her. 'You'll get your drink after you've told me what you're up to.'

'I'm not up to anything,' she replied. 'I'm just bored saying all the right things to the right people.'

'You astonish me,' I said. 'From the way you handled the wrong things I got the impression you had had plenty of practice.'

Alix blinked as if suddenly unsure of herself. 'You're not a complete phoney,' she said, 'but you do work hard at it.'

I gave her a straight look before turning away. 'I've got work to do,' I said, and I headed for the kitchen without looking back. But she followed after me, came right into the kitchen and closed the door behind her.

'What do you want?' I asked.

'I don't want anything.' She sighed with what appeared to be exasperation. 'I'm just trying to help, that's all.'

'Help?' I said.

'I was warned off.'

'What do you mean?'

'I was told to leave you alone, not to bother you, not to upset you.'

'By whom?'

'By your darling Alexis, of course.'

'When?'

'When your back was turned.'

Drawing the skin of my bottom lip between my teeth, I bit on it gently. 'What exactly did he say?'

'He said you weren't ready for the likes of me,' laughed Alix.

'I'm apt to agree with him,' I replied.

'Do you agree with everything he says?'

'I neither agree nor disagree.'

'Oh, very philosophical,' retorted Alix. 'You'll be telling me next that what he talks to you about just floats through your head.'

'You could put it that way,' I said.

'Then you are a phoney,' she said in a hoarse whisper. 'He's tying you up like a chicken and you haven't even got the sense to see it.'

'I'll tell you one thing I do see,' I said quietly. 'If I laid one finger on you it would be the end of me.'

Her face contorted into a grin. 'And yet you'd love to, wouldn't you,' she said. Before I could reply her face softened, became almost childlike. 'I couldn't destroy you even if I wanted to. All I want to do is help you to overcome your fear.'

The way in which she could shift from one emotional platform to another intrigued me. Either she had an extraordinary control over her personalities, or they were so out of control she couldn't keep track of them. 'That's very kind of you,' I replied sarcastically. 'But I have the feeling that the only fear you want me to overcome is my fear of you.'

'You're getting very near to the truth,' replied Alix, 'but it's not the truth you envisage.' She sighed to herself, stared at me. 'You've got it into your head that I'm some kind of destructive force, but I'm not. I wouldn't have told you about Alexis warning me off if that were my game.'

I laughed nervously, shook my head, searched for the correct words. 'I'm sorry,' I said, 'I just don't believe a word you're saying.'

'You're a fool,' replied Alix. 'And that is over and above being a phoney.'

Her words stung me. She returned my gaze without flinching, took a step towards me, noted my reaction, and stopped. 'You want me more than anything you've ever wanted in your whole life,' she said, eyeing me suggestively, 'but you're afraid to admit it to yourself.'

I was shaking and there was nothing I could do about it. 'What makes you think you're so desirable?'

'The sweat on your brow.' She laughed suddenly. 'You really are sweating.'

'It's the curry,' I said.

She giggled and the tension between us broke in spite of my wariness.

'This is a set-up, isn't it?' I said.

'Of course it's a set up,' she replied.

'Sabazius didn't say anything to you.'

'Of course not.'

I relaxed somewhat, leaned back against the kitchen wall.

She came closed, much closer. 'You're very lucky having Alexis,' she said, her hands going up round my neck. 'He's got quite a reputation.'

I stood very still and watched her face; her eyes were magnificent, almost luminous. Her head tilted slightly as she brought her full, red lips up to mine. But it was her eyes that held my attention – they were now enormous, and glassy. I stared into those eyes, felt everything give way. And then I felt her lips touch mine, ever so gently, then with a little more pressure, and then more pressure, and then they slowly parted and the wetness of her mouth engulfed me. I was sinking; she was pulling me down, her body flat against mine, her mouth working on my mouth. I tried to resist, but it was impossible; she had me on my knees and she was still kissing me, her mouth parting further and further until I had the sensation of my whole head disappearing into her mouth, my whole head, and then my neck and shoulders, chest and waist …

I fell through into her blackness, into her darkness, wanted to scream, but it was too late for that. She had captured me somehow, captured me and imprisoned me with her eyes and I was now helpless. Looking up into that darkness I saw those eyes watching me, like a cat's eyes, like a cat that wants to play lethal games. Knowing that I must not look at those eyes directly, I dropped my gaze and waited for the attack – it came immediately. The eyes blinked, and in the same moment I heard the far-off sound of beating wings. Breathing out into the darkness I relaxed myself as best I could. The sound of the wings grew louder. I looked at the darkness rather than into it, for it was an impenetrable black soup. Panic. The desire to flee and hide. The cold realization that escape was impossible.

She was coming for me. She was coming out of that point of midnight below the eyes which were not really her eyes. She was powerful. Her talons were strong enough to debowel my mind. There was only one weapon capable of defeating her, and she knew of this weapon, knew that I knew of it, but considered me too weak to find it. For had I not already been caught and devoured by her, rendered naked and helpless for the kill? The sound of her approach intensified my search for that hidden strength, and even though I had not found it when she struck, she must have sensed that I was near to it, for the angle of her whistling, screaming advance was imperceptibly altered, and some part of her grazed my head and shoulder. As she curved up into the dark reaches of that space which was her space, I felt her anger and frustration press in on me from all around. She had missed me once, but it was unlikely that she would miss me twice. I waited. What a fool I had been to think I could deal with her alone. Was I going to die, or simply be taken over because I could not find the space of non-retaliation? But how was it possible not to fear the very essence of fear, to stand before it without a quiver, without a thought of risk or loss? I did not know. All I knew was that that was what I had to do, and quickly. The sound of wings dinning towards me, wings cutting through the darkness like black knives. In a fumbling, incomprehensible manner, I breathed toward her and attempted to locate myself as an actuality, a 'something' beyond sum and substance. Feeling. A glimmer of strength as this feeling multiplied out of itself and shakily constructed the invisible barrier. Failure. And yet another long breath, an open-mouthed breath forming itself into a long A and M, a sound which made my life flicker and dim, slip away from me as it enveloped me in an impenetrable bubble.

Light.

I saw her swerve, saw her huge, blackened body twist grotesquely away in haste. And then just as suddenly it was dark again and I was standing alone and unshielded. Alone. Vulnerable and without the strength to remain vulnerable. Another sound. A faintly familiar sound. Voices talking and laughing distantly. A normal darkness without fear. Opening my eyes I looked around me. The kitchen. The piled paper plates. The little window which looked out onto the gardens. As I took my first step a spasm of pain stopped me. I gasped for air and held onto the table for support. And then I was sick, sicker than I had ever been in my whole life. Yes, I was alive, but I had a scar within me as deep as a trench, a scar which would remind me for the rest of my days that the world was composed not just of earth and sky, but also of forces beyond imagination.

29 ❋ *A series of dream visions*

Having cleaned up my vomit I went straight to bed. Any idea of continuing at the party would have been a nonsense. I lay awake for some time listening to the rise and fall of my breathing, then with a sigh of relief and tiredness allowed myself to sink toward sleep. But I was soon awake again, stark awake and open-eyed. A voice had articulated my name clearly and unmistakenly. Placing my hands on my chest in a criss-cross fashion I acknowledged the voice with a curt movement of my head. A few seconds passed before anything happened, then I felt a tingle of energy pushing its way up. When this energy reached my head, the cave of moist, blue moonlight formed.

A huge hood of blue-white light.

A cone of moist blue stretching up into the dizzy heights of a cave. I did not have to look up to know this. One does not have eyes in the cave, just awareness – perfect sight without seeing. On this occasion, however, what Sabazius had said about my falling asleep in the cave modified the quality of the experience in some unknown way. I was not to fall asleep. If I did, something would pass me by.

A second or a century? Who knows. All I know is that after what seemed an endless moment of waiting, I became aware of a flicker of light at the cave's apex, and as I sat there in the blue-stillness, I was carried up toward that light, and in some unimaginable manner penetrated the top of the hood. A figure. The figure of a woman in white. A terrifyingly beautiful woman with a sword in her hand. And yet even as I looked at her she became something else – a mother, a caring vessel, a matrix out of which life could spring endlessly. I acknowledged her presence, her power, her ability to kill me or kindle me, her right to judge or care, flay or caress, raise up or cast down. I knew that the sword in her hand was double-edged, a terrible weapon which could tear my heart out, or signal a return to life in fullness. Scrutiny. Not the eyes of the Predator this time, but the eyes of a prepotent being, a being with the power to transmit its own characteristics to another, and in doing so, free that other from limitations.

The razor's edge.

To seek knowledge without love is to unwittingly throw oneself into the arms of a castrated vision – it is to be torn apart by the White Goddess. Whatever the direction chosen, the White Goddess has to be faced. It is not enough to have the burning power of passion, or an insatiable hunger for knowledge – passion and knowledge have to be transformed into love and wisdom. Only through such a transformation can the harshness of both be removed, or cancelled. For human need goes far beyond love for love's sake, or knowledge for knowledge's sake. To manufacture love out of desire alone is to make everything one touches into a possession, and to seek knowledge as a mere possession is to kill the essence of knowledge. Which is to say that truth cannot be sought out as a thing in itself, as a thing isolated from life and living – it can only be sought and found out of the clear recognition that it is not static. A static truth is no truth at all; it is a blight on the face of reality.

A blurring. A long, white corridor. A corridor with white-washed walls. There's a door on my left and I open it and walk into a large lounge filled with furniture. A woman and a small fair-haired boy are playing together. The boy is asking his mother questions which she cannot answer, or will not answer. I listen to one of the questions and start to answer it in a slow, monotonous voice. The boy looks up at me with a puzzled expression. Although I'm talking to the boy, I'm looking at the mother, sort of testing her by proxy. The boy says something, questions my answer, and I smile at the mother. She gives me a pained look, says something about my answer being too obvious, and I reply that the obvious is never obvious. She nods and intimates that I must leave. I open the door and step out into the white corridor. It looks the same, but it feels different. Sensing now that I must be ultra careful, I flatten myself against the right-hand wall and stare up the corridor's length. I'm having difficulty in breathing. It is as if my throat has locked off somehow. Spreading my arms against the wall I try to fight the sensation of choking; but it intensifies. I can hear the hoarse rasp of my breathing all around. Must move. Must keep on the move. I edge my way along the wall and come to a stairwell. Stone steps going down to the right. I turn onto the steps and press my back against the wall. Must get to the bottom of the steps. My breathing worsens. I'm surrounded by the harsh, heaving note of my own breath. And then suddenly there are vaguely formed figures to my right and left. Uniformed figures with shiny helmets on their heads and weapons in their hands. I can see the stairwell through them; yet I know they aren't phantoms. One of the figures raises his weapon and strikes me with it. There is a searing pain in my chest. And then they're all at it, smashing and plunging the butts of their weapons into my body. The pain is so severe that it becomes an intangible feeling, a feeling which goes beyond pain and allows me to witness my tormentors and myself with a kind of stupified clarity. Insensible insensibility. A terrible knowledge of human suffering. All the pain of man ground into one experience. A focal point of hatred, viciousness, cunning and coldness. Nothing left. Nothing left to feel with. A body as beyond feeling as those attacking it, a pulp of flesh robbed of form. But not dead. Somehow alive to know, to realize, to see, to understand, to penetrate the numbness of pain and remain standing.

Alone.

My breathing is normal again and the stairway is empty of horror. I push myself away from the wall and walk down the remaining steps into a large, vaulted chamber. Straight ahead are a number of pillared arches. The spaces between the pillars to right and left are in darkness. But the space immediately before me is lit up inside with a rich, amberish glow. What am I looking at? Some kind of nativity scene with mother and child? The scene vanishes and is replaced with two figures standing deep within the arch. On the left is a tall, blonde-haired woman wearing a tight-fitting black jacket, fish-net stockings and high-heeled shoes. On the right stands a man in black evening wear, heavily moustached, complete with topper and cane. A magician entertainer and his assistant. While staring at these figures they enter into a song and dance routine without my being able to hear the song. After a few seconds of this they stop and look at me intently. They exchange a few words which I again cannot hear, turn and move apart. The nativity scene, complete in all respects re-appears, only this time it looks like a cardboard cut-out. 'Don't forget the baby,' says the blond-haired woman. 'You mustn't forget the baby.' With that said the scene dissolves and she takes the man by the hand. They move behind the pillar to their right. As I want to know what the woman means, I move into the archway and follow them. To my surprise, they simply dart round the pillar and back into the chamber. A buffet? There is now a long table in the chamber with many types of food on it. Both the woman and the man start to eat. Standing next to them I ply them with questions, but the woman's deliciously rounded buttocks distract me from the answers. Unable to stop myself I start to caress her body. At first, she pays no attention to me, then with a sudden look of annoyance she brushes my hand aside and rebukes me. Feeling ashamed, I step back and away from her into the arch.

A kind of darkness.

I'm standing on a beautiful beach which stretches as far as the eye can see to right and left. There are a few trees in the background, and beyond the trees a scrubby wilderness. The light is very bright, the sky very blue. I look at the ocean and am mesmerized by its calmness. Voices. The voices of children playing in the sun. Maybe ten or fifteen children, some in the water, some playing on the almost white sand. Laughter. Lots and lots of laughter. I move nearer but they cannot see me. Why can't they see me? I can feel the sun's rays on my body, so why can't they see me? The light begins to fade, and the sea turns from the colour of the sky to another colour, the colour of a growing shadow. Where are the children? I'm alone and my feeling of invisibility has gone. How warm the approaching darkness feels. How bright the shadows are as they eat up the landscape. A filter of blue, an encrustation of amber light and blue mixed together into a fluorescent darkness. Everything feels alive. The landscape and seascape are breathing life into the darkness. But there is someone there, one of the children, a boy, a small boy with an almost glistening white skin and a shock of golden hair. He's standing looking out to sea. So small, yet so strong, so young, yet so full of intent. He turns toward me and demands something, something which fills me with fear. He wants to go out onto the sea, wants to reach some destination that only he knows about. I refuse. I try to explain that there is no boat available, and that even if there were it would be useless in the approaching storm. He frowns and looks back towards the sea. And then to my horror runs down and into the water and starts to swim. I'm paralysed for a moment, afraid to move, afraid of the boy and the sea, afraid to follow after him. But he has to be followed, and the knowledge that he has to be followed makes me plough into the sea and swim after him.

But it's no use. He seems to have the strength of a fully developed man. All I can do is struggle on behind and hope that I can be of some use when the storm breaks. And it does break. Even as the thought forms in my mind the waves rise up angrily. Surely nothing can survive in this? And yet I can see him, see him pushing forward, see his head in the water like a floating gold stone. What courage! I'm shouting to him to turn back, to go back to the safety of the beach, but he doesn't seem to hear, doesn't want to hear. He's being driven by a huge determination which does not fear fear, and even the ocean does not seem to have the power to stop him. Wait for me! I'm shouting. Don't try to get there by yourself! And as I'm shouting I know that it is I who will run out of strength, I who will fail, I who will need saving. But what's happening out there? The boy is rising out of the water, being held above the white-nailed fingers of the sea by some dark form. He's sitting above the waves shouting to me to catch up, to make one last effort. What is he sitting on? It looks like a huge fish, a smooth skinned fish, and it seems to be under the boy's control. I've reached them and my legs are straddling the fish's body. My right arm is about the boy's middle. We're moving. We're moving across the surface of the sea, gathering speed, defeating this watery element with its own content. The fish is a blue-black dolphin with a beautiful head. I can see its eyes as it heaves itself out of the water and buckles its body forward. I'm shouting to the boy to hold tight to the dolphin's fin, and as my words spill out, I'm somehow above the scene and in it, experiencing it and witnessing it simultaneously. My body is violet-blue, violet-blue against the white of his skin, my hair black against the gold of

280

his hair. 'The island!' shouts the boy. And again: 'The island!' What island? All I can see is the black mouth of the sky lying on the surface of the ocean. Where are you taking me, little boy? Am I really with you? I can see both of you as you slowly disappear into the mouth of the sky. You are being drawn away from me, and I can only wonder at what you are attempting, you and your violet-blue passenger.

The room of a house.

I'm standing in the middle of the room and I have an egg in my right hand. The egg is warm and has a fairly distinct crack in it. I show the egg to someone, and say that whatever is in the egg must be given assistance. As I crack the egg gently, a piece of the shell breaks off leaving the thin elasticated membrane visible. Something within the egg responds immediately and begins to push against the membrane. I'm pointing at what is taking place with great excitement, for I know that the egg's content is about to be born, and that this birth is going to take place in my hand. But what is in the egg? I can see a dim shape behind the membrane, a shape which presses and pushes. I feel sure that it must be some kind of bird. But as the membrane breaks, and the occupant appears, I realize that I'm mistaken, for what I thought to be a bird is actually a furry caterpillar, a black and gold-ringed caterpillar of great beauty. As this strangely beautiful creature winds its way out of the egg, it defies the dimension of the egg by growing immediately. Within a few seconds it is larger than the egg and my hand. The speed of its growth amazes me. It is now so large that it is draped across both of my hands; and still it continues to grow. All I can do is offer it the support of my upturned palms.

This was the last of the visions. It was five in the morning when I opened my eyes. Everything was quiet. I lay looking at the dim outline of the ceiling and wondered what it all meant. There was no use in trying to interpret what I had seen, I had to let it work on me, let it grow like the caterpillar.

30 ✻ *Journey to chaos*

The moment I entered his flat, he directed me physically toward the centre of the room and made me stand there. I stood motionless and stared at the wall. He appeared within my line of vision three times, but did not seem to be looking at me. On the third occasion, as he passed, he made a curious gesture with his left hand and cracked the bones in it loudly. And then nothing. Not a sound from behind, not even the feeling of being watched.

'You look okay to me,' he said suddenly.

'What were you looking for?'

'I was looking for nothing,' he replied obliquely, 'and I found nothing.' He laughed, walked across to the window and picked up a brown canvas duffle bag. 'We've got a plane to catch.'

'Where are we going?'

Reaching into his jacket he produced two air tickets. I looked at the tickets in disbelief, they were return flights to Athens for ten o'clock that evening.

'Okay?'

'I suppose so.'

'You will need to get some things.'

'What will I need?'

'Your passport and strong footwear.'

Opening the door he ushered me out into the corridor. 'Our bus leaves for the airport at eight-thirty.'

'It's six-thirty now.'

We walked out into the slightly chilled sunlight. 'Then we've got just enough time to pick up what you need,' said Sabazius.

As we walked down to the corner to get a taxi, I said: 'How long are we going for?'

'Not long.'

'I haven't got much money on me.'

'Where we're going a man could live on a few pounds for a week,' he replied. 'That's the least of your worries.'

As from that moment everything moved so fast I began to feel dizzy. We collected my bits and pieces from the flat, grabbed another taxi and headed for the Phoenix Road bus terminal at King's Cross. It was eight o'clock when we arrived. Sabazius paid the taxi and I followed him into the strange greenish light of the terminal lounge. There were only about a dozen or so people around. By eight forty-five we were seated on the bus and already on our way to Gatwick.

'How do you feel?' asked Sabazius.

'Rushed,' I said.

He chuckled to himself and settled deeper into his seat. 'We'll be there before you know it,' he said.

I sighed and looked away from him, looked out through the expanse of reflecting window at the still and colourful darkness of the suburbs. 'This is the first time I've ever gone abroad without being on business,' I said. 'It feels strange.'

'Have you been to Greece on business?'

'Only twice, and only for a few hours. I virtually flew in on one plane and out on the next.'

'Yet you speak Greek fairly well.'

'I learned it along with five other languages, but hardly ever used it.'

'That is a great pity,' replied Sabazius. 'To know the Greeks one must be able to appreciate the tiny changes of inflection in their speech. Our language is very subtle and very beautiful.'

'And very difficult,' I added.

He nodded in agreement. 'The subtle and the beautiful are often difficult to grasp.'

After a pause, I said: 'Where are we headed?'

'We are going to a place where the trees talk and the stones weep. It is a place of great mystery and many fear it.'

'Is it an island?'

'Yes.'

'Is it the island in my dream-vision?'

'You could say that.'

'Does it have a name?'

'It does, but it would not be meaningful to you.' He turned his head slowly and looked at me. 'If you would like it to have a name, then I suggest you think of the island as being called *Chaos*.'

I nodded my acceptance of the name. And then I said: 'Have you been to the island of Chaos often?'

'Nine times,' he replied.

'So this will be your tenth visit.'

'You could say that.'

I digested his tone. 'But you would not say that?'

'No, I would say something else.'

It was in my mind to ask him what that something else might be, but he stopped me by turning away and closing his eyes. I sat looking at him for almost a minute, watched him breathe, wondered why he had cut me off in such a fashion, and then I too closed my eyes and lay back. When I opened them again it was because Sabazius was nudging me.

'We've arrived,' he said.

I stumbled out into the aisle clutching my duffle bag. Everything looked fuzzy and unreal. A stewardess in a yellow jacket was standing on the platform. We stood waiting for those in front to struggle into their coats and gather their hand luggage together, and then we inched our way down the aisle and out into the sharp, night air. Whitish-blue light and a sense of emptiness. A short, hurried walk across a stretch of concrete and into a low building. Customs officials sitting within box-shaped desks like school teachers robbed of their students. And then suddenly we were speeding down one of the many long corridors in a ragged stream, and there was a sense of urgency, a feeling that we might arrive too late, that the plane might have closed its doors and be already on the move. But of course it was not. It was sitting quite still, its grey and yellow striped body etched into the darkness like a fluorescent painting.

The flight, like all the flights I had ever been on, was totally uneventful. The plane droned through the blackness, bucked a little now and then, passed over towns and cities and mountains. We slept for almost the whole journey sitting upright in our seats, only vaguely aware of the sounds and movements around us. It was like being in a trance. When I came out of this trance it was two-thirty in the morning and the brilliant, light-studded coastline of Greece was already in view. We banked steeply to port above the bay of Saronikos, levelled out, and began our descent. There was a sudden roar as the air-brakes regulated our speed and allowed us to float gently down toward the inky surface of the sea like a mechanized leaf. A few minutes later we were bumping along the invisible line of our approach-path to Athens airport, and not far below, self-illuminated and ghostly, an occasional island or ship appeared and vanished. Greece. The land where the Olympian Gods had ruled, and still ruled. A bowl of soft light and whispering winds where the presence of the world was as thick as the scent of jasmine. There was no escape. I had come to be civilized, to be changed irreversibly.

We stepped out of the plane and boarded one of two Olympian buses. The bus carried us through a maze of new buildings and jolted to a halt beside a concrete ramp. I followed Sabazius up the ramp and into the terminal building. Stewardesses in a multiplicity of coloured uniforms moved this way and that like non-combatant troops. I felt displaced and ill at ease. Within a few minutes we were through passport control and standing at the currency desk. I was handed an assortment of notes and coins. Having no luggage to collect, we moved rapidly across the main hall to the customs exit, waited for but a moment while our duffle bags were checked, and a few minutes later emerged from the terminal building to hail yet another taxi. I drank in the sweet, early morning air as Sabazius informed the driver where we wanted to go, and then suddenly I was in an enclosed space again and we were hurtling out onto a dual carriageway at breakneck speed.

'I feel dazed,' I said.

'You'll feel even more dazed by the time we reach where we're going,' replied Sabazius. 'We've still got a one-hundred-mile journey by sea ahead of us.'

'Are we heading for the port now?'

He nodded. 'The *Ionion* leaves at nine, so we've got a five hour wait ahead of us.'

Our taxi arrived at the port of Piraeus at exactly four-thirty. We got out directly opposite the shuttered door of the ticket office. It was my turn to pay for the taxi.

'When the shops open we can buy some fruit,' said Sabazius. 'We can have some for breakfast and keep the rest for the voyage.'

'It's quite light now,' I said.

A feeling of strangeness. The light of a Greek dawn eating into the sky above the city, infusing the dark, star-studded canopy with moving fingers of brilliance. A sprawling giant shrugging itself awake, shaking itself awake with a clatter of shutters and a revving of engines. Voices shouting at each other across the quay, issuing instructions, laughing and joking about incomprehensible niceties of the day's task. A completely different world.

'I'm in Greece,' I said.

'You look as if you've left your head back in England,' replied Sabazius mirthfully. 'And maybe that's not such a bad thing.'

When the shops opened we bought fruit, that is, I bought fruit. Sabazius said that I might as well get used to speaking Greek to Greeks. I was quite pleased with my effort, and returned carrying a number of paper bags containing pomegranates, apples, and grapes.

'Are these the only words you could remember?' asked Sabazius. 'Where's the bread, and the cheese?'

The result of my second journey seemed to satisfy him. We sat down on the pavement outside the ticket office. Sabazius pulled off a piece of bread and handed it to me along with a pomegranate. 'You bought them, you eat them,' he said.

'I haven't got a knife.'

'You've got teeth.'

I smiled and began to bite off the skin of the pomegranate. 'Isn't this the fruit which binds one to the Underworld?'

'It had better not be in your case,' replied Sabazius.

He had made the remark casually, but there had been a barb in it, an insinuation which wiped the grin off my face. 'What exactly are we here for?' I said.

'To see what kind of man you are. If you're the kind of man you've led me to believe you are, then everything will be okay, but if you're not ...'

'It's some kind of test, isn't it.'

'If it were only some kind of test there would be no problem,' said Sabazius, 'but your days for tests are over.'

'What ... '

I didn't complete my sentence; a man suddenly appeared and

began to undo the padlock on the ticket office door. Sabazius addressed him and they fell to conversation. My unease returned. I tried to translate the conversation to take my mind off what had been said, but I couldn't concentrate and the words turned into a jumble. Confusion. A moment of blind panic when I felt as if I wanted to rise and run, hide myself somewhere where Sabazius could not find me. And then suddenly my perspective shifted, lightened, came back into focus and what Sabazius was saying to the man began to make sense.

'The ship's leaving early?' I said.

'Eight-thirty instead of nine,' replied Sabazius. 'It's a new time-table.'

'When can we board?'

'Any time after seven.'

We completed breakfast, bought our tickets, chatted for a while about inconsequentials, and then made out way over to the quay. The *Ionion* was lying off the end of the quay with its stern doors wide open. We boarded her and passed along the lower gangways. Quite a number of people were already seated, some with crates of chickens on their laps. An extremely old woman dressed completely in black was stretched out on the bench seat. She was groaning quietly to herself and moving her head from side to side. A young girl in a flaming red dress was sitting beside her eating an apple. Sabazius uttered a sharp retort at the girl and she immediately placed a hand on the old woman's shoulder. A little further on we climbed a steep stairway and were back in the growing sunlight. Keeping close to Sabazius, I followed him through a large, comfortable lounge filled with high-backed seats, and then we again entered into the light and warmth.

'Where would you like to sit?' asked Sabazius.

I looked up and down the deck. 'There's a nice spot up there next to the First Class entrance,' I said. 'And there are plenty of empty chairs.'

'You're right, that is a good spot,' he said, nodding at me. 'When the wind comes up we'll be sheltered there.'

'What wind?' I asked.

He glanced at me and laughed. 'By ten o'clock this evening everyone will be hiding in the lounge. It can get very cold out on the sea at night.'

When we were settled, I said: 'Will we still be on board ship at ten this evening?'

'We will indeed. At this time of year it takes about fourteen hours to get where we're going.'

We had placed our chairs next to the rail and put our duffle bags into the shallow drainage system. I sat looking out at the straggling body of Athens, at the low hills where the light was gathering, at the other ships in the bay. It was beginning to get hot.

'Would you like an apple?' asked Sabazius.

I took one from him and bit into it. 'I've never travelled so far by ship,' I said.

'By the time we leave Greece you'll never have travelled so far ever,' he replied, winking at me.

And so we sat and waited, waited for the ship to fill up with people and cargo. I thought the moment of departure would never come. I walked down to the stern of the ship at least three times to see if they had closed the giant double-doors. And then suddenly I heard them close, and in the same moment the engines sprang into life.

Leaning on the rail, I watched Piraeus slide slowly backwards. Within ten minutes it was indistinguishable from the rest of the coastline. Further down the deck, a transistor radio hammered out some jaunty, repetitive Greek song about a young man drinking wine and teasing girls. I smiled to myself and bit another chunk out of the apple in my hand. What a country. It had all the trappings of Western civilization, yet there was something very odd going on underneath. In my mind's eye I could see Greece lying between two distinct geographical hemispheres, almost like a beautiful woman between two strangely different men. She knew both intimately, yet she belonged to neither. She was not of the East, and she was not of the West, she was rather an overlapping space between the two where both struggled to exist with difficulty. She was, as the Greeks themselves said – an *anomalia*. A curious thought sprang into my mind. Maybe Greece did not actually exist the way the other two hemispheres existed. It was just possible that she was a kind of hole in the earth's psyche, an aperture through which an altogether different light from that of the sun had access to the world. Out of her had been born almost everything which elevated the human spirit. Through her growth and evolution man had become truly man – man the thinker, man the resolver of problems. And yet that in itself had caused a problem, for her gift of reasoning had been pulled out of its sacred context and made into a mechanical toy. We had, without realizing it, taken her greatest gift and changed it into a parody, a burlesque imitation of itself. The essence of Greek reason had evaporated at our touch and fled back to its origin, back into the landscape itself, back into the air and the light.

It took a full six hours of sailing before I fully appreciated that light. Over the first few hours I kept on inventing reasons for getting up, for shifting my chair, for going to the lounge bar, for talking; but as the sixth hour approached I found myself staring dreamily into the deep and endless blue of the sky with hardly a thought in my head. All I was aware of was the change in the light, a slow, sensuous change which softened the hard-edged glitter of the sea and turned the sun from an equally stark yellow ball into an amber-yellow disc. The ship was also much quieter, many of the passangers having taken leave of us during our two stops. Others had boarded, but they were fewer in number and seemed to bring with them a curious stillness. From the stern of the *Ionion* I had stood fascinated at the rail and watched the life of the islands take its daily course; but now I was sitting very still and quiet, and all I could hear was the drone of the ship's engines and the sound of my own breathing. Something was happening to me, something I could not understand and did not have the power to stop.

It was pitch dark and chilly when we reached the island of Ikaria. I had slipped on a sweater a couple of hours before. Most of the passengers were gone now, and those that remained were sitting in the lounge, or playing cards in the bar room. An old Greek with a sour face was sweeping up the debris from the deck. It was not actually cold, but after the heat of the day my skin was sensitive to the slightest change in temperature. Sabazius and I leaned on the polished wooden rail and watched as two people went ashore to be greeted by friends. There were only about ten people on the quay. Three came aboard. And then we were underway again, moving out into the thick night of the ocean, the greenish-hued shoreline of Ikaria melting into itself as the ship lunged forward on the last lap of its journey.

'We will soon be there,' said Sabazius.

'In the dark,' I said.

A slight shudder ran through the ship and into my body. I closed my eyes and listened to the engines push the whole mass a few more feet. How extraordinary it was that I was in Greece and not in London. It was like a dream in which one wakes up to the fact that one is dreaming without being able to shrug it off. But this was no dream, I knew that only too well. The ship, the card players and the old man sweeping the deck were all quite real. So was the apple I had eaten earlier, and the curious round ring of bread I had bought from the man with the basket, and the slice of coarse watermelon which had melted away in my mouth like a soft, red ice cube. I was in Greece, and in an odd kind of way, Greece was in me.

I was not at all sure where I was or what was happening when Sabazius shook me awake. A jumble of atmospheres struggled in my mind for precedence. He said that we were approaching the island and I got up and followed him through the lounge to the other side of the ship uncertainly. Straight ahead, moon-silvered and distinct, lay the outline of Chaos, its massive shoulders tapering down into the sea. Far over on our left, in almost a direct line with the ship's prow, a yellow dot of light flashed every few seconds.

'It looks pretty rugged,' I said.

'It is both rugged and beautiful,' replied Sabazius.

Fifteen or twenty minutes later we passed the light and began to slow in preparation for our turn. The engines of the *Ionion* died slowly and came to a momentary halt. Through the impetus of her own weight, the ship spun dizzily into position. Shielding my eyes against the glare I hung out as far as I could to catch a glimpse of the quay. The engines came back to life, checked the swing and forward movement, and with a juddering of steel plates we entered the narrow harbour entrance.

Ever so slowly the faces on shore took on substance, and then suddenly we were there, and the ropes were being thrown, and there was a clanging of bells and a whirring sound as the doors on the stern opened and the ramp was lowered into place. Sabazius grabbed me by the arm and hurried me down through the ship. We had to wait for a few minutes in a queue until the vehicles next to the ramp were driven off, then, on a signal, we were ushered into the central cavern and allowed to disembark. Before I could adjust to the fact that the journey was over, we were off the *Ionion* and striding along the quay.

As we drew away from the crowd, the noise of their voices and that of engines being revved up slowly lessened. With every step a new sound gained strength, the strange and continuous sound of crickets calling to each other. I looked back as we walked, looked at the huge shoulder of rock rising up black against a black sky behind the port. I was not at all sure where the rock ended and the sky began. Every so often a private car laden with passengers would blare at us with its horn and pass by at full pelt. And then the lights and the sounds of the port gave out altogether and we continued in darkness.

'How do you feel now that you've arrived?' asked Sabazius.

'Tired,' I said.

'Shall I walk more slowly?'

'Not if we're heading for a bed,' I said, glancing at him. And then I added: 'Are we?'

'We are indeed,' he replied. 'I have a friend in the town who owns a little hotel, so we will be quite comfortable.'

'That's marvellous,' I said.

'But there will be no beds after that,' he added quickly, 'at least not the kind you're used to.'

We walked on in silence for some minutes, then I said: 'Are we going to be sleeping out?'

'By late tomorrow afternoon we'll be in the mountains,' said Sabazius. 'High in the mountains.'

The sound of an invisible sea rolling up onto an invisible shore, and above that sea a blanket of stars. Sabazius pulled me into the side of the road as another car approached, raced past us and disappeared into the darkness ahead. That was when I saw the neon cross on the hill.

'It serves as a cross and a beacon,' said Sabazius. 'We Greeks are very practical.'

I stopped and stared up at it. 'Then it serves as a blessing and a warning,' I said.

'Just so,' he replied.

31 ❀ *Transfiguration*

A seam of strong sunlight cut into the room from between the metal shutters of the window. I lay looking at it, realized that I was awake, that my eyes were open, that I had moved from sleep to wakefulness without noticing the transition. I looked at my watch, but it had stopped. I wound it up and shook my wrist, but it refused to start. Pushing back the light covering of bed clothes, I got up, went straight to the window, undid the bolts on the shutters and flung them open. A blaze of intense colour, light and heat fell into the room as if I had unwittingly opened the door of a furnace. Mountains. An horizon of green-sloped mountains tumbling upwards ridge upon ridge, and behind them, higher still, a rounded summit of yellow rock pushing defiantly at the sky.

The little room I had been given lay at the end of a long, high-ceilinged corridor. It was simple and functional. There was an extremely large double bed, an army-style locker for clothes, a small table, a straight-backed chair and a washhand basin with a mirror above it. A tiny square of worn carpet beside the bed stopped the icy coldness of the terrazzo floor from inflicting instant lockjaw. All in all it was a very pleasant room. I sat on the edge of the bed and examined my watch, but it still refused to work. Getting up, I wrapped a towel around me and headed down the corridor to the shower room. The water was stone cold and sent me scurrying back within minutes. When I re-entered the room Sabazius was sitting on the bed smoking. He greeted me and asked me what I thought of the island.

'It looks like a veritable paradise,' I said.

'And the yellow mountain?'

'Gave me the shivers.'

He watched me rub at the still wet parts of my body. 'The yellow mountain is not our destination,' he said, 'but we will be very near.'

As I dressed, I looked out of the window at the range. 'How do we get up there?' I asked.

'By bus.'

'Bus?'

'Not all of the way. There is a little village high up in the mountains called Petalothes. The bus stops there and turns.'

'And then?'

'And then we walk. There is a Metochion higher up on the range. It takes a good hour to get to it.'

'What's a Metochion?'

'You do not know the word?'

'No.'

'It refers to a simple building which is neither a church nor a monastery, but a bit of both. Most people call it a monastery however.' He laughed and added: 'It is an *in between place*, if you see what I mean.'

'Will there be just the two of us?'

'No, there will be three others.'

'Friends of yours?'

'Well they're not enemies.'

Smiling, I left the top button of my shirt undone and slipped on my jacket. 'I've just realized what the name of that village means.' I said. 'The village of butterflies?'

He nodded. 'There are many such names in the mountains. Some are very beautiful, and some are full of dread.'

'What would be a dread-name?' I asked.

'Well, the name of the district in which the Metochion lies is Kakoperato.'

'Which means?'

'It has two meanings. On the one hand it means "difficult to pass", and on the other, "should not be passed".'

'Then I have a decision to make,' I said.

'Yes, you have a decision to make.'

We left the hotel soon afterwards and made our way to a small taverna on the outskirts of the town. Sabazius said that the name of the town was Elios, and that although the word meant 'sun', it should be understood as meaning 'sunflower' or 'flower of the sun' in relationship to the town. As we walked through the narrow, white-edged streets I began to understand the reason for this. There were sunflowers everywhere. Every so often I caught sight of them delicately looped and tied back against the buildings. When we entered the taverna, a large, slim man with thinning red hair and a heavily lined face rose to greet us. I stood aside as Sabazius and the man hugged one another. To my surprise, Sabazius introduced him as Hippokratés (pronounced Hippo-kratés), and informed me that he was an expert in all things to do with the land. Hippokratés spoke very good English, but in an extremely deliberate manner. Each word reverberated around the room as if produced by a unique musical instrument. He was roughly the same age as Sabazius, and had a natural dignity which made me feel curiously privileged to be in his company.

'Hippokratés is coming with us to the monastery,' said Sabazius, dispensing with the word Metochion. 'He has not been able to go up there recently because of a bad back – but he is better now.'

I acknowledged what had been said by nodding at Hippokratés, then I asked Sabazius whether the other two people were joining us before we left Elios.

'There is really only one other person,' replied Sabazius. 'The third is a nun who lives at the monastery most of the year round.'

'Won't she mind?'

He laughed at my expression. 'Don't confuse Yarondisa with the prissy-faced nuns you've seen in England,' he said, chuckling merrily. 'She is an old, battered woman with the spirit of a lion and the experience of a gladiator. If she does not want us around she'll throw us out on our ear.'

'Is she some kind of recluse?'

'Not in the least. She loves company, but she has taken it upon herself to seek out her God alone.'

We were seated now, and I could smell roasted meat and vegetables cooking. Hippokratés bent across the table toward me. 'When darkness comes,' he said in a rumbling voice, 'she speaks with the angels.' And then with a malicious twinkle in his eye, he added: 'Male angels of course.'

Sabazius burst out laughing and slapped the table. 'I had forgotten about that,' he said, winking at Hippokratés. As it was obvious to both of them that I was at a loss, he continued: 'Hippokratés once asked her if the angels she spoke to were male or female. She smiled at him and said that they were always male.'

'I don't understand,' I said.

'Listen,' said Hippokratés. 'Angels, even if they have the names of men and women are not different from one another. They are just angels.' He rapped a finger on my arm. 'They don't have what it takes to be a male or female!'

They laughed together as I tried to digest their statements. Then I said: 'Will she be helping us in any way?'

'Not directly,' said Sabazius. 'But she will certainly be of help if you get into any kind of trouble.'

'How could she be of help?'

'Because the mountain knows her and respects her. So if she prays for you, it will probably respond by sparing your life.'

He had said this in a very matter-of-fact way, and although I tried to assimilate it in the same spirit, the idea of the mountain trying to kill me made me shiver. I asked him if it were likely that the mountain would react unfavourably.

'It might,' he replied. 'The mountain knows why you are here. She has been watching you for months.'

'Watching me?'

'She has been waiting for you to come.'

'Mountains are very good waiters,' said Hippokratés, 'much better than the one in this taverna.'

When our amusement abated a little, Sabazius pretended to scold Hippokratés for making light of a serious situation, and Hippokratés responded with a look of fake terror which made me laugh all the more.

'I knew this man would cause trouble,' said Sabazius. 'He has a knack for it.'

When the waiter finally appeared I ordered the Greek equivalent of mince and potatoes. When it arrived I was glad that I had.

Sabazius eyed the dish of food in front of me and said: 'If you eat all of that we'll have to carry you up the mountain.'

'You'll have to carry me up if I don't eat it,' I replied. 'I haven't had a decent meal since I left England.'

'I have never been to England,' said Hippokratés. 'If I come, can I stay with you?'

'You would be most welcome,' I said.

'Then I will come,' he said immediately.

'When?'

'Soon. I will come soon.'

The atmosphere seemed to change in that moment. I sat for a second or two watching them eat, then I lifted my fork and applied it to the mound of food before me. No one said anything until the meal was over.

'Where is Takis?' asked Hippokratés.

'He is persuading his father to look after the shop for the rest of the day,' replied Sabazius. 'It is not an easy task, for he is continually persuading his father to look after the shop for the rest of the day.'

Hippokratés smiled and nodded. 'He is a fine boy,' he said. 'I sometimes feel like a father to him myself.'

'Then maybe you had better look after the shop,' said Sabazius quickly. 'I'm sure his real father would be delighted.'

The two men continued in this vein for some minutes, then Sabazius pushed back his chair and got up. 'We had better move,' he said, beckoning the waiter. 'The bus will not wait for us.'

It was a ten minute walk from the taverna to where the buses were. When we arrived, the bus for Petalothes was already full of people (many of them standing) and had its engine running. The driver, a powerful looking man with his shirt sleeves rolled tightly up above his elbows, was busy pushing a sack of something into the luggage compartment. He slammed the doors shut and locked them. I remarked to Sabazius that I was surprised by the newness of the buses.

'If they were not in good condition they would never handle the roads,' he replied.

It was Hippokratés who spotted Takis. 'He is already on the bus,' he said, pointing toward one of the windows where a young man with a bushy moustache, dark glasses and a sombrero-type straw hat on his head was grinning out at us. The young man got to his feet, undid the catch on the window and shouted that he had already bought our tickets. We moved around to the other side of the bus and boarded. Sabazius, his jacket over his arm, and his shirt open halfway down his chest, cleared a path through the tightly packed passengers.

'Have we got seats?' I asked.

'If we have tickets, then we have seats,' he replied.

When we reached Takis, Sabazius took the tickets from him and checked the numbers. Handing me one of the tickets, he edged himself around and pushed me into the seat beside Takis. I looked up and down the bus but could not see another available seat, never mind two. Sabazius began to examine the numbers on the seats adjacent. Within seconds a rumpus started. I asked Takis to explain what was happening. With a flick of his hand he said that some people got on the buses without getting tickets first, and to have a seat one had to have a ticket. When I turned back to see how Sabazius was doing, I was amazed to find both he and Hippokratés already seated. The people they had displaced were attempting the same thing on the passengers behind. And then it dawned on me what was going on. The seat numbers, which were on the back of each seat, did not refer to the seat facing it, but rather to the seat itself. So in all probability some of the people on that side were in the wrong seats whether they had tickets or not. Sabazius and Hippokratés were already talking and had washed their hands of the matter. As the bus moved out of the depot, the game of musical chairs slowly enveloped more and more of the passengers, and within a few minutes had reached those who did not have tickets.

'We are a very crazy people,' said Takis.

'In England we would say colourful,' I said.

He shook his head adamantly. 'No, crazy is better.'

The driver sounded his horn at each corner as we wound our way up through the broader streets of Elios. He swung the bus energetically within a few inches of the buildings. I could see his dark face reflected in the central mirror. Just below the mirror, an ikon of a saint with a little unlit candle perched in front of it stared balefully up the aisle. A number of other trinkets – including a bunch of plastic flowers – were attached to the metalwork. And then over and above the heavy drone of the engine came the music, that jaunty and effortless music I had heard in Athens, on board the *Ionion*, and almost everywhere else since. It sprang out of the speakers and cut through the silky air insistently. Turning to Takis, I asked him where he had learned his English.

'At school,' he said.

'Have you ever been to England?'

'No, but England has been to me,' he said, grinning. 'My father owns the hotel you stayed at.'

About half an hour later – I wasn't sure of the time because my watch was still jammed – we were a good few miles out of the village and climbing steadily. All I could see out of the windows were vineyards and olive groves; apart from the occasional glimpse of the mountains or the sea which the turning and twisting of the bus sometimes allowed.

'He's a very good driver,' I said.

'The whole family is driver,' replied Takis.

A beautiful white church with moorish arches set in a grove of tall, elegant cypress trees, followed by piles of grey lava rock shot through with quartz blasted out of the hillside to widen the road. A tiny, domed shrine painted in blue and white with its saint cemented in behind cracked glass, and behind it, a donkey with its head bowed standing absolutely still in the drenching heat. Suddenly, the smooth surface of the road gave way to a dirt track strewn with stones. I held onto the seat in front and watched unbelievingly as we rounded one incredible bend after another, creeping often so near to the crumbling edge of the road that one had the sensation of being momentarily suspended in mid-air. The music hammering out of the speakers could not contend with the mountain horn which sprang to life at each dizzying turn.

And then a village.

A straggling double row of decrepit houses leaning one against the other like a mouthful of decayed teeth. Faces. The faces of children and adults staring into the bus from their windows and doorways. Eagle-eyed faces burned out by the sun staring at my face, penetrating it as if it were a soft cheese which innocence could devour. We moved slowly up the steep main street and stopped. The driver got out, opened the luggage compartment and threw the sack onto the roadway. When I turned to ask Takis what the name of the village was, I found myself staring straight into the face of an old woman leaning on her window sill. Takis said something to her through the glass. She responded with a curt nod of her head, but did not smile.

'This is a very poor village,' said Takis. 'They have to work

298

very hard to live.'

We left the village soon afterwards and continued toward Petalothes. Each time the bus swung round a huge expanse of glittering sea heaved up at an odd angle and caught me off guard. I closed my eyes and opened them again to straighten out my sense of equilibrium. Never, never in my life had I experienced anything quite like it, or indeed seen anything quite like it. It was almost as if the bus were trying to leave the ground and claw its way up into the sky without the aid of wings. No wonder the old woman had not smiled. She knew that wings were necessary if one wished to fly.

Petalothes.

Our bus bucked and juddered on the last few yards of track before reaching the circular plateau of concrete which served as the entrance to the village. It was like driving onto the flat top of a round tower, only there was no tower, just the mountain. Beyond the plateau, the village of Petalothes grew out of itself like the treads of a staircase, each level appearing to be both rooftop and foundation simultaneously. Looking at the village was like looking at a trick photograph where a human being is seen to be standing on the hand of another. From the window of the bus I could see children apparently playing on the rooftops with the certainty of acrobats. And the light did not help either. It was as if someone had draped a silken blanket across the village to stop the sun from burning it up. The sun was there, but its fierce power was being filtered through the light which it was responsible for, yet somehow separate from. In Petalothes, the light sprang out of the air, out of the altitude and atmosphere alone, and the sun, almost as white as the moon, was governed by its intervention. Stunned by what I could see and feel, I clambered out of the bus with Takis and joined the others. Sabazius said immediately that I should change my shoes and socks. Going over to the little whitewashed wall which circled the plateau in twelve equidistant sections, I dug out my walking boots and fresh socks and did as he had asked. When I returned, Hippokratés inspected my feet. It was time to move on.

The village proved to be a maze. At certain points, concrete ramps had been built to replace parts of the old streets which had completely disintegrated. These ramps also stopped the equally old houses from collapsing onto the ones below. The streets were a mixture of cobbles, pebble-concrete and slabs of hewn slate, and some of the stairways had been cut out of the solid rock. The houses leaned this way and that, supporting one another uncertainly, and the doors and window-frames fought the pressure with ever decreasing success. As I struggled ever upwards – sometimes on all fours – I had the impression of being in a large, roofless house full of irregular corridors and distorted junctions. Only those who had been born in the village had any chance of finding their way through the natural labyrinth which had grown out of necessity and cunning. Even Hippokratés had to stop on occasions and check his bearings. I was glad of those stops. My chest was already heaving because of the pace, and I couldn't help wondering what it was going to be like in the mountains. Was I going to disgrace myself by not being able to keep up? Sabazius, Hippokratés and Takis had greeted the villagers almost constantly, whereas I hadn't said a word; yet they seemed to be in full breath.

The halfway mark in the village turned out to be a water trough. It was there I learned my first lesson in mountaineering. When I saw the tap sticking out of the rock I made straight for it. Some of the villagers stood aside to let me drink. But no sooner had I bowed my head toward the tap than I felt a hand on my shoulder. It was Hippokratés. He drew me away from the tap and said politely that I was not to drink the water. I asked him if there was something wrong with it. He said that the water came from the mountains and was perfectly good, but that it would do me harm if I drank too much of it. Still not understanding what he meant, I questioned him further. He shook his head as if I were a child being distrustful of a parent. It was quite simple, he said. The water would only make me more thirsty, and probably give me stomach ache into the bargain because it was so cold. When a man goes into the mountains, he said, he must learn to control his natural appetites, for if he does not, then the mountain pounces on him, and that is the end of the man. So I was allowed to swallow one mouthful of water, and we moved on up through the village to where the streets gave out and the track began. A few minutes later we left the last straggling houses of Petalothes behind, passed a windowless wash-house where a number of women were scrubbing and singing, and struck out into the wild, thorny landscape towards Kakoperato.

On the other side of the hill lay a deep valley. The path wound and looped its way down into the valley through a series of vine terraces. Hippokratés took the lead, followed by Takis, Sabazius and myself. At first, thinking that the path was just like any other path, I allowed myself the luxury of looking around, but after two falls it became clear that the best place for one's eyes was on the path itself. If we had been travelling more slowly, then both might have been possible, but Hippokratés was pounding ahead, and the sheer speed of our descent into the valley, and subsequently up and around the other side of it, demanded steady concentration. These men were not out for an afternoon's walk in the hills, they were heading for a destination as if their lives depended on it. Stumbling on the loose rocks and slithering down the steep inclines, I kept up with them as best I could. On two occasions the gap between Sabazius and myself grew alarmingly. I had to push myself to the limit to catch up. That was when I realized what Hippokratés had been getting at earlier, for the one mouthful of ice-cold water I had swallowed was lying in my stomach like a ball-bearing.

Up and down we went. The going down, although treacherous in itself because of the sharp, flint-like rocks, at least gave me time to catch my breath, but the going up steadily eroded my strength and made me feel as if I were being subjected to an unfair test. It crossed my mind more than once to simply sit down and give up, but the suspicion that if I did I would be left to fry and find my own way to the monastery kept me on the move. If there had been one distinct path then I might very well have taken the risk, but there were lots of paths, some narrow and some broad, some ascending and some descending, some looking important and some hardly resembling paths at all. The number of times I was fooled by the appearance of the path annoyed me. On the second of the two occasions when I fell back and almost lost sight of the others, I had found myself choosing paths which carried me away from them, and had had to clamber about at right angles to the paths until I picked up their slurred footprints. Not once did they look behind them. As far as they were concerned, it was my job to keep up, not their job to slow down.

When we entered the dips where the trees thickened and the bushes dragged at our clothes, the burning sunlight was replaced by fly-infested shade. I had never encountered such angry flies. They threw themselves at us like miniature dive-bombers and followed us into the open in clouds. Breaking off a bunch of ferns I used them to protect and cool my face. Pleased with my make-shift fan, I pushed on and attempted to keep the distance between myself and Sabazius down to a minimum. Hippokratés, his red hair covered now with a floppy straw hat, stopped suddenly at a bluff which only he could see over and raised his hand. In the same moment he leapt aside as a mule with chains attached to its heavy collar struggled into view pulling a felled log. A young boy with a stick in his hand followed close behind. When I saw the size of the log, it dawned on me immediately why so much of the path was ankle deep in finely ground soil. It also explained why sharpened branches had been driven into the side of the path at intervals. When a log was forced to turn a sharp corner on the hillside, these simple stakes stopped it from rolling off the path and carrying the mule with it. The mule passed us in silence, its head bent low, its hooves gripping doggedly into the sand and rock in a steady forward rhythm. And then came the boy, his face and eyes bright with excitement at seeing strangers. As I watched, the log jammed on a rock and pulled the mule's head up sharply. The boy shouted something, grabbed a branch, inserted it expertly beneath the log and levered it free. I turned to say something to Sabazius about how well the boy had handled the situation, only to discover that he and the others were already over the bluff and out of sight. The suddenness of their departure drove home the fact that I was not there to gape at beautiful or interesting things, but to reach the monastery, to keep up with their hectic pace and not get left behind like some bedazzled tourist.

The last part of the journey, apart from one final and exhausting climb, proved easy and refreshing. We descended from a hillside into a little gorge, forded a stream, wound our way upwards through a boulder-strewn bottleneck, and emerged into a cool glade of fir trees. This glade, however, was completely hidden by an overhang of rock, and as the path did not pick up again until one was well into the bottle-neck, the chances of finding it, or realizing that that was the direction one should be going in, were slight. We walked slowly down through the glade and into a natural basin filled with soft light. The ground was soft and springy underfoot, almost moist because of the canopy of firs. Not far away on our left, a herd of goats, some with huge twisting horns, and almost all with a little bell tied around their neck, watched us motionlessly. The boy in charge of the herd was lying flat out and fast asleep beside them. As we passed, they edged back nervously and their bells sounded off hollow and empty in the still air. Seconds later, as if in answer to a danger call, a larger bell beat out a series of hard, monotone notes, stopped, and then continued its strange reply in a frenzied clanging which echoed throughout the glade like a challenge. For a moment, I found myself visualizing a giant goat about the size of a house shaking its head angrily, the bell around its neck thrashing from side to side, its horns carving the air like spiral-bladed knives. Then it dawned on me what it really was – it was the monastery bell declaring that Yarondisa the nun was alive and kicking, and that she knew we were near at hand.

Although lying virtually straight ahead of us, the monastery remained invisible because of its position. We were almost through the gate before I realized we had reached it. This was because the builders had cunningly chosen a site on the other side of a dry river bed where the trees ended and the land sloped upwards and became a hill. The monastery was tucked into the side of the hill just beyond the trees, and because of its slightly higher elevation, and the fact that one naturally followed the contours of the land around, and down, it remained hidden behind the fir canopy. Even the little hump-backed bridge and stone gateway were camouflaged, and it was only when the logs of the bridge focused into a structural shape that the gateway itself became noticeable. And still the bell rang. We crossed the bridge one at a time, passed through the arched gateway and climbed a few stone stairs to the monastery forecourt. Two dogs tethered in a corner barked as our heads and shoulders came into view. One of the dogs was so old it could hardly rise. Following the others, I stepped out into the brilliant sunlight, and there, dressed all in black, her hand still swishing the short, knotted bell-rope backwards and forwards, stood Yarondisa.

She let go of the bell-rope immediately and came towards us, the sound of the bell dying and following after her like the reverberation of a dumb-noted triangle. She greeted us warmly with a mixture of prayer-blessings, hand-clutching and sober politeness. Sabazius displayed great formality when addressing her. When she reached me, she stared into my face as if trying to read it, and then she closed her eyes and launched into a long, complicated prayer to a saint I had never heard of. As she prayed, her expression and the movement of her head and hands stamped the prayer into my mind. She then welcomed me to the monastery and said that she hoped I would be comfortable during my stay. Addressing her as *Metera* (mother), I thanked her for her blessing and said that it was my hope she would live as long as the oldest tree on the island, and that each of her blessings would return four-fold. My statement surprised me more than it surprised or pleased her, for when I opened my mouth no such words had been in my head. Taking me by the hand, she led me across the courtyard and made me sit next to her open-air kitchen. I was to rest, she said, and while I rested she would prepare sweet coffee.

We spent what was left of the afternoon sitting around the kitchen area talking, and in the evening when the air turned chill and the shadows ate into the landscape like the fingers of a giant hand, we stirred up the fire and fed it with dried fir cones. How brightly they burned, and how quickly they were consumed. Hippokratés informed me that Yarondisa was seventy-two years of age, and probably one of the only remaining nuns in the whole of the Aegean to have chosen the solitude of the mountain fortress in which to worship, and die. She had lived a full and busy life, he said, and during the second war when *Wotan* had threatened the Greek freedom and made his presence felt through the islands, had worked with the local resistance movement and supplied them with baskets of grenades and ammunition disguised as fruit and vegetables. Her life had always been on the line, said Hippokratés, and it was no different now that she was old and stiff. That was when I understood what Sabazius had meant when he said that she had 'the spirit of a lion and the experience of a gladiator'. And yet Yarondisa was a tender spirit, for when it got really dark, and I was forced to fold my arms to retain the heat of my body, she produced a blanket and laid it across my shoulders. Sitting not far from the hawthorn tree where the bell hung, I watched the firelight dance in the courtyard and elongate our shadows as far as the monastery door. The black cross on the door stood out starkly against the orange-painted woodwork. Yarondisa, her face cowled with a black, lace shawl, stood near to the fire and tried to control the sparks as they leapt upwards and singed the leaves on the tree which overhung the kitchen. Dissatisfied with her efforts, she dampened the heart of the fire with water and scolded Takis for putting on too much wood. As she remonstrated with him a strange sound echoed out of the darkness – the sound of an owl and a cockerel calling to one another across the dark reaches of the mountain. I listened to this unusual combination thinking it to be a mere coincidence of timing, but the more I listened the more obvious it became that it was an intentional act, and not just a fluke of the night.

The doorway.

While those sounds were going on, I happened to glance at the monastery door – it was open. As no one had crossed the courtyard since I last looked at it, and there was no wind to speak of, I could not understand how it had opened. Disturbed by that wedge of blackness, I allowed my eyes to move away from it and take in the shape and presence of the monastery itself. It was a small building about twenty yards long roofed with large grey slates. Behind it, although still attached, a higher section with green-shuttered windows loomed up and merged with the dark outline of the hillside. At ground level, to the right of the door, a small, deeply-set window reflected the light of a solitary candle and the glint of a silver-framed ikon. In the wavering light of the fire, the monastery changed shape as the shadows fled and re-grouped on its sacred walls. Shivering involuntarily, I turned towards the fire wondering how Yarondisa could stand living alone in such a place.

I drew the blanket in close, held it from the inside and watched Sabazius as he talked to Hippokratés – the two men were sitting one end of a long table next to the fire. They were deep in conversation, but speaking in such low tones that I could make out only the occasional word. Takis was standing next to Yarondisa in silence; he watched as she placed a long-handled metal coffee pot onto the ribbed grill above the fire, then wandered off towards where the dogs were. I sat back into the old wicker chair I had found and closed my eyes. What would the morrow bring, I wondered. Then suddenly, compulsively, I was on my feet and Sabazius and Hippokratés were looking across at me. What had made me rise? I questioned Sabazius with my eyes, but he just sat there and stared at me. I took a deep breath and turned towards the parapet, but not of my own volition; it was as if a pair of hands had grasped me by the shoulders and forced me to turn around. I let out a little yelp of fear and stared into the darkness fully expecting the predator to come flapping out of the night and attack me, but no such thing happened.

Then quite without knowing why I found myself walking across the yard, fully conscious of what I was doing, yet at the same time driven by an inner compulsion which I could not countermand. It was as if I had split into two, and the other half was in control of volition. I was making the decisions, but it was not the 'I' of my personality. Continuing to hold the edges of the blanket from the inside, I pulled it tightly around me and headed down the concrete ramp for the exit gate at some speed. When I reached the dogs, they stood up, but did not bark. Takis allowed me to pass without comment. Then with the same sureness I walked through the arched gateway, crossed the bridge and made off into the semi-darkness without once questioning what I was doing. Ahead of me, just visible, was the path; it was now a faintly illuminated grey-blue ribbon disappearing among the trees to my right. Following that ribbon, I was led down into a dry riverbed and upwards onto the hillside where the path became easier to follow. Behind me I could hear the shuffle of feet and the breathing of men. Moonlight. A shift in the clouds and the darkness dispelled by a sheen of silvery brilliance. Tiny animals scurrying through the undergrowth and dozens of paths, formed by the winter rains, falling away down the hillside. But only one with that curious luminescence, that beckoning blue-greyness.

We came out of the trees far up on the mountain side and followed the path to a point where the darkness became quite impenetrable. The blue sheen of the path twisted sharply to the left as it met this darkness and plummeted downward at an angle of forty-five degrees. It was a very difficult descent, and I knew without having to be told that the black nothingness on my right was empty air, and that one wrong step would hurtle me to a certain and totally invisible death. And yet how magnetic that darkness was. It tugged at my imagination and suggested against all reason that I could step out onto it without mishap, indeed, that I ought to step out onto it to prove that I could support my own weight with the strength of mind alone. Time and time again my feet strayed toward it as my mind attempted to accept the challenge and my eyes were drawn into its hypnotic density. And yet on each occasion something drew me back and allowed me to continue. We were almost halfway down the path when I suddenly stopped and realized where I was. It was as if a flash of light had illuminated the whole landscape. I was standing on the narrow, precipitous path of my dream-vision where the Predator had almost bruised my head as it skimmed by and dropped into the gorge. How strange it was that I had not recognized the gorge sooner, for I had stood that very afternoon and stared down into it from the monastery wall. The point, however, was that I recognized it now, knew why I had been driven from the safety of Yarondisa's fire. I had been driven by my knowledge of the steps, the steps I had once stood on but had not been allowed to climb. With even greater care I moved forward and completed the descent. As we passed the spot where the white-washed crosses were barely visible, Sabazius touched my shoulder gently and took the lead. And in that same moment, Yarondisa began to thrash the monastery bell.

A spiral of stone steps carried us up into a large cave. We had to literally crawl upwards because of their steepness. I could see nothing of the cave when we entered it, but I could feel its hollowness stretching up and out in all directions. Sabazius stopped me with his hand and told me to stand still. He then moved off into the darkness and I heard what sounded like a door being pushed open. When he returned, he was carrying a tiny dish of oil with a lighted wick floating in it. By the aid of that light I was able to see the shadowy outline of a small building on my left. A black wooden cross on the door signified that it was a church of some sort. Cautioning me to watch every step, Sabazius held the lamp out in front of him and inched forward. On having covered a few feet he stopped again and beckoned to us. When I reached him and saw what he could see I froze. Directly in line with the gable-end of the church, and running right across the width of the cave was the edge of a pit. I asked Sabazius how deep it was. He said that it was not as deep as it looked. He then sat down on the edge of it and began to feel about with his feet. Lowering the lamp as best he could, he took a quick look over the edge and allowed his body to slip forward. Instead of disappearing into the darkness as I expected, he stopped short at shoulder height. 'This is the first of the steps,' he said, turning himself around slowly. 'Be very careful, each step is roughly five feet deep and not terribly steady.' When he had gone down two more steps, I lowered myself after him with help from Hippokratés. It was a hair-raising business. The light of the lamp was inadequate, and the steps, no more than roughly hewn stones, sank into the damp earth under our weight. Tying the ends of the blanket in a knot at my middle, I negotiated those Titan steps one by one, and helped those behind me whenever possible. Down we went, step by step, into the fathomless darkness. I'm uncertain how long it took us to reach the bottom, but it seemed like a long time.

The floor of the pit was chilled with an icy draught and the darkness around the little lamp so intense it hardly gave out any light at all. I stood very still and close to the light wondering why I had come to such a desolate spot. Of all the places in the world I could have imagined going to, the bottom of a pit inside a mountain on an island in the Aegean Sea was not one of them. And yet I myself had led the way, first by seeing a little golden haired boy who had acclaimed its existence, and second by leaving the monastery in a kind of dream and following that blue, irridescent path to where the white-washed crosses intimated mystery. I only had myself to blame, or thank, and as I stood there facing the darkness, I was not sure which was the most appropriate.

'Now you must go on alone,' said Sabazius.

'Where to?'

'There is a tunnel to the left which leads to a larger chamber.'

'Can't you come with me?'

'Only one person can enter the chamber at a time. If two people entered, the whole mountain would collapse in on itself.'

'What do I have to do when I reach the chamber?'

Sabazius chuckled and handed me the lamp. 'There isn't anything to do in the chamber. All you have to do is reach it, that is enough.'

'You won't have any light when I'm gone.'

'There are plenty of lights down here,' he replied. 'I'll show you what I mean.'

He moved over to the left and struck a match. The flare of yellow light revealed a white-painted shrine with long-chained lamps hanging on either side. The lamps were of filigreed brass and studded with coloured glass segments. Sabazius examined the lamps in the dying light, removed their lids, struck another match and managed to ignite one of the tiny candles each lamp contained. I was only able to see into the shrine properly when the second candle spluttered into life. Instead of the usual ikon, or cross, two exquisitely carved white marble figurines about ten inches in height stood facing one another in the recess. The figure on the left was female and almost naked except for a girdle of finely sculptured cloth. In her right hand, which was extended, she proffered a thin-stemmed goblet, or chalice, to the other figure, which was male. The male figure had magnificent horns growing out of his head and a serpent coiled around his waist. Behind them, and centrally situated at head height, a black sun had been painted on the white rock. Thin spikes of blue, yellow and red light streamed from the lamps into the arched interior of the shrine like a dissembled rainbow. Sabazius allowed me to gaze into the shrine for a few seconds, then, taking me by the arm, he turned me toward an inky corridor where the light retreated weakly before the blackness. He indicated that I should start walking by applying a gentle pressure to my back. I took a few steps away from him and stopped where the rainbowed light gave out and my own lamp became the only source of illumination. Realizing that one false step could extinguish that naked flame in the oil which fed it, I bent low to study the ground. Each step would have to be enveloped in concentration, for there was no way of knowing what lay between me and the chamber.

Black silence.

I did not look back as I moved further and further from my friends; although I was conscious of them looking at me, conscious of them watching my form and the little light being swallowed up in the black stillness of the mountain's heart. After a few yards, the corridor changed into a perfectly round tunnel, dipped slightly, became less rugged and rock strewn, and took on a sandy smoothness which allowed me to travel more easily. The glass crystals in the sand caught the light of my lamp and reflected it back like a host of miniature cat's eyes. Because of this extra light, and the fact that I could now discern areas ahead where rocks stuck up out of the floor, I was able to let my back straighten fractionally and reduce the pressure on my spine. It was however still very dark, and the weight of that darkness above the glint of the sand crystals made me feel dizzy. After what seemed like an hour, I guessed that I had covered perhaps quarter of a mile. I was now almost straight-backed. The walls of the tunnel became progressively smoother, and the amount of light available doubled due to the rock and sand giving way to gleaming quartz. It intrigued me that so much light could be generated by so little a lamp. Being careful still to hold the lamp level and not spill the oil, I forged ahead. It was like being inside a sphere of light travelling along a tube. As I moved, the light moved, and as the light moved into the darkness to reveal each successive section of the tunnel, the same darkness pushed at me from behind like a chilled hand. And then I saw something in the distance which slowed my breath to a whisper – a tiny, fluctuating spot of intense blue. I moved toward it cautiously, using my peripheral vision to watch it and my direct vision to hold the lighted area of the tunnel floor in focus. The quartz walls added a curious effect to the whole scene. It was as if a hidden sun were shooting its rays over the circular edge of a black ring. Hardly daring to breathe, I followed the tunnel on its subtle descent and slowly approached that spot of colour. As I drew nearer, the walls gathered up the blue light and sent it streaming in a wild dance of advancing and withdrawing beams. And then the wind came and the light of my lamp was extinguished.

Having no longer any need of the lamp, and surrounded

now by the Damascus blue of the mountain's inner life, I walked the few remaining yards to the end of the tunnel and entered the chamber. It was like walking into the heart of a huge diamond. The interior of the chamber, composed of interlocking crystals, rose majestically to a point like a pair of hands with the fingertips touching. The floor, polished as finely as a mirror and as large as a lake, reflected a deep and convincing duplicate of what lay above. Making my way to the centre of the chamber, I undid the knot I had tied in Yarondisa's blanket, and sat down. My head immediately fell forward as if pushed from behind. Unable to move, I stared down into the mirrored floor of the chamber. In the same moment I noticed that I did not have a reflection. In an odd kind of way, I was looking through myself without seeing myself. And yet I was there, incontrovertibly there, as real as the cavern's inverted image, as real as the little extinguished lamp lying in my cupped hands. As I watched, the sharp-edged interior of the crystal mountain became milky and indistinct. Within seconds it was no more. In its place appeared the same chamber, only at a different angle. From where I sat in the centre of the chamber, it seemed that I was standing at the tunnel entrance looking at myself sitting at the centre of the chamber.

Before me a white egg balanced on its tip, and about the size of a man. Next to it a spear, its point downwards, hanging without support. I watched myself rise and approach the egg, grasp the spear firmly, bring its metal point up and drive it towards the egg. But instead of penetrating the shell, the metal tip of the spear simply cracked the egg and bounced back. Watching from the sidelines, I saw the egg crack vertically and fall into two halves. Within the egg the figure of a naked man perfect in form, indeed so perfect that the sight of him made me gasp. Then to my astonishment I realized that I was looking at my self, at a perfect self, a self so perfect, so beautiful, so extraordinary that it shocked me. I stepped back afraid of this perfect thing, stared at this impossible possibility and felt anger at its very being there. I began to shake. The anger came up out of me as a roar, as a volcanic eruption of hate and loathing for this perfect figure, this man that I could never ever be. Incensed by his presence I swung the spear round to drive it into him, to kill him, but stopped short in this act because of his look. A long moment, then the gentle drone of bees overhead, and a dizziness, and a melting away of that terrible anger. The perfect man no longer visible. The halves of the egg no longer visible. The spear no longer visible. Just a man sitting shrouded in a patterned blanket in the middle of a cave, weeping, his shoulders heaving as he sobbed the anger out of himself.

Release.

I got up and walked across the mirror-like floor to the tunnel entrance. I did not look back. On reaching where the blue light of the chamber weakened, I halted, held up the lamp and watched it splutter back into life. Moving along the tunnel quickly, I came to a second tunnel and entered, followed it until I reached a small, circular room. There was no door. At the centre of this room, on a platform of smooth rock lit by two candles, lay the body of a man wrapped in a wool cloak. Only his face was visible. On the floor, its eyes fixed on me, lay a magnificent white goat with twisting horns. I looked from the goat to the man's face – it was the face of my friend and mentor, Alexis Sabazius.

'Alexis?' I said.

There was no reply.

And again I said his name. 'Alexis?'

The eyes opened; he turned his head towards me. 'What do you want?' he asked.

'Want?' I said.

'You woke me from a deep sleep for no reason?'

I frowned.

'It's the middle of the night,' he said, pushing himself up on an elbow. 'What do you want?'

I looked around me. The courtyard was just visible in the gloom; the embers of the fire Yorandisa had dampened earlier glowed dully over to my right. Wrapped in a wool cloak, Sabazius was lying on a wooden bench only a few feet away from where I sat, the side of his head supported on the palm of his right hand.

'I must have had a dream,' I said.

'You awakened me because you had a dream?'

'I haven't left here?'

'Left? Where would you go?'

I looked toward the parapet, 'Out there,' I said.

He laughed at me. 'You wouldn't last ten minutes out there.'

'I've been inside the mountain.'

'You have?'

'There's a little church inside the mountain. And a pit with steps. You showed me a shrine with figures in it.'

'I've been asleep.'

'You were all down there with me,' I said, ignoring his claim. 'It was not a dream.'

Sabazius drew breath, exhaled audibly. 'There is a church inside the mountain,' he said back. 'And there is a shrine.'

'And steps?' I asked.

He nodded, waited for me to continue.

I described everything that had happened, felt tears come to my eyes as I described my anger and anguish at seeing my incomprehensibly beautiful twin.

'He was well-formed? Complete?'

'Me as I'll never ever be,' I replied hopelessly.

He laughed softly to himself and stared at me. Then he said, 'Peter, what you have witnessed tonight is the result of the work we have been involved in almost every minute since we met in Johannesburg. It was for this end that we worked, for no other. The beautiful man you saw is not someone who will exist later; he is not a potential Peter Derwent belonging to some indeterminate future. He exists *now* on another level of being. You created this beautiful creature, and what you have to do is join with him. This is what I saw sticking out of your energy cloud when we first met. I saw *you* emerging.'

'But he was extraordinary,' I said.

'You are extraordinary,' he replied. 'Any human being who takes on the challenge of Being is extraordinary.'

'I'm a fool.'

'No, not a fool, Peter. A butterfly … at last.'

I sat very still and thought about that. Then I said, 'Where are the others?'

'They haven't returned yet,' he replied.

'Returned?' I said.

He smiled at me innocently. 'I was the only one who could keep up with you.'

313